# A Field Guide to the
# MARINE FISHES
# of WALES
### and Adjacent Waters

### Paul Kay and Frances Dipper

Marine
Conservation
Society

Cyngor Cefn Gwlad Cymru
Countryside Council for Wales

Noddir gan
Lywodraeth Cynulliad Cymru
Sponsored by
Welsh Assembly Government

Published in 2009 by
Marine Wildlife,
Vine Villa, Mount Road,
Llanfairfechan,
Conwy LL03 0DW
Wales

www.marinewildlife.co.uk

10 9 8 7 6 5 4 3 2 1

A catalogue record for this book is available from the British Library.

ISBN: 978-0-9562048-0-6

Designed and produced by Fluke Art, Cornwall

Printed in Slovenia on behalf of Latitude Press Limited

Recommended citation:
Kay, P. and Dipper, F. 2009. *A Field Guide to the Marine Fishes of Wales and Adjacent Waters.* Marine Wildlife, Llanfairfechan.

Front Cover – Corkwing Wrasse at Sarn Badrig, Paul Kay.
Back Cover – Upper – Tompot Blenny off Porth Dinllaen, North Llŷn, Paul Kay.
Back Cover – Lower – Nursehound in Cardigan Bay, Paul Kay.

# Contents

# Foreword

Rydw i wedi bod efo diddordeb ysol mewn pysgod erioed. Pan oeddwn i'n hogyn bach yng Nghanolbarth Cymru ers talwm, roedd yn rhaid imi fodloni ar ychydig o frithyll a phennau lletwad yn nentydd yr ucheldir. Ond wrth chwilio trwy byllau glan môr yn Sir Benfro y taniodd fy nychymyg mewn gwirionedd. Roedd pysgod o bob lliw a llun i'w cael yno ym mhob pwll mawr – rhai'n cuddio dan y gwymon ac eraill yn nofio'n rhy gyflym i'r rhwydwr ifanc eu dal.

Ar y pryd, doedd gen i ddim syniad beth yn union yr oeddwn i'n edrych arno. Ond hyd yn oed yr adeg honno, roeddwn i'n gwybod ei fod yn rhywbeth arbennig iawn. Cefais weld pa mor arbennig bron i ddeugain mlynedd yn ddiweddarach wrth ddeifio yng ngorllewin Cymru. Gan ddeifio mewn dyfnder o ddim is na 10 metr mewn dŵr clir fel grisial, cefais fy rhyfeddu gan amrywiaeth aruthrol y pysgod a welwn. Roeddwn i'n teimlo fel pe bawn i ym Môr y Caribî neu yn y Môr Coch; ond dan y don yn Sir Benfro heulog oeddwn i, mewn gwirionedd.

Roedd yno wrachod lliwgar, morgwn, llysywod môr arswydus yr olwg, a heigiau o forleisiaid. Hefyd, roedd yno lymrïaid ariannaidd, llyfrothod â chuddliw gwych, gobïod, chwyrnwyr, a thoreth o greaduriaid eraill nad oeddwn i wedi eu gweld o'r blaen. Yn anffodus, wnes i ddim llwyddo i ddod o hyd i arweinlyfr da a allai roi gwybod imi beth yr oeddwn wedi'i weld – na 'chwaith ddau lyfr a oedd yn cytuno ar yr enwau!

Erbyn hyn, diolch i'r drefn, mae llyfr o'r fath i'w gael. Dyma'r arweiniad maes mwyaf cynhwysfawr ar bysgod môr Prydain, ac mae'n amhrisiadwy i hogiau bach 10 oed sy'n chwilio trwy byllau glan môr, i bysgotwyr, i naturiaethwyr ac i ddeifars fel ei gilydd. Ynddo fe gewch chi wybodaeth werthfawr a lluniau rhagorol, ac mae wedi deffro awydd ynof i ddeifio yn nyfroedd Cymru unwaith eto.

Heb amheuaeth, fe fydd y llyfr yma'n bwysig o ran dod â physgod môr i lygad y cyhoedd, gan helpu i sicrhau y bydd y creaduriaid diddorol yma'n rhai y gall cenedlaethau'r dyfodol eu mwynhau hefyd.

I've always been fascinated by fish. When I was a young lad growing up in the heart of mid-Wales, I thrived on a meagre fare of trout and bullheads in upland streams but it was whilst exploring rock pools in Pembrokeshire that my imagination really caught fire. Every large rock pool had fish of different sizes and colours, some hiding beneath seaweed whilst others moved too quickly even for a young boy's net.

Back then, I didn't have a clue what I was looking at but even my undeveloped mind told me that they were special. Just how special, I discovered nearly 40 years later on a diving expedition to west Wales. At a depth of no more than 10 metres, in a crystal clear sea, I was stunned by the sheer variety of fish. I felt as though I should have been in the Caribbean or the Red Sea, but here I was beneath the waves in sunny Pembrokeshire.

There were multi-coloured wrasse, shark-like dogfish, gruesome-looking conger eels and shoals of pollack. There were also silvery sandeels, perfectly camouflaged blennies, gobies and gurnards and a myriad of others that I had never seen before. Frustratingly, in the following weeks, I couldn't find a comprehensive guide book that could tell me what I'd seen or even two books that agreed on their names!

Now, thankfully, such a book exists. This is the most comprehensive guide to marine fish in Britain and is an invaluable tool for 10-year-old rock poolers, fishermen, naturalists and divers alike. The informative text is accompanied by excellent photographs which have whetted my appetite to dive again in Welsh waters.

There is no doubt that this book will play an important role in putting marine fish in the public eye and help ensure that these engaging creatures are around for future generations to enjoy.

Iolo Williams
October 30, 2008

# Acknowledgements

This book has been produced for the Marine Conservation Society and was made possible by grant aid from the Countryside Council for Wales and many thanks are due to both organisations for their help and support. Any book such as this one relies on a great deal of help from many contributors. Ivor Rees, Lin Baldock and Doug Herdson deserve our special thanks for the amount of time and effort both have put in to researching, identifying and providing information on many fish. We would also like to thank Andy Woolmer for his enthusiasm and information on fisheries; Mandy McMath for ensuring the viability of the project and Marc Dando for his design and drawing and who provided far more than he was originally asked to do. Finally we would especially like to thank the following people who provided many of the photographs without which this book would be populated by far fewer fish:

Lin Baldock (p30B, p31T, p33BL, p73B, p215T); Janet Baxter (p118B, p233L); David Bird (p19upperBL, p47both); Dan Bolt (p234); George Brown (p111B); David Connor (p223); Sue Daly (p110B, p113B); Dylan Evans – Anglesey Sea Zoo (p151T); Tony Gilbert (p166B, p179T, p182, p184); Jim Greenfield (p16upperBR, p17TR, p94B, p96T&B, p100B, p101T, p103T, p139, p142inset, p153, p155, p161, p192B, p226, p227T&B); Jason Gregory (p209B); John Gwyn (Aden Productions) (p46); Sven Gust (p93, p99); Melanie Harding (p39, p84); Derek Haslam (p61T); Ben Hextall (p170B); Chris Holden (p86B); Rohan Holt (p77T&B); Robert Irving (p183T&B); Lucy Kay (p43T, p75 BL &BR, p104T, p112B, p144, p156B, p158T, p179B, p230T, p231T, p238B, Inside back cover L); Richard Lord (p86T, p122R, p210T); Eoin McGreal (p118M); Mandy McMath (p14TL, p107); Andy Murch (p15BL, p53); Dave Peake (p16BL, p85T, p88T&B, p168); Bernard Picton (p105, p113T, p152T, p210M&B); Linda Pitkin (p60); Declan Quigley (p109); Ivor Rees (p69, p72); Trevor Rees (p132T); Bill Sanderson (p84); Sue Scott (p18BL, p64T, p85B, p98, p118T, p132B, p142main, P224T); Shark Trust (p31B); Sally Sharrock (p27B, P169T); Liz Sides (p30T); Steve Trewhella (p14BL, p28B, p80, p108T&B, p115, p122L, p123T&B, p155B, P184inset, p216, p225T); Mark Woombs (p92); ;D P Wilson/FLPA (p59), Peter Wirtz (p16lower TL, p131T&B, p138, p165, p171B, p174T&B); School of Ocean Sciences, University of Wales, Bangor (p181); National Museum of Wales (p239)

All other photographs are by Paul Kay with the exception of those on p31B, p49 and p83 all three of which have been supplied for use without credit. Photo of Paul Kay by Lucy Kay, of Frances Dipper by Elizabeth Wood.

T = top, B = bottom, M= middle, L = left and R = right.

ALL the excellent illustrations throughout this book have been drawn by Marc Dando.

# Introduction

In 1907 H. E. Forrest published *The Vertebrate Fauna of North Wales*, a substantial piece of work which contained nearly 100 pages on the fishes found off the North Wales coasts. Much of the information that he included is still valid and whilst many of the scientific names of species may have changed, most of the locations he described can be revisited and many of the fish he described can still be found.

In the intervening 100 years since Forrest's book was published, our knowledge has moved forward. Most of the information that Forrest compiled came from the field naturalists of that time who made careful observations the importance of which should not be underestimated. Now with the advent of scuba diving we can extend those first hand observations underwater and observe directly many fish species in their own environment. Undoubtedly, the early naturalists would have been delighted to know of this future ability which was, in their day, mere science fiction!

Despite our increased knowledge and technologies, there is still an awful lot to learn about Welsh fish. In fact during the writing of this book it became very evident that we lack a great deal of information about many fish, their life histories, behaviour and distribution. So this book is a mere 'snapshot' of the data collected and collated by the authors in 2008. It should be regarded as 'work in progress' and it is hoped that it will stimulate the collection of more data and information and so quickly become outdated!

No doubt mistakes will be found and some images may even have to be re-identified as more material comes in. The relatively recent advent of digital photography has already had an impact on our abilities to instantly, and effectively, record subjects such as fish – above or below water – and as this technology matures it will mean that many more images of fish become available.

This book is the first photographic field guide to the sea fishes found in Welsh waters and is designed to help users identify any fish found in the area. Although live features that allow identification on the shore and underwater have been emphasised, other identification features of use to anglers and fishermen who may have a fish in the hand have also been included. Where useful photographs were not available, drawings have been used instead. The text is derived both from the enormous amount of existing published data on these fish, and from unpublished data and observations collected by the authors and other recorders. It is not claimed to be definitive because, although some fish have been extensively studied, others have not and for them, details such as life history are still very sketchy.

# WHAT IS A WELSH FISH ?

The title of the book refers to Wales and adjacent waters. Whilst it is possible to draw boundaries which are halfway between the coasts of Wales, England, the Isle of Man and Ireland (and these are shown on the map opposite), fish know no such boundaries and are free to swim and drift as they please. They are however, at the mercy of currents and may be affected by prevailing weather, ocean fronts where temperature and salinity can change abruptly and many other factors such as finding suitable habitats. So it is difficult to be specific about what precisely a 'Welsh marine fish' is.

Every effort has been made to determine which fish have been recorded within Welsh boundaries but this is not straightforward as records are not always easy to access or verify. Some fish are very difficult to identify with precision or may have been confused with other species and misidentified. Some fish, which are clearly within their global range in Welsh waters, have not as yet been recorded from Wales – a good example is the Red Blenny (page 219) which was only 'discovered' around Britain and Ireland within the last ten years and prior to this has been mistaken for the Tompot Blenny. In fact there appears to be no published 'definitive' list of the species of fish found around Britain and Ireland, partly, it has to be said, because defining the existence of a fish in a specific area is actually far from easy.

## RED BLENNY

The Red Blenny (page 219) has only been 'discovered' around Britain and Ireland within the last ten years although it has undoubtedly been present here for far longer and has been mistaken for the Tompot Blenny prior to this. A blenny was photographed by Paul Kay (one of the authors) off the Arran Islands in Galway Bay, Ireland in 1998. Its patterning and colour were unusual and finally it was conclusively identified as a male Red (or Portuguese) Blenny in breeding condition. Once this was ascertained it was possible to identify this blenny in other photos and in the field. It is now known to have been photographed previously (but misidentified as a Tompot) and has been positively identified from recent photos in a variety of locations around the west coasts of both Ireland and Scotland (as far north as St. Kilda), although not within Welsh waters as yet (see Goodwin & Picton, 2007).

With the potential of global warming to alter climatic conditions, there is the possibility of shifts in the distribution of some fishes. There is already evidence that this is happening, with some species, that are normally only summer visitors from further south, now remaining and possibly breeding in British waters. Increased seawater temperatures may lead to more 'southern' fish (and other) species being recorded in British, Irish and Welsh waters. Disorientation due to shifts in temperature and/or current patterns may result in increased numbers of vagrants being spotted and normally deep-sea dwelling fish being observed at shallower depths.

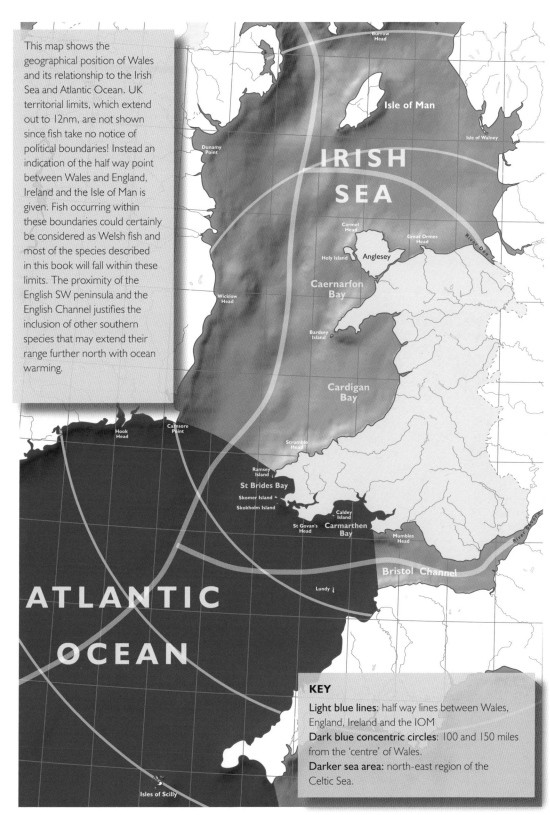

This map shows the geographical position of Wales and its relationship to the Irish Sea and Atlantic Ocean. UK territorial limits, which extend out to 12nm, are not shown since fish take no notice of political boundaries! Instead an indication of the half way point between Wales and England, Ireland and the Isle of Man is given. Fish occurring within these boundaries could certainly be considered as Welsh fish and most of the species described in this book will fall within these limits. The proximity of the English SW peninsula and the English Channel justifies the inclusion of other southern species that may extend their range further north with ocean warming.

**IRISH SEA**

Isle of Man

Burrow Head

Isle of Walney

Dunany Point

Carmel Head

Great Ormes Head

River Dee

Holy Island    Anglesey

**Caernarfon Bay**

Wicklow Head

Bardsey Island

**Cardigan Bay**

**ATLANTIC OCEAN**

Hook Head

Carnsore Point

Strumble Head

Ramsey Island

**St Brides Bay**

Skomer Island

Skokholm Island

St Govan's Head

Caldey Island

**Carmarthen Bay**

Mumbles Head

**Bristol Channel**

Lundy

River Severn

Isles of Scilly

**KEY**

**Light blue lines**: half way lines between Wales, England, Ireland and the IOM
**Dark blue concentric circles**: 100 and 150 miles from the 'centre' of Wales.
**Darker sea area**: north-east region of the Celtic Sea.

Finally there is the contentious issue of fisheries. If stocks shift, for whatever reason, numbers of a particular species may increase or decrease and the species available to catch may also change as stocks of traditionally targeted species wane and other species move in to replace them. There is therefore the possibility of a loss of both numbers and/or fish species available to fishermen.

Forrest's book mentions some fish species which we no longer seem to record within Welsh waters. One of these, the Wolf-fish (page 226), is a northern species and is generally considered to prefer cooler waters than those found around the Welsh coast at the moment. However, its is known to be in Cornish waters so may well still be present around Wales. The Common or Blue Skate is now considered to be effectively extinct around Wales today due to being over-fished a long time ago. Its life history reveals that it is a slow growing, long-lived fish that matures late and so is vulnerable to over-fishing for these and a variety of other reasons, few of which were appreciated when they were considered a common and cheap food source many years ago.

Recording which species are found where in Welsh waters will help to highlight what changes in fish populations, if any, are taking place and understand at least some of the above issues. This book aims to help readers to do this by making sure they are able to recognise and identify the fish they see.

It is to be hoped that in this, the 21st century, we are able to use the knowledge which we have amassed to help us to identify sea fishes, understand their distributions and abundances and take note of any changes, so that we may alter our policies and actions to ensure our impact on them is sustainable. If this book helps to foster an interest in Welsh marine fishes and achieve the above, then its authors will be satisfied that it was worth publishing.

# How to use this Book

The fish in this book are arranged in 'scientific' order. That is firstly within each of the three major fish groups Jawless fishes (lampreys and hagfish), Cartilaginous fishes (sharks, rays and chimaeras) and Bony fishes. If you have no idea at all what sort of fish you have, then turn first to the introductory pages for these three groups and decide which one your fish fits. Within each of these three main groups the fish are arranged in 'Families' within larger 'Orders', for example Codfish (Order Gadiformes) includes the Cod family (Gadidae), the Hake family (Merlucciidae) and the Rockling family (Lotidae). So you will then need to look through the book at the introductions to the orders or families or at the first example given for each family until you make a match. Once you know what sort of fish you have, for example a blenny or a gurnard, then you can work through those pages to decide which species it is.

Of course if you already know what sort of fish you are looking at, for example a goby, you can turn straight to the pages covering the Goby family. This is the first step in fish identification – learning the main identification features of each fish family or order. For example a fish with three dorsal fins and two anal fins will be a member of the codfish family (Gadidae).

To help you find a particular fish group quickly, each page is colour coded in the top corner. The colours represent the different 'Orders' of fish (such as Codfish) or groups of Orders (such as Sharks). These colours are shown in the Contents pages and are also reflected in the fish list in Appendix I.

The images used here have been chosen to try to illustrate either 'standard' versions of a species or specific identifying characteristics. Obtaining 'good' photographs of all these species has proved to be difficult and in some cases it has not been possible to do so. Illustrations have been used for species where good images were not readily available and also to highlight particular features.

However, as with all identification guides this book needs to be used with some acceptance that individuals may vary considerably from the 'standard' descriptions given here. This is especially true of colour which can, in some species, vary substantially, and is influenced by habitat, time of day, sexual state and other factors. There is often considerable variation between adult males of territorial species and the females and immature fish. Dead fish can change colour dramatically too and this is often confusing especially as early, and even some current, fish books were and are based on descriptions of dead fishes. Many original scientific descriptions were based on preserved specimens and so relied on persistent characteristics such as scale and fin ray counts. It is also worth remembering that colour patterns often fade in fish kept in aquaria.

For each species the text is arranged under different headings as described below. Where a fish is especially rare or little is known about it, the text may be condensed.

Whilst the sections on 'Key identification features' and 'Similar species' will perhaps be the most useful in terms of identifying your fish, other very useful clues will come from the 'Habitat' and 'Behaviour' sections. This is especially the case if you were not able to see or photograph all the physical features required. In the authors' experience a 'holistic' approach to fish identification is the most successful. Making notes on where (including habitat, depth and geographic location) and when a fish was seen or caught and even what the weather was like, will all help in identification. This is especially true of fish which are seen for only short periods of time because they have darted away to hide or because they have been released back into the sea. Traditional identification 'keys' used in many books require that specific features be seen and this is often not the case. So whilst we would encourage readers to use such keys as they become more experienced, we have not attempted to provide a key to Welsh fish identification here.

Left: Male Butterfly Blennies can now be observed in their natural habitat and can be seen to defend their eggs against other fish interested in a quick meal!

CLINGFISHES

# TWO-SPOTTED CLINGFISH

## Glynwr deusmotiog
### *Diplecogaster bimaculata bimaculata*

Other names: *Lepadogaster bimaculatus* (synonym)      6cm

**KEY IDENTIFICATION FEATURES** This little clingfish is difficult to distinguish from Small-headed Clingfish in the field. Males have two purple spots outlined with yellow on the sides behind the pectoral fins and if these are visible then identification is certain. These are quite low down and a close look may be needed to see them. This (and Small-headed Clingfish) have their single short dorsal fin set well back near the tail which distinguishes them from Shore and Connemara Clingfish. Individual fish vary in colour but many are a blotchy red with blue and brown spots.

**SIMILAR SPECIES** It is not possible to distinguish female Two-spotted Clingfish from Small-headed Clingfish in the field. Both are similar in size, shape and colour. In the laboratory, differences in fin ray counts, head size in relation to body size, and teeth help identification.

**BEHAVIOUR** These small fish tend to be rather secretive – their small size makes them a target for predatory fish – but if exposed by turning over stones for example, they often stay still, clinging on to the remains of their hidey hole.

**HABITAT** This clingfish lives mainly below the shore down to at least 55m, possibly 100m, but is sometimes found in rock pools near low water. It seems to prefer stony areas rather than bedrock and is also found on sediment where it hides in or under shells and stones. It has also been found in beds of bivalves such as horse mussels.

**DISTRIBUTION** Two-spotted Clingfish can be found all round the Welsh coastline, though they are not especially common or at least are not often seen. This is the only clingfish to extend as far north as Norway. It extends south round the British Isles and down into the western Mediterranean.

---

**The information provided for each species is as follows:**

**COMMON NAME** In general the Common name used is that given in www.fishbase.org (a freely available database of information on all the known fish species in the world). Occasionally a different name in more common use in Wales and the UK is used instead. Alternative common names are also given under 'Other names'.

**WELSH NAME** The Welsh name used is, wherever possible, the name adopted by Cymdeithas Edward Llwyd, but where no name has been adopted, the one shown has been taken from a list of marine species compiled by Dr B. Griffiths and Dr Llŷr Gruffydd.

**SCIENTIFIC NAME** The Scientific name used is that given in www.fishbase.org and where this has been updated in recent times, well known synonyms are also given under 'Other names'.

**SIZE** The size given for each fish is the approximate maximum total length. In heavily fished species this will often be greater than most fish caught today. In little recorded species it may be less than the true figure.

**KEY IDENTIFICATION FEATURES** The most important features for arriving at a correct identification are given.

**SIMILAR SPECIES** The species with which the fish is most likely to be confused in the field are highlighted along with a resume of how to tell the difference. In some cases, other very rare species or those just outside the range covered by this book are mentioned in case they turn up.

**BEHAVIOUR** Specific behaviour that might be observed underwater or in rock pools, and which might help identification, is described.

**HABITAT** The usual habitat of the species is described as this can help identification of similar species. Depth limits are not always known with accuracy and we would expect (and hope) to receive records outside the limits stated.

**DISTRIBUTION** This describes whether or not the fish has been recorded in Welsh waters (if known), its wider distribution around the British Isles and its approximate world distribution.

**NATURAL HISTORY** Details the life history, feeding habits and other information as currently known.

**SIGHTINGS** Briefly lists the people most likely to come across the fish, whether it is fished commercially, any landing restrictions and conservation status.

---

The 'spot' on the side of this male Two-spotted Clingfish is just visible and is a Key Identification Feature that helps to distinguish it from a Small-headed Clingfish. It is living on shell gravel and stones, a typical Habitat for this species. It is using its pelvic fin sucker to cling onto an empty shell, which is classic Behaviour for clingfishes.

# Identifying, Watching and Recording Fish

## IDENTIFYING FISH

Identifying a fish from a dead specimen ought to be easy you would have thought! However, even with the fish in front of you and available for detailed examination this can sometimes be difficult. Dead fish lose their 'posture' and colour and may suffer damage depending on how they were caught. In this book we have used photos of live fish wherever possible simply because it is far easier to visualise a dead fish when looking at an image of a live one than it is to work the other way round. So when examining a dead fish, it is important to use both the images and the text as your fish may look very different from the photograph.

Trying to identify a fish underwater can be a frustrating business as few fish will pose for you! However, if you know beforehand which features are most likely to help in your identification, then this will help considerably. Relying only on your memory after a dive is at best unreliable (at least we find it is!). So either a simple writing board ('dive-slate') or a camera, or preferably both, will help enormously.

### FISH SHAPES

The first thing to note is the general shape of the fish. Sometimes this in itself is sufficient for a positive identification, for example the unmistakable outline of a John Dory. More usually it will narrow the field down to a number of possibilities, for example a long thin eel-like or snake-like fish is likely to be either an eel, pipefish, Ling, rockling, or perhaps one of the blenny-like fish such as a Rock Gunnel. Again sometimes the colour pattern of a fish is unique allowing a fish such as a Cuckoo Wrasse to be recognised instantly.

John Dory

Horse Mackerel

Ling

Short-snouted Seahorse

Cuckoo Wrasse

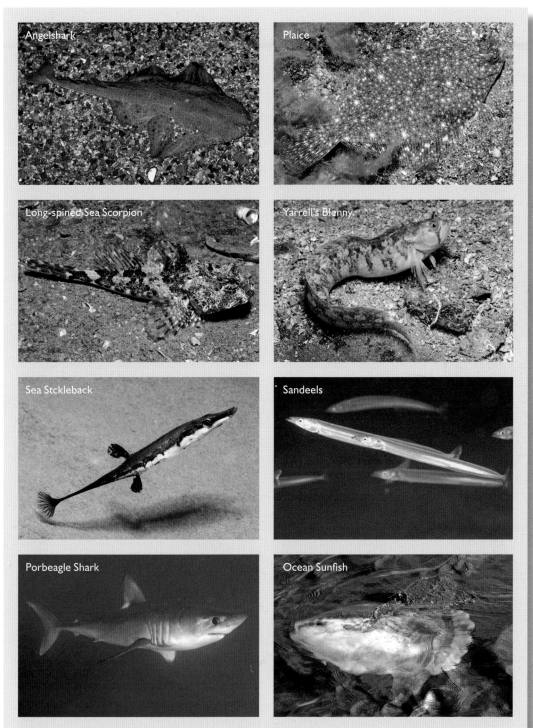

Most people can recognise a shark as such, from its characteristic outline, underslung mouth and gill slits. However, an Angelshark is more like a ray in shape. Most rays and skates have a very similar outline and it is quite easy to learn to recognise them as such. The same applies to flatfish, and their outline will even show up through a light covering of sand. In contrast the bizarre shape of a seahorse or an Ocean Sunfish could cast doubts on whether these were fish at all!

After this initial (two second) look, it is helpful to record the following in rough order of priority:

## FINS: the number of dorsal and anal fins and their shape as well as the shape of the tail.

Small-spotted Catshark: two dorsal fins close together near tail.

Spurdog: two dorsal fins with dorsal fin spines.

Black Scorpionfish: one dorsal fin, divided into two types of fin rays.

Whiting: (and all in the family Gadidae) have three dorsal fins.

Dragonet: two dorsal fins, the first triangular.

Three-bearded Rockling: one long dorsal fin, one anal fin, convex tail fin.

Sea Trout: Small adipose (fatty) fin; straight-cut or slightly concave tail fin.

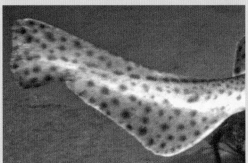

Small-spotted Catchark: unequal (heterocercal) tail fin.

**LATERAL LINE: the shape of the lateral line if evident e.g. straight, curved, not visible.**

Pollack: lateral line curved.

Saithe: lateral line straight.

Atlantic Cod.

Horse Mackerel.

Red Gurnard.

Tub Gurnard.

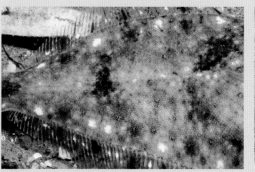
Dab.

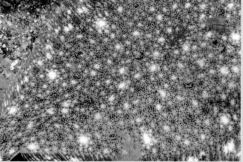
Plaice.

**EYES: position and size e.g. on top of head, bulging.**

Flatfish: on top of head, bulging.

Sand Smelt: on sides of head, large.

Dragonet: on top of head.

Ray: on top of head, bulging.

Pipefish: near top of head, large.

Catshark: pupil has diagonal orientation.

Montagu's Sea Snail: on sides of head, tiny.

Black Goby.

**MOUTH: whether the jaws are equal, or either jaw is longer than the other.**

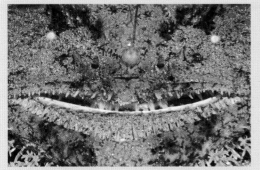
Anglerfish: huge mouth.

Lumpsucker: thick lips.

Cod: upper jaw longer than lower and barbel.

Conger Eel: upper jaw longer than lower (just).

Plaice: small mouth.

Lamprey: sucker mouth.

Greater Pipefish: tubular mouth.

Pollack: lower jaw longer than upper.

## MARKINGS: distinctive spots, lines, colour etc.

Nursehound: blotches, saddles and spots.

John Dory: distinct ocellus.

Atlantic Cod: spots and reticulation.

Anglerfish: cryptic coloration.

Mullet: lateral stripes.

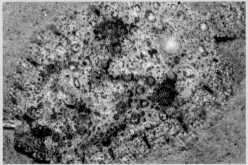
Cuckoo Wrasse: distinct coloration.

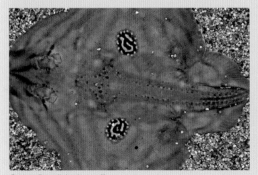
Cuckoo Ray: distinctive ocelli.

Eckstom's Topknot.

**SIZE: an approximation of the size compared to say a hand or arm.**

Remembering the mnemonic FLEMMS that is spelt out by the initial letters of these features, you can make very quick notes or drawings on a board that will in many cases be sufficient to identify the fish even without a photograph, though the latter will help greatly.

So for example a fish with three dorsal and two anal fins, a gently curved lateral line, the upper jaw overhanging the lower which has a single chin barbel, banded with brown and white vertical stripes is a Pouting or Bib *Trisopterus luscus*.

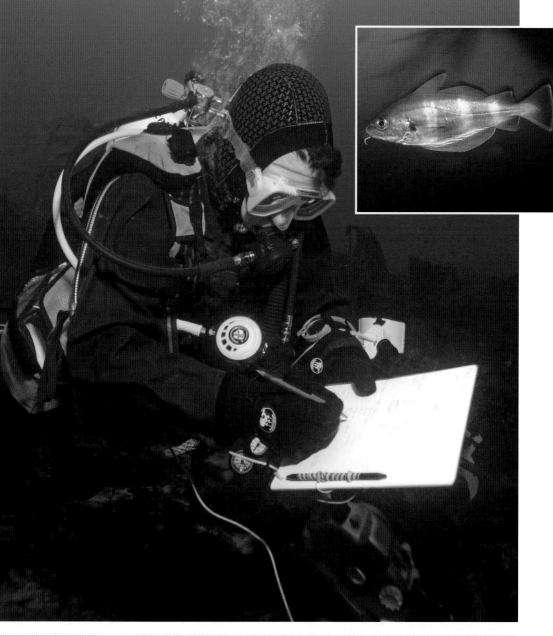

# WATCHING FISH

Obviously if a fish is dead then it can be examined at leisure and this is clearly the case with fish washed up on the strandline or commercially caught. Anglers may have both live and dead fish. Examining dead fish, even those bought for your supper, will help hone identification skills. Little more need be said other than to comment that colour changes can be substantial when a fish dies affecting both tone and patterning. So colour is not always a very useful identification feature in dead fish. Dead fish are often damaged when captured and it is important to remember that fins may be broken or even missing making identification even more difficult.

Watching live fish is possible for just about anyone but divers are in many ways in the best position to watch fish in their own environment. Perhaps the most important attributes for fish watching divers are good buoyancy control along with both patience and a patient diving buddy! But this has to be tempered with an understanding that time underwater is precious and is always curtailed by decompression requirements.

Many fish are frightened by divers' exhaled bubbles – they can feel the vibrations that these cause in the water. So breathing gently and evenly is helpful. Some fish can be enticed closer or lured out of their hidey-holes by gently scrabbling fingers in the sediment or undergrowth. Gobies and blennies will often come over to look for titbits rather like a garden robin does. Others such as wrasse are naturally curious and are attracted by the glint of a camera, watch or even diving knife!

Opposite. Man made objects are all too often discarded into the sea. Some such as this empty beer bottle prove useful to some marine life. Here the bottle serves as a handy refuge for a Black Goby.

Below. Curiosity has won over fear with this Ballan Wrasse. Many wrasse, blennies and gobies can be enticed nearer for a close look and portrait photo by the gentle glint of a camera or white fingers. This is especially so in areas where divers are the 'norm'.

Looking for fish is not always easy, many take refuge from intruding divers and as they live in dark, murky and often difficult to access environments, finding some species can be difficult.

Watching live fish in an aquarium is the closest many people will come to seeing them underwater. However, even for divers this can be a useful (and warm!) way of learning more. Knowledge of how they swim, move and feed can not only help identify fish but will also allow you to pinpoint any unusual behaviour. It will also help you to recognise that individual fish of a particular species vary just as humans do, especially between sexes, juveniles and adults.

As more experience is built up, the easier recognition becomes. Once familiar with a particular fish or type it becomes easier to anticipate and recognise their behaviour and so once back underwater not miss out on a fish building a nest or spawning. You may then also recognize that the behaviour you are seeing may never have been recorded or photographed before!

Rock pools also offer a chance to watch living fish although unless one is caught, then glimpses of fast moving, darting fish are the usual reality. If fish are caught then ensure their welfare by examining them quickly and returning them as soon as possible. Always put them back into the pool that they were caught in, as some are territorial.

Lastly there are opportunities to see, if not actual fish, then fishy traces! Look for eggs under seaweed on the shore, egg cases on the strandline, or even feeding marks made by fish in shallow water when the tide is in, which are revealed in the sand as the tide ebbs.

# RECORDING FISH

Many divers, anglers and seashore naturalists keep records of the fish they have seen and identified simply to increase their knowledge and for their own interest and satisfaction. There are however, many routes through which this vast store of useful information can be made available to a wider audience. There are a number of schemes to which records can be submitted. Details of current (2009) schemes are given in Appendix II (see page 250) and we would encourage all 'fish watchers' to submit their records to one or more of these.

For anglers, the main emphasis is likely to be records of weight and size and Welsh records can be submitted through angling clubs, competition organisers and associations. Divers however, are in a unique position amongst fish watchers to record much more than just where and when a fish was spotted. They can also make first hand observations of fish behaviour. For example recording the presence of juveniles of a southern species in Welsh waters at a size and at a time of year when they could not have migrated north from warmer waters, would indicate that a species was now breeding in Welsh waters.

So just what is a record? When a species new to science is discovered and described, then protocol insists that in almost all cases a specimen in needed which can be kept in a museum. However, in Welsh waters it is far more likely that a 'new record' will be of an already recognised species that has not previously been recorded from Welsh waters. In this case a simple record if it is an easily recognised species will suffice or a photograph or even a detailed description if it is more unusual.

Even records of common Welsh fish can be very useful if details of place and habitat are supplied. In this way it may be found for example, that a fish previously thought only to live offshore is found in rock pools at a certain time of its life.

For any record the minimum information needed is Date, Location, Depth (if applicable) and Recorder's name and contact. The type of record, i.e. photograph, drawing, specimen etc. will help those using the records to ascertain its reliability. Different recording schemes may ask you to input additional or different parameters.

A female Black Goby has laid eggs in the scallop shell and these are now being guarded by a male.

# Parts of a fish

Knowing your way around the parts of a fish will help you to record your fish quickly and efficiently as identification often relies on the presence, absence, shape or position of a particular fin or other body part. The following labelled drawings provide names and examples of fish parts in sharks, rays, fusiform bony fish flatfish and seahorses. All the examples shown have the same set of fins but these vary in size and position. Compare the different diagrams to become familiar with each body plan. Pectoral and pelvic fins are always paired. In sharks the pelvic fins are set far back and could be mistaken for an anal fin if only one is seen. Dorsal and anal fins are always single, though there may be more than one. Compare the photograph and diagram of the Bass. In the photograph the Bass has lowered its first dorsal fin and therefore appears only to have one – another potential source of confusion. In rays, the dorsal fins are set far back on the tail and most have no tail (caudal) fin. In flatfish the pelvic fins are difficult to see. Spot them and it will tell you that this is the ventral (belly) side of the fish. This will help you to envisage the fish swimming 'upright' and so you can then tell whether it is 'left-eyed' or 'right-eyed' like this plaice (see page 143).

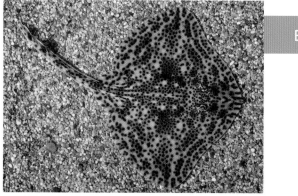

## EXTERNAL FEATURES OF A RAY

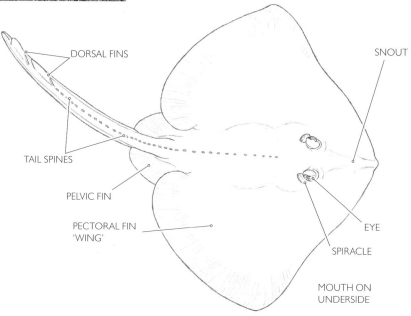

DORSAL FINS

SNOUT

TAIL SPINES

PELVIC FIN

PECTORAL FIN 'WING'

EYE

SPIRACLE

MOUTH ON UNDERSIDE

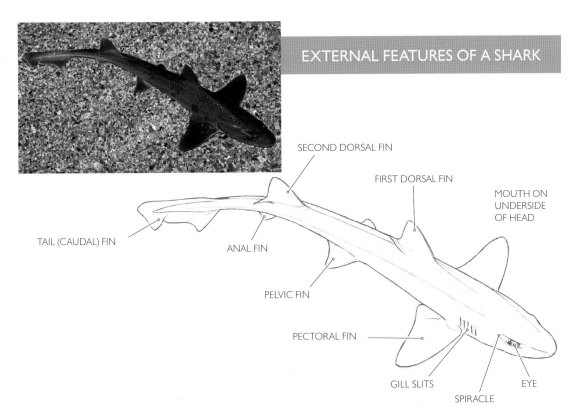

## EXTERNAL FEATURES OF A SHARK

SECOND DORSAL FIN

FIRST DORSAL FIN

MOUTH ON UNDERSIDE OF HEAD

TAIL (CAUDAL) FIN

ANAL FIN

PELVIC FIN

PECTORAL FIN

GILL SLITS

SPIRACLE

EYE

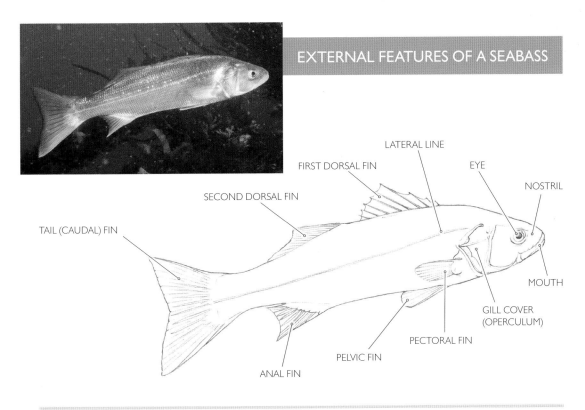

## EXTERNAL FEATURES OF A SEABASS

LATERAL LINE

FIRST DORSAL FIN

EYE

NOSTRIL

SECOND DORSAL FIN

TAIL (CAUDAL) FIN

MOUTH

GILL COVER (OPERCULUM)

PECTORAL FIN

PELVIC FIN

ANAL FIN

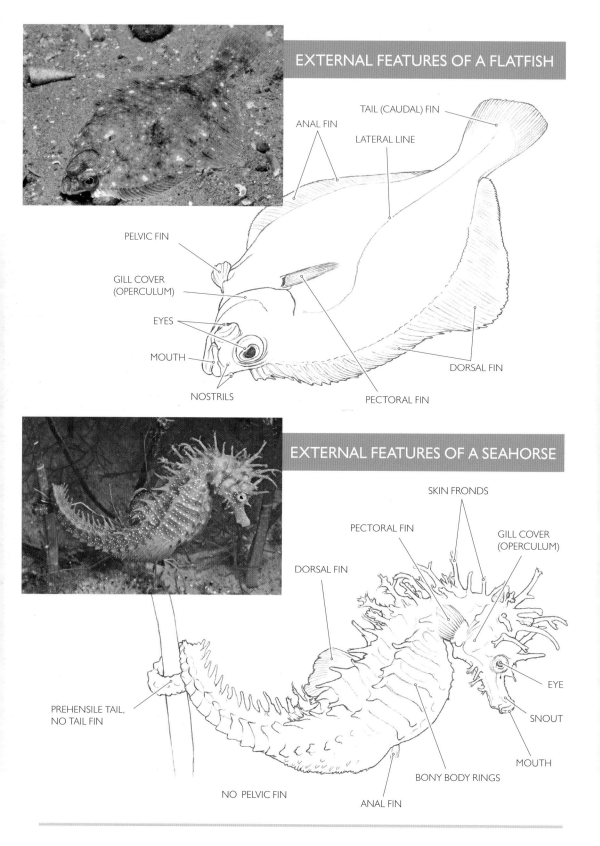

## EXTERNAL FEATURES OF A FLATFISH

ANAL FIN

TAIL (CAUDAL) FIN

LATERAL LINE

PELVIC FIN

GILL COVER
(OPERCULUM)

EYES

MOUTH

NOSTRILS

PECTORAL FIN

DORSAL FIN

## EXTERNAL FEATURES OF A SEAHORSE

SKIN FRONDS

PECTORAL FIN

GILL COVER
(OPERCULUM)

DORSAL FIN

EYE

SNOUT

MOUTH

PREHENSILE TAIL,
NO TAIL FIN

BONY BODY RINGS

NO PELVIC FIN

ANAL FIN

# Where and How to See Fish

Strolling along the strandline of a sandy beach, searching in rock pools on a rocky coastline, diving and angling from boats and shore and being on board a commercial or research fishing boat, all provide opportunities for seeing and studying fish. The following pages describe where and how to make use of these opportunities and what you might expect to see.

In addition, a visit to a local aquarium will help you to become familiar with different fish groups and allow you pick out identification features without even getting wet! Take this book along for practice and try taking digital photographs (if allowed) for later use. Anglesey Sea Zoo **www.angleseyseazoo.co.uk** and SeaQuarium **www.seaquariumrhyl.co.uk** both have reasonable collections of local fish species.

Public aquaria are one place where it is possible to see some of the larger Welsh fish alive and in conditions which are similar to their natural environment.

# THE STRANDLINE

Anyone who has ever visited the seashore, especially a long sandy one in winter, will have come across the debris collected by wind and waves and dumped unceremoniously as the tide recedes. Seaweed, shells, plastic and fishing debris are all commonplace, but as fish can swim against a current and most are never found out of water, the strandline does not immediately come to mind as a good place to search for them. However, after winter storms and occasionally at other times, fish get caught out and are deposited on the shore amongst the other debris.

Most stranded fish are inshore dwellers and some are actually caught out by their own behaviour. The Lumpsucker (see page 141) is one such fish, because the male guards the eggs laid by the female and is so zealous, that even where they have been placed in a very shallow location, he will not leave them. In stormy weather, his strong sucker may not be enough to prevent him being washed ashore and sometimes large numbers are stranded. Small lumpsuckers, dressed in their blue or green juvenile colours can also be stranded. Pipefish and seahorses live entwined in seaweed and seagrass and may be washed ashore along with their weedy home during violent storms.

Some fishes appear to be thrown ashore when weakened or killed by cold winter waters. This applies especially to fish with a predominantly southern distribution that move north into our waters in the summer. Triggerfish (see page 164) wash up in late autumn, and often appear to be in poor condition. Atlantic Pomfret (see page 181) get trapped by influxes of cold water when making their way back south in autumn. This is a common occurrence in the southern North Sea.

Above. Wave action proved too much for this young Lumpsucker, which has washed ashore.

Left. Triggerfish that stray too far north in summer may not make it back to warmer southern waters in autumn.

Sometimes far more unusual fishes are found on the shore – the swordfish on page 239 for example – and these can include some very strange fish indeed. Deep sea species do, on occasion, wash up although why they do so is not always clear. Some, such as the Lantern Fish or Pearlside shown here, clearly carry out vertical migrations at night and this combined with bad weather is probably responsible for their demise. Similarly oceanic fish are sometimes carried to our shores by strong or aberrant currents. For many of us this is the only opportunity we will ever have of seeing such strange and unusual fish.

The strandline also contains other fish-related material. Whilst 'mermaid's purses' are discussed on page 75, the strandline offers another opportunity to examine these and collect data on species, numbers and location. Such information gives us useful clues as to where the fish are breeding. Many of these eggcases soon darken and can be very difficult to distinguish from the dry seaweed with which they are often found. But fresher eggcases are much lighter and those from the Smallspotted Catshark and from the Nursehound are relatively easy to spot and identify (pages 58 to 61). Reports of such finds or the egg cases themselves can be sent to the Shark Trust **www.sharktrust.org** for their Great Eggcase Hunt. Collated data from this project is providing a better picture of the localities in which these fish lay their eggs.

Above. A Pearlside or Lanternfish *Maurolicus muelleri* lives up to its name, its light organs gleaming even after it has been tossed ashore.

Right. After hatching, this ray or skate eggcase has been tossed ashore as a 'Mermaid's purse'.

# ROCK POOLS

Life on the shore can be hard. With the tide out, seashore animals and plants are exposed to hot sun in summer, freezing snow in winter and diluting rain. It is therefore perhaps surprising that the seashore is an important habitat for fish. Rock pools are one of the reasons for this. A deep rock pool lined with stones and seaweed provides a habitat for small fish where they will be safe from large predators. Some fish such as the Shanny are specialist shore dwellers and can squirm from pool to pool even with the tide out. Most are camouflage experts. Long-spined Sea Scorpions match their colour to the background whilst Worm Pipefish mimic long brown seaweed strands.

## WHERE AND WHEN

The greatest variety of shore fish are found in the south west of the British Isles including southern Wales, and the shores of Pembrokeshire and the Gower Peninsula are good hunting grounds. However, whilst shore fish can live under and between boulders and seaweeds, most live in rock pools and the presence of pools depends on geology and wave exposure. So shores with a varied topography, good seaweed cover and deep rock pools will support the most fish. In northern Wales, good shore pools can be found on the Llŷn Peninsula, Anglesey and the offshore islands.

Spring and summer are usually the best times to find shore fish because, whilst some are all year residents, many others move off the shore in winter to avoid the cold. Juveniles of many other species such as Sand Smelt use the shore as a nursery but move away as they grow.

### Common Welsh Rock Pool Fish

Shanny page 215
Rock Gunnel page 221
Rock Goby page 203
Shore Rockling page 102
Five-bearded Rockling page 102
Shore Clingfish page 113
Worm Pipefish page 122
Long-spined Sea Scorpion page 128
Corkwing Wrasse page 189

A careful scrutiny under seaweeds can turn up the unexpected. These eggs probably belong to the Long-spined Sea Scorpion and have been stuck down to bedrock below seaweed.

## HOW TO SEE

Most rock pool fish stay out of sight at low tide to avoid the unwelcome attention of seabirds and otters. So watching them in their natural habitat is not easy. Gobies and blennies will sometimes perch out in open sunny patches in their pools but will dive for cover at the hint of a shadow or noisy footstep. Try lying at the edge of a large pool and using a face mask to peer below the surface. Or make a pool goggler from plastic drain pipe with Perspex fixed into one end with silicone sealant. Of course the time honoured method is to use a small hand net to catch fish hiding under curtains of seaweed and between rocks. But this is not easy! Put the fish into a white bucket or tray and then return them as soon as possible to the same pool. Turning boulders is often rewarding but remember to turn the rocks back again.

As the tide recedes the shallow water may reveal plentiful sea-weeds under which fish can lie in the damp conditions until the sea returns.

Looking down on a fish gives a quite different view of it. Here a Rock Goby is quickly identified by the scales on its nape.

Worm Pipefishes lie in rock pools and require a lot of looking for. Their long, thin, brown body merges into the seaweed, in which they are often found, extremely well.

Rock pools are not always sculpted out of bedrock. Many are formed as boulders are washed out of the shore and pools are formed between these and the cobbles, pebbles and sand surrounding them. Such pools are a good place to look for fish as the boulders offer plenty of good cover for them and they often hide underneath such shelters.

# DIVERS AND FISH

As divers are able to enter the underwater world directly, they are clearly in the best position to view fish in their own natural environment and to be able to record what they see. Until the advent of scuba diving, the presence and abundance of fish species could only be ascertained through fish catches. Small, cryptic species such as the Leopard-spotted goby that live in rock crevices and burrows are rarely, if ever caught. Diver records are essential for determining the distribution of such species. Not only does direct observation allow for identification of many fish *in situ*, it also allows behavioural information to be gathered and documented using still or video cameras. Furthermore the documented behaviour will be natural and not influenced by the animals being within the confines of an aquarium. Even today it is quite possible to record behaviour that has never been observed before, let alone photographed.

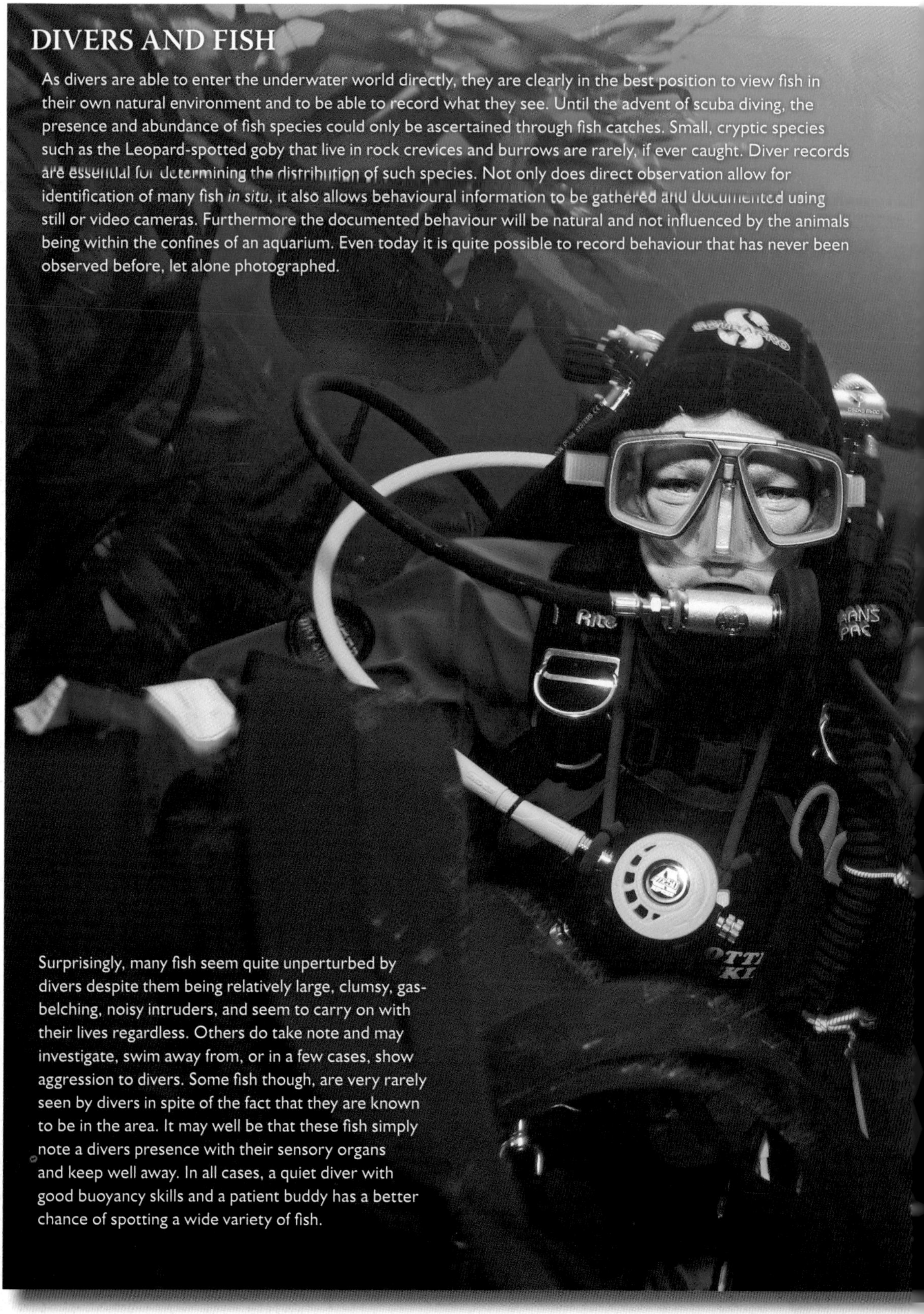

Surprisingly, many fish seem quite unperturbed by divers despite them being relatively large, clumsy, gas-belching, noisy intruders, and seem to carry on with their lives regardless. Others do take note and may investigate, swim away from, or in a few cases, show aggression to divers. Some fish though, are very rarely seen by divers in spite of the fact that they are known to be in the area. It may well be that these fish simply note a divers presence with their sensory organs and keep well away. In all cases, a quiet diver with good buoyancy skills and a patient buddy has a better chance of spotting a wide variety of fish.

Divers are often only familiar with a relatively small number of different fish. These are usually the bottom dwellers, many of which will remain still for inspection thinking they can't be seen. Perhaps the least familiar are the fast moving species. In the low contrast, dimly lit undersea world, a fleeting glimpse of such fish is often all that is obtained and this is hardly sufficient for easy identification. Despite this, knowing what to look for (such as the shape of the lateral line and barbel on silvery shoaling fish) can allow accurate identification from even such tantalising glimpses.

With cameras it is possible to capture images that will allow for accurate identification after the dive. Even without a camera a diver can note down details about the fish or sketch unusual fish which cannot be identified during the dive itself. As has been previously mentioned, familiarity with the pertinent features of fish will make it easier to record the important details so that an accurate identification can still be made later on.

Any knowledge gained about fish features on dry land will allow you to make the most of your short observation time underwater. However, not all fish can be identified underwater, especially some of the closely related species and it is important not to guess an identity if there is any doubt about just which fish you have seen.

# SEA ANGLING

The well-known conservationist, Dr David Bellamy, once described anglers as 'the eyes and ears of the water environment', and sea anglers are likely to be amongst the first people to notice changes in the marine environment. Any records of the fish they catch are therefore of great importance.

Welsh sea anglers are very fortunate as they fish along a coastline that stretches from the Severn estuary in the south to the Dee estuary in the north. This coastline provides a huge variety of shores and types of seabed and this variation attracts many different species of fish.

Angling is one of Britain's favourite participation sports – more people go fishing on a weekend than play football or rugby – and angling is a lifelong passion for many and is particularly popular with young people. Fortunately, much of the coastline of Wales is very accessible and provides a great variety of excellent shore angling locations.

There are exposed surf beaches, such as those of Llangennith, Freshwater West and Hells Mouth (Porth Neigwl) which are hotspots for Bass and mullet. Black Bream, wrasse, large bass, and Pollock find that there are plenty of hiding places for them along the rocky reefs of Gower, Pembrokeshire and the Lleyn Peninsula, whilst the sandy estuaries of the Burry Inlet and the Dyfi and Tywi rivers are home to a variety of flatfish as well as migratory Salmon and Sewin (Sea Trout). Many angling locations such as Penmon (shown here) are spectacular.

In addition to shore angling, boat based fishing is also very popular around Wales. Most Welsh ports and harbours have charter boats run by experienced skippers who have a wide knowledge of the local marks (fishing spots). Favourite species for boat anglers include Seabass and bream around the rock marks, flatfish and rays over the sandy marks and sharks, including both the Blue and Porbeagle are caught in hotspots along the west coast. Being out at sea also means that there is the possibility of catching more unusual and less seen species and of seeing giants such as Sunfish and Basking Sharks swimming at the surface.

**Dabs can be recognised from the hump in their lateral line and their orange pectoral fin which retains its colour even in a dead fish.**

Male Cuckoo Wrasses are strikingly colourful and are immediately recognisable.

Active sea angling clubs are based all along the Welsh coast. Some of these clubs run local and regional as well as national competitions and offer a focus for local anglers to develop their sport. Many clubs now promote a 'catch-and-return' policy, advocating that, even though freshly caught fish is wonderfully tasty, anglers should only take what they can actually eat. Sea angling clubs and their umbrella organisations also lobby government to ensure better management of fish stocks and the wider marine environment. It is important to ensure that the seas around Wales remain both healthy and productive in terms of fish numbers and diversity of species.

Sea anglers and angling clubs are able to contribute towards our knowledge of Welsh fish by participating in recording schemes and can supply details of their catches and other wildlife observations. See Appendix II on page 250 at the end of the book for details.

# COMMERCIAL FISHING IN WALES

Welsh fishermen and fishing communities have been catching and supplying fish for thousands of years. The stone-age people who transported stones from the Preseli Hills almost certainly traded for fish from Milford Haven. Early fishermen would have worked from both the shore and small boats and have used a variety of ingenious methods including hook and line, nets and traps, to catch their fish. These age-old, artisanal techniques are now considered to be the most sustainable ways of catching fish and cause the least impact on the marine environment.

With the exception of advances in boat design and build, these traditional methods of fishing probably changed little until the advent of sailing trawlers in the 16th and 17th centuries. Wind provided sufficient power to allow fishermen to pull trawl nets over the seabed and catch larger quantities of fish.

The steam engine revolutionized fishing as it did life on the land. In the 19th century, steam trawlers gave fishermen the capacity to catch far larger quantities of fish and the improved transport on land provided them with access to new and expanding markets in the big cities. The industrialisation of fishing saw the rise of large fishing ports in Wales including Milford Haven in the south and Holyhead and Conwy in the north. These ports were home to large fleets of trawlers and the smaller herring drifters. By 1924 Milford Haven was home to 101 steam trawlers and upwards of 170 herring drifters.

The large fishing fleets, improved vessels and effective fishing gear landed huge quantities of fish for the markets, but to the detriment of the fish stocks upon which they relied. Over-fishing and poor management caused many of the most important fish stocks to show a significant decline by the mid-20th Century.

The Welsh fishing industry is now striving to address this previous overexploitation. Today, many of the current fishing vessels are now small boats (under ten metres long), manned by either a few crewmen, or just a skipper. Many now pursue a variety of fish species utilising various traditional methods, such as static nets and hook and line. These time-honoured methods are intended to ensure that top quality fish are landed to market with minimal impact.

At the time of writing, changes in the way that fisheries are managed in Wales are imminent and it is anticipated that Welsh fishermen themselves will play a more active role. Adopting co-management approaches, advocated by many conservation groups and independent experts, should place fishermen and scientists at the heart of the management process as they work in partnership with fishery managers and government. As a result, Welsh fishermen should be able to operate within well-managed fisheries, which have long-term sustainability, whilst also ensuring a healthy and diverse marine environment.

Fish have traditionally been an important part of the Welsh diet. They are an excellent source of protein and provide a variety of different essential vitamins and minerals. Oily fish such as herrings and mackerel are rich in Omega-3 fatty acids, which are beneficial for heart health and are also necessary for brain development, joint function and healthy skin.

# Photographing Fish

The digital revolution has transformed photography. The accessibility of digital recording equipment (cameras, mobile telephones and video systems) and the ease and low cost of use of capturing images, means that most people are now able to photograph subjects which they would never have considered trying to take images of on film.

This applies to fish too! Whether the fish have been caught by anglers, found washed up on a beach, are seen in rock-pools, at a market or even underwater, they can be photographed. Underwater photography, once the preserve of just a few enthusiasts, is now being undertaken by more and more scuba divers. Cost of equipment has come down substantially and its effectiveness has improved dramatically.

Fish though, can be difficult subjects to photograph wherever they are and in whatever condition.

## Equipment

Image capturing equipment falls into several categories – not all of which are primarily cameras! Equipment in the first category is essentially designed to take images as a secondary function. Some mobile phones fall into this category and they can produce remarkably good results. It is also possible to use video cameras to shoot stills (some have this function), or frame 'grabs' can be taken and can be very useful (some of the images in this book are from frame 'grabs').

The second category of equipment is the so called 'compact' cameras which are easily portable but which vary in their abilities. Many are highly automated and users can rely on them to produce good images with little input from the photographer. Some are capable of producing extremely high quality images, but do so without the absolute precision of the third category.

This is the digital single lens reflex camera. These are capable of the highest quality results but require the highest level of skill and understanding by the photographer.

Whatever your equipment, it is important to remember that because the fishes in this book are all marine, it is likely that taking photographs of them will mean using your equipment near or even in salt water. Salt water and electronics do not mix! Even splashing electronic equipment with salt water can destroy it. Care should be taken to ensure that dry hands are used to handle phones and cameras, or if possible, they are shielded inside purpose-built waterproof housings or sleeves of which there are many available.

## Techniques

Different image capturing devices (it is difficult to describe a telephone as a camera) require different techniques to produce useful images but the one technique which is both obvious and simple is always to take lots of photos and from lots of angles. Taking digital photographs is inexpensive, so err on the side of taking too many. Then review all the images to make sure they are acceptably sharp and show all the details that seem relevant.

Always get as close to the fish as possible and as well as taking pictures of the whole fish also take detail shots of fins (preferably open if the fish will cooperate) and any other specific details which look like they may be useful. Dead fish should be photographed with their fins extended to show their shape, size and the number of rays.

As fish are wet a big problem is that of reflections when photographing them out of water. The water on them reflects light extremely well and this shows up as areas of white with no information in them. One solution is to photograph them in water. This generally only applies to smaller fish and involves putting the fish in a bowl or tray (preferably white) of water. They can then be photographed. Try using a piece of black card (with a hole for the lens) in front of the camera to reduce reflections. Ideally lights can be used either side of the fish at 45° to the water to illuminate it to best advantage.

Although not usually feasible underwater, whenever possible a scale (such as a coin or ruler) and neutral reference colour (grey) together with a label (date and location) should be included in the photograph as these can help to record both size and to some extent colour.

Cheaper cameras generally produce Jpeg or possibly Tiff files. Whilst these are usually perfectly adequate for most uses, if it is at all possible, it is best to shoot RAW files as well (some cameras will produce BOTH Jpeg and Tiff files). These files contain much more information than either Jpeg or Tiff files and can allow more data to be extracted from them during post-processing on a computer. They are especially useful in low contrast conditions such as those often found underwater. Substantial adjustments are sometimes possible to RAW files with appropriate software and these

Underwater photography requires a high degree of diving competence if large, sophisticated cameras are to be used.

may dramatically change an image and allow useful details to be enhanced that may help identification. Colour balance is much easier to adjust, especially if there is an item of 'neutral' colour included in the photograph (white or grey) and this can allow for better appreciation of the colour of the fish which has been photographed.

# Underwater

Underwater photography requires a high degree of diving competence if large sophisticated cameras are to be used. The biggest problem when taking photographs underwater around Wales is that of underwater visibility. Again it is best to get as close to the subject as possible, but many fish are wary of divers and so it isn't always easy or possible. Underwater photography is a specialised photographic genre and any divers who take it up will soon learn of the pitfalls which can only be overcome by reading up on the subject and talking to as many other underwater photographers as possible. Whilst practise and experience will allow high quality images to be shot, knowledge of the subjects being photographed (such as fish) is also essential.

# Metadata

The traditional method of adding metadata to an image is straightforward – simply add a label and scale onto an image. Today, digital files automatically carry metadata – that is embedded textual information about the image file and its contents. Some information is automatically embedded in the image file by the camera when the image is taken (details such as date and time for example). More can be added later and this can include the photographer's name, contact details, location of image (and this can even come directly or indirectly via software, from a GPS unit), identification of the subject and a great deal more.

Embedding metadata requires appropriate software and an understanding of how it all works, but is a very useful way of retaining information and as it is embedded within image files, it is far safer than most other ways of recording it. Various software solutions exist to enable metadata to be added to image files and this is an area where developments are still advancing quickly. Web searches will reveal more about metadata as well as current software and how to use it.

Metadata is potentially a very powerful tool for imagery because it can add an immense value to each image, as it retains information that may prove to be extremely useful if the image is later used to confirm the presence of a species, or even the identity of an unusual species.

Above. Rare sights such as shoals of fish feeding are photographed opportunistically – here simply by snorkelling amidst them.

Below. The eggs of this Butterfly Blenny have been laid in an empty whelk shell and are guarded by the male who will also ensure that they have water gently 'blown' over them to maintain their well-being, for as long as it is needed.

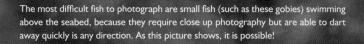

The most difficult fish to photograph are small fish (such as these gobies) swimming above the seabed, because they require close up photography but are able to dart away quickly is any direction. As this picture shows, it is possible!

# Fish Identification

The next section of the book is an identification guide to the many fishes which are or which may be found in Welsh waters. As already mentioned in the section 'How to use this book' (see page 11) the photographs we have used here represent the 'norm' for each species but the ones you see may vary from this. So it is important to use both the photographs and the text. Also remember that information such as maximum depth or size may change as more observations are made.

With most fish it is easy to see where its back (dorsal) side is and where its belly (ventral) side is and so count the relevant fins etc. This is much more difficult in flatfish (pages 143–163) and so a brief explanation follows. Flatfish start out life as normal larval fish swimming upright in the plankton. As they develop, they become thinner and flatter, start to swim on their side and eventually settle on the seabed lying on either their left or their right side. This means that one eye is now underneath but soon this eye migrates round until it is close to the other eye on the upward-facing side. Different species end up either with both eyes on what was their left side (left-eyed flatfish) or both eyes on what was their right side (right-eyed flatfish). To visualise the fish upright and so tell which is which, remember that the pectoral fin will always be below the lateral line.

The general shape, single long dorsal fin, large scales and bright coloration identify this as a Rock Cook wrasse in its breeding colours.

# Jawless Fish

Hagfish (Myxinidae) and lampreys (Petromyzontidae) are strange eel-like fish which do not have proper biting jaws. In fact they do not have much of a skeleton at all. Although considered as primitive vertebrates, they do not have a proper backbone, but instead a flexible rod of cartilage runs the length of the body. Although superficially similar in appearance, these two groups of fish evolved separately. One species of hagfish and two lampreys are found in Welsh marine waters. Brook Lamprey *Lampetra planeri* are only found in rivers and streams.

Hagfish live their whole lives in the sea whereas lampreys migrate up rivers to spawn. Hagfish feed on carrion and are expert scavengers consuming dead and dying fish, and tearing chunks off whale and dolphin carcasses. They will attack fish caught in nets and on long lines if these are left in place for too long. They can also eat crustaceans and other invertebrates. In contrast Sea and River Lampreys are mostly parasitic on live fish. They fix themselves to large fish or marine mammals with their sucker-like mouth and gradually rasp their way in using horny teeth. They feed for a few days and then drop off. The victim, especially if it is large, may survive though River Lampreys often kill their smaller fish hosts. They can cause considerable damage to fish stocks especially to captive fish in fish farms.

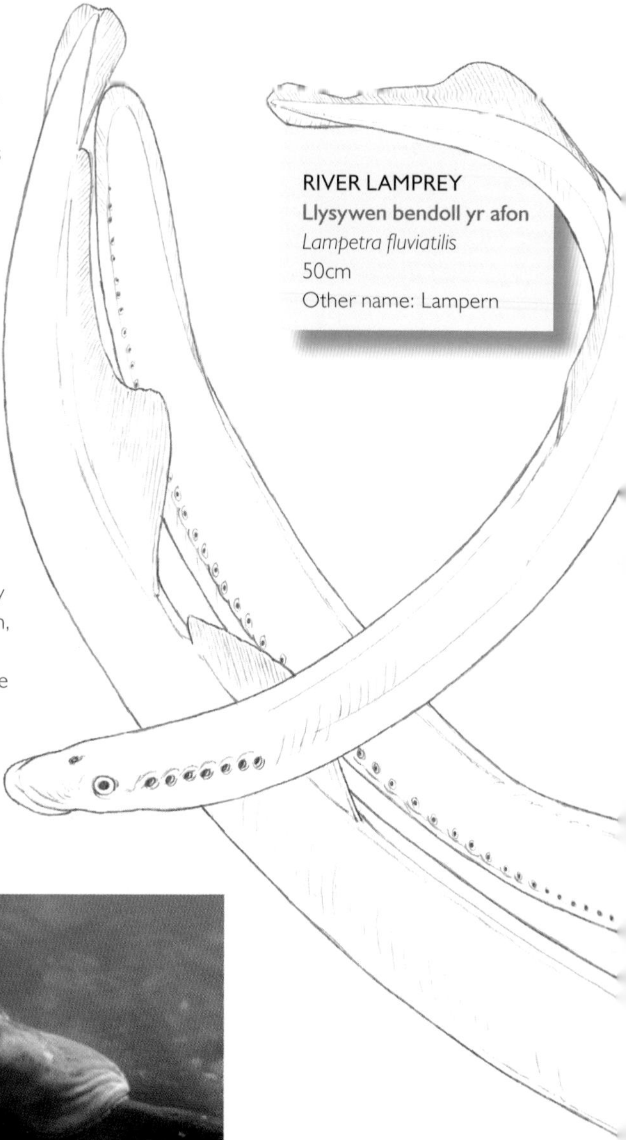

**RIVER LAMPREY**
**Llysywen bendoll yr afon**
*Lampetra fluviatilis*
50cm
Other name: Lampern

Sea Lampreys use their sucker-like mouth to cling onto rocks as well as for feeding. They can even move stones around when preparing a site to lay their eggs. (Image from video sequence from 'Natur Cymru' by Aden Productions for S4C).

**KEY IDENTIFICATION FEATURES** These fish can be identified in the field with a high degree of certainty. They are long, thin and eel-like, with slimy skin and no scales. Lampreys have a line of small, round gill openings behind the head, whilst Hagfish have a single opening on each side well behind the head. Instead of jaws, lampreys have a round sucker for a mouth which is lined by concentric rows of horny teeth. Hagfish have a slit-shaped mouth surrounded by fleshy barbels and vestigial eyes. Adults of the two lampreys can be told apart by their colour. Sea Lampreys are a pale brown mottled with dark brown or black. River Lampreys are a uniform greenish-brown fading to white on the belly.

**SIMILAR SPECIES** At first sight, jawless fish could be mistaken for eels but are easily told apart by looking at their mouth and gills.

**BEHAVIOUR** Hagfish spend most of their time buried with only the top of the head showing, coming out at night to scavenge. They can be attracted by setting bait. Sea and River Lampreys will hide amongst rocks when not actively searching for hosts to feed on.

**HABITAT** Hagfish burrow in soft mud from 20m down to at least 1200m depth and cannot tolerate low salinity or warm water. Adult Sea Lamprey swim freely in the water column but can also be found in rocky areas from close inshore to at least 650m. Adult River Lampreys live close inshore and in estuaries.

**DISTRIBUTION** Jawless fish are uncommon but widespread in Welsh waters with only a very few records for Hagfish. They occur all round the British Isles, north to Norway and south to Morocco and the western Mediterranean. Hagfish and Sea Lamprey are also found along the coast of North America.

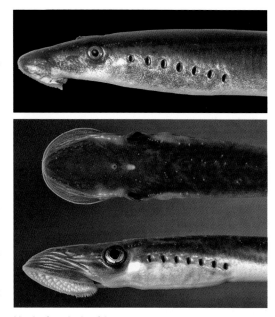

Heads of two jawless fish.
Top. River Lamprey, *Lampetra fluviatilis*.
Bottom. Young Sea Lamprey, *Petromyzon marinus*.

**NATURAL HISTORY** Hagfish are entirely marine and lay their few large, sausage-shaped eggs on the seabed. These hatch into miniature adults. Sea and River Lamprey migrate up rivers to spawn in clean gravel areas. Their eggs hatch into worm-like larvae called ammocoetes that change into the adult form and migrate out to sea.

**SIGHTINGS** These fish are rarely seen by divers but both Sea and River Lamprey might be encountered in estuaries. Most sightings are of Sea Lamprey attached to fish caught by anglers or in trawls. Young River Lamprey feed on fish such as herring and flounder in estuaries and so sometimes come up in trawls and nets. Sea Lampreys are also spotted attached to slow moving Basking Sharks. Hagfish have been filmed by remote cameras in deep water, baited with dead fish. Sea and River Lampreys are classed as 'Least concern' in the IUCN Red List because although still rare, populations in Europe have recovered from earlier river pollution problems.

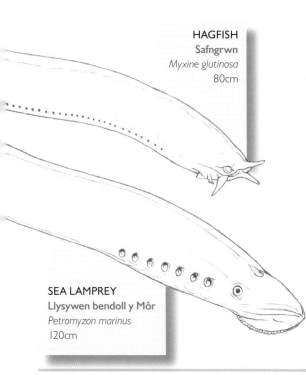

**HAGFISH**
Safngrwn
*Myxine glutinosa*
80cm

**SEA LAMPREY**
Llysywen bendoll y Môr
*Petromyzon marinus*
120cm

# A KNOTTY PROBLEM

Hagfish use their extreme flexibility and large amounts of slippery slime to literally tie themselves in knots. This gives them leverage against the carcass they are feeding on. A Hagfish can fill a bucket with slime if it is caught and this normally deters would-be predators.

# Sharks

Sharks are cartilaginous fish and belong to a group (Class) of fish called Chondrichthyes. As their name suggests they have a skeleton made principally of flexible cartilage rather than bone. Sharks are generally easy to recognise as such. Their mouth is on the underside of the head, rather than at the end as in most bony fish and they have five pairs of gill slits (six or seven in a few rare deepwater species) on either side of the head. Their fins are stiff with relatively short bases and the tail fin is uneven with the top lobe longer than the lower one. A shark's skin is protected not by scales but by tiny backward-pointing dermal denticles, like miniature teeth. This is evident if you run your hand along a shark from back to front, something usually only possible in dead sharks! Sharks have several rows of teeth with the inactive rows lying flat behind the active ones. In this way individual teeth can be replaced as often as necessary. Shark teeth vary in shape depending on what the shark eats and can be useful in identifying dead sharks.

Of the 500 plus known sharks in the ocean, 21 are found in British waters and 13 of these have been recorded from Welsh waters. All these are described here, with the exception of the Bramble Shark *Echinorhinus brucus*. This is a deepwater shark that has been recorded from the Bristol Channel. The remaining eight sharks found in British waters all live in deepwater.

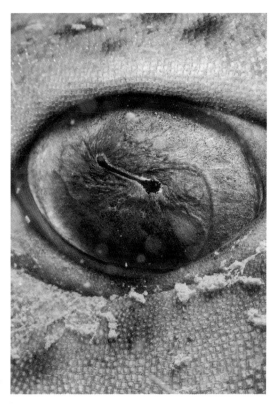

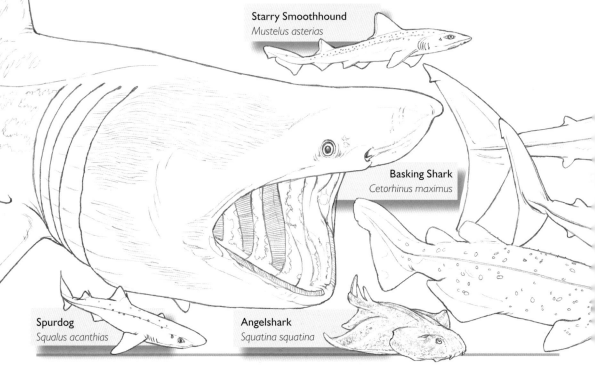

**Starry Smoothhound**
*Mustelus asterias*

**Basking Shark**
*Cetorhinus maximus*

**Spurdog**
*Squalus acanthias*

**Angelshark**
*Squatina squatina*

# A SAD TAIL

Like Cod, Spurdog were once extremely abundant and may once have been the most numerous of all sharks. We know more about their life history than any other shark and yet have been unable to prevent a catastrophic decline in their numbers. Spurdog are now in the 'Vulnerable' (IUCN Red List) category globally and in the 'Endangered' category in the northeast Atlantic where there is no effective management. There is a minimum catch size in force in Norway. In 2006 ICES recommended a zero quota but this has not been implemented by the EU. Unlike populations of many commercial bony fish that produce millions of eggs and have the potential to recover fairly quickly if fishing pressures are reduced, Spurdog reproduce extremely slowly and recovery is a very slow business after collapse of a stock.

**Smooth Hammerhead**
*Sphyrna zygaena*

**Shortfin Mako**
*Isurus oxyrhinchus*

**Tope**
*Galeorhinus galeus*

**Porbeagle**
*Lamna nasus*

**Bramble Shark**
*Echinorhinus brucus*

**Blue Shark**
*Prionace glauca*

# SPURDOG                    Picwd                    *Squalus acanthias*

**Other names: Piked Dogfish, Spiny Dogfish**                    100cm

**KEY IDENTIFICATION FEATURES** This small shark can be identified in the field with a high degree of certainty. It is the only common small Welsh shark with a sharp spine in front of each of two dorsal fins, and no anal fin. Divers need to look carefully as the paired pelvic fins are set quite far back towards the tail and could be mistaken for an anal fin. It is a slim, streamlined shark with a pointed snout and large eyes. The usual colour is grey with a few scattered, distinct white spots. Larger older fish don't always have these spots. Most grow up to about 1m long but given the chance they can reach 2m.

**SIMILAR SPECIES** Tope *Galeorhinus galeus* and smoothhounds *Mustelus* spp. are a similar size, colour and shape but do not have spines or an anal fin. Other sharks that have dorsal fin spines that might be found in offshore deepwaters in the area covered by this book include gulper sharks *Centrophorus* spp., and lantern sharks *Centroscyllium* spp.

**BEHAVIOUR** Divers may see solitary individuals in shallow water resting on the seabed or swimming slowly just above it. However, they usually gather in large schools especially in areas where there is plenty of food in the form of shoals of Sprat, Herring, Cod or similar fish or rich sediments with crustaceans and other invertebrate food. The schools usually consist of one sex or size of fish; immature fish, mature males, large mature (often pregnant) females or large but immature females.

Some populations are resident in one area but tagging has shown that many populations migrate north–south or between deep and shallow water in response to changing water temperatures.

**HABITAT** Spurdog can be found from the surface to the seabed in coastal waters but in deeper water over the Continental Shelf, they are usually found near the bottom. They also inhabit oceanic surface waters far offshore. They are most common down to 600m but may extend to over 1400m depth. Nursery grounds are mostly in soft sediment bays and estuaries.

**DISTRIBUTION** This widespread and common small shark is found throughout Welsh waters both inshore and offshore and all round the British Isles. Elsewhere it has an extensive and almost worldwide distribution except for the tropics and northern Arctic and Antarctic waters.

**NATURAL HISTORY** This is one of the longest living sharks with individuals estimated to reach 70–100 years old. They also grow very slowly and need to be between 10–25 years old before they reproduce. Females give birth to live young (ovoviviparous) usually in sheltered inshore nursery areas. The number of young and the time they take to develop (gestation period) varies between regions. Litters of 1–32 and gestations of 12–24 months have been recorded.

**SIGHTINGS** Of all sharks in Welsh waters, this is the one most likely to be seen. It is a very important commercial species with target trawl and line fisheries. It is also caught by sports anglers. It is sometimes seen by divers but prefers soft sediment areas whereas most divers prefer rocks and wrecks. It is also a popular public aquarium fish and is used in research and teaching laboratories.

# ANGELSHARK                    Maelgi                    *Squatina squatina*

**Other names: Monkfish**                                                          180cm

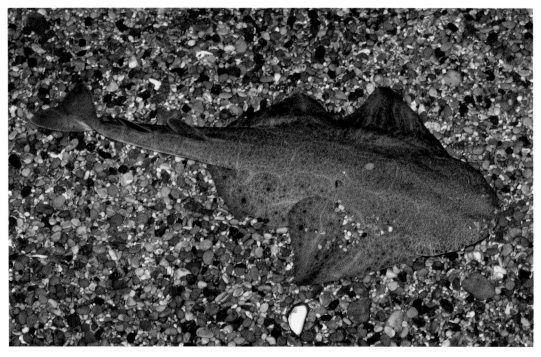

**KEY IDENTIFICATION FEATURES** The bizarre shape of this shark means that it would be hard to mistake it for anything else and it can be identified in the field with a high degree of certainty. It is in effect, a squashed shark with a broad head and terminal mouth (unlike rays) and large, broad-based pectoral and pelvic fins. There are two small dorsal fins near the tail which has a relatively small un-sharklike fin. Most are a greyish, greenish or reddish-brown with scattered, small dark blotches and white spots. Young fish often have thin white lines forming a reticulate pattern and large dark blotches. Adults can reach around 1.8m long possibly even 2.4m.

**SIMILAR SPECIES** Two other angelsharks live in the Mediterranean but do not extend as far north as the British Isles. Other flattened bottom-living fish include rays, flatfish and anglerfish but it should be easy to distinguish these from Angelsharks. Underwater it is usually possible to see the characteristic outline of the shark even if it is partially buried.

**BEHAVIOUR** During the day Angelsharks lie hidden on the seabed partially buried and often with only their eyes protruding. At night they swim up off the bottom using their tail to skull along (unlike rays which swim by flapping their expanded pectoral fins) and hunt for seabed creatures such as flatfish, skates, crustaceans and molluscs. They are ambush predators and will rear up suddenly from the seabed to catch passing fish. Although not aggressive they can and will bite if handled. This shark is an important predator in the few places where it remains common.

**HABITAT** This strange shark is adapted to living on the seabed and is generally found in sandy, muddy and gravelly areas from close inshore, in as little as 5m of water, or even in the intertidal down to at least 150m. It is also found in estuaries and brackish water.

**DISTRIBUTION** There are records of Angelsharks all round the Welsh coastline but sightings are now rare. It was historically common in the Bristol Channel. Angelsharks were recorded in low numbers in Cardigan Bay during the 1980s but CEFAS trawl surveys report just one individual in the last 15 years from this area. Its range extends all round the British Isles, north to southern Scandinavia and southwards to the Mediterranean, Canary Islands, and Mauritania. However it has now been declared extinct in the North Sea, is no longer found in many parts of the Mediterranean and is rare throughout most of the rest of its range. Numbers increase in summer around Wales and the British Isles in general with migrations north from more southern populations.

**NATURAL HISTORY** Females give birth (ovoviviparous) to between 7 and 25 young in June and July in English waters but there is not a lot of reliable information available. Much of their life history such as longevity, mortality and reproductive age is still unknown. It is not known whether they breed in Welsh waters.

**SIGHTINGS** If they are lucky, divers may come across this shark lying quietly on the seabed especially in the warmer summer months but this is now a rare fish. It is listed as 'Critically Endangered' in the IUCN Red Data List. Its demise is due to intense bottom trawl fisheries and bottom longlines throughout its range, mostly targeted at other species. It has been proposed for legal protection in Great Britain but this has not yet happened. Anglers sometimes catch this fish from boats and from the shore. They can also be seen in public aquaria.

# BASKING SHARK          Heulgi          *Cetorhinus maximus*

**Other names: Basker**                                          1100cm

**KEY IDENTIFICATION FEATURES**   There is no other shark in Welsh waters that looks remotely like a Basking Shark and so they can be identified in the field with a very high degree of certainty. This is the second largest fish in the ocean and total length can reach 11m with a weight of 4.5 tonnes. It has a distinctive pointed snout and huge mouth with tiny teeth that are not easily visible, whilst its gill slits go almost right round the head. It has two dorsal fins, the first much larger than the second and it is the large, triangular first dorsal fin that gives the fish away as it swims along at the surface. The tip of its tail may also stick out of the water. Most Basking Sharks are greyish brown on the back with white undersides but some individuals are grey or almost black.

**SIMILAR SPECIES**   When only their rather triangular dorsal fins are spotted above the surface, Basking Sharks are sometimes mistaken for predatory sharks including Great Whites whose existence in British and Irish waters has not been confirmed (see page 61). However, Basking Sharks move very slowly and can often be closely approached.

**BEHAVIOUR**   Basking Sharks are active all year round and do not hibernate as was once thought. In summer they feed at the surface, their mouths wide open filtering out plankton with their gill rakers. In winter they move offshore into deeper water where they track and feed on deepwater plankton and so are not usually seen. Satellite tracking has shown they may swim thousands of kilometres a year in search of good feeding areas which they can detect from many miles away, presumably by smell. Although mostly solitary, they sometimes gather in large groups of over 100 individuals. Occasionally one will breach, leaping clear of the surface and crashing down again in a welter of spray. No-one knows exactly why but it may help to dislodge parasites or be a social display as this behaviour has only been seen in groups of sharks.

**HABITAT**   Basking Sharks mostly swim in surface waters but in winter months spend more time in deeper water down to around 900m. They approach quite close inshore but are also found offshore to at least the edge of the Continental Shelf. They often congregate at water fronts where the plankton on which they feed is concentrated.

**DISTRIBUTION**   Basking Sharks are regularly sighted around the Welsh coastline and are found all round the British Isles with 'hot spots' around the Isle of Man, south-west England and the Hebrides in Scotland. Further afield they extend as far north as Iceland and the Barents Sea and have a worldwide distribution in cold to warm-temperate waters.

**NATURAL HISTORY**   Very little is known about how basking sharks reproduce. They give birth to live young and there is a catch record of a single pregnant female which was carrying six embryos. Juveniles are rarely seen. Females may not mature until around 8m long, males around 5m and both sexes may be as old as 18 years before they reproduce for the first time. Recent work suggests a gestation of around 14 months. Basking Sharks periodically shed their gill rakers during winter but do so a few at a time allowing new ones to grow so that feeding is not interrupted.

**SIGHTINGS**   In the summer months basking sharks can easily be spotted from cliff tops and boats as they cruise along at the surface with their dorsal fins sticking up out of the water. Divers and snorkelers have a good chance of swimming with these mighty fish if dropped in the water at the right place and time. Divers and boats should not approach too closely and should follow the Shark Trust Code of Conduct. The Marine Conservation Society Basking Shark project collates records of these amazing fish. Basking Sharks are protected in UK territorial waters and some other countries and are listed on CITES Appendix II under which trade in their meat and other products is closely controlled. They are listed as 'Vulnerable' in the IUCN Red Data List.

# PORBEAGLE                    Morgi Mawr                    *Lamna nasus*

**350cm**

**KEY IDENTIFICATION FEATURES**   This shark can be identified with a high degree of certainty in the field. Underwater sightings are rare but even here size, colour and shape should make identification certain. It is a heavy, deep-bodied shark with a large first dorsal fin and very small second dorsal fin. There is a small anal fin beneath the second dorsal fin. Like all mackerel sharks (Lamnidae) it has an almost crescent-shaped tail. This is a grey shark with a white belly and a distinctive white patch covering the free rear tip at the base of the first dorsal fin. Maximum recorded size is 3.5m.

**SIMILAR SPECIES**   The only other mackerel shark in Welsh waters is the Shortfin Mako *Isurus oxyrinchus*. The British Isles are at the northern distributional limit of this shark and it is a rare visitor to Welsh waters. It is slimmer than the Porbeagle and predominantly deep blue or blue-grey.

**BEHAVIOUR**   Porbeagle migrate moderate distances; individuals tagged off southern England have been recovered from waters off Spain, Denmark and Norway. It is potentially dangerous because of its size but there are few if any reported attacks.

**HABITAT**   Young Porbeagle up to about 40kg in weight come relatively close inshore but adults live mainly offshore over the Continental shelf. They are most common around offshore banks where there are plenty of fish and hunt from the surface down to around 700m.

**DISTRIBUTION**   Porbeagle range throughout Welsh waters and all round the British Isles. They are a cold water shark preferring temperatures from 1–18°C and in the North Atlantic, extend into the Arctic Circle. In the southern hemisphere they have a circum-global distribution in a band of temperate cool water in the south.

**NATURAL HISTORY**   Females give birth to between one to five large young (ovoviviparous) in spring in European waters, after an estimated gestation of eight or nine months, though this may be longer. They are active hunters feeding mainly on bony fish and squid and have been seen to take seabirds from the surface. They are warm-blooded like other mackerel sharks (Lamnidae) and so can remain active in water temperatures as low as 2°C.

**SIGHTINGS**   Divers are unlikely to see this shark unless on a specific shark watching expedition and would have to be lucky even then. Sport fishermen catch this shark in offshore areas in south and west Wales and occasionally small ones from the shore. It is commercially exploited throughout Europe. There is no target fishery for this species in Wales but they are sometimes caught as by-catch and are retained because of their high value. Populations have been seriously depleted worldwide especially in the North Atlantic and it is listed as 'Vulnerable' in the IUCN Red List. It is included in Annex 1 (Highly Migratory Species) of the UN Convention on the Law of the Sea (UNCLOS). As this shark has declined so greatly in numbers, all records from Welsh waters are of interest and as much information as possible should be recorded (size, sex, location etc.).

# CATSHARKS

## FAMILY Scyliorhinidae

Nursehound and Smallspotted Catshark belong to a family of small sharks called Catsharks (Scyliorhinidae). This is by far the largest shark family with at least 160 species worldwide but only these two species are regularly found in Welsh waters. The Blackmouth Catshark, Morgi cegddu, *Galeus melastomus* has been recorded from nearby deep waters including the Isle of Man, below about 200m. In Norwegian fjords this species is found as shallow as 22m. New undescribed catshark species are frequently discovered worldwide now that boats are fishing deeper waters.

These well-developed Smallspotted Catshark embryos are safe within their tough eggcases.

## CONFUSED DOGFISH

In Wales and Great Britain, catsharks (Scyliorhinidae) are often called dogfish. Most divers and many fishermen will be used to calling a Smallspotted Catshark a Common Dogfish or a Lesser Spotted Dogfish. True Dogfish Sharks belong to a separate Order (Squaliformes) that contains several families and includes Piked Dogfish or Spurdog *Squalus acanthias* (see page 50). Other deepwater examples include Black Dogfish (Centrophoridae), Birdbeak Dogfish and Velvet Belly (Centrophoridae) drawn here.

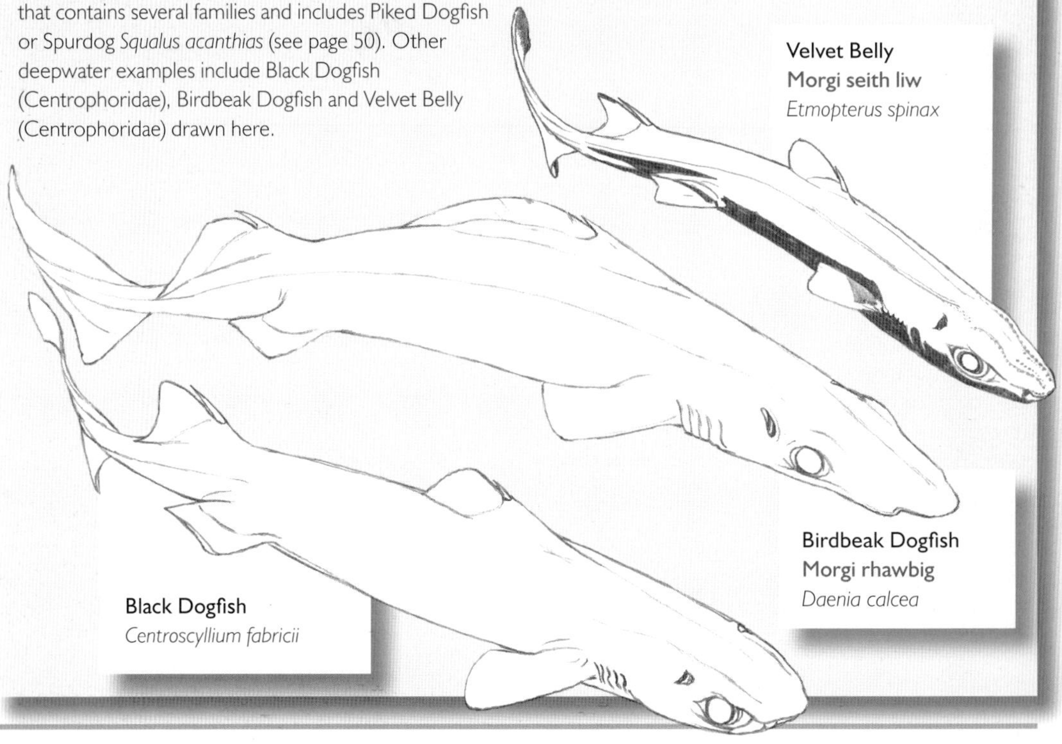

**Velvet Belly**
Morgi seith liw
*Etmopterus spinax*

**Birdbeak Dogfish**
Morgi rhawbig
*Daenia calcea*

**Black Dogfish**
*Centroscyllium fabricii*

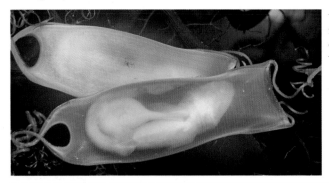

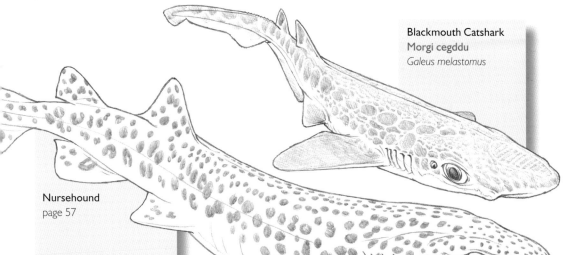

**Blackmouth Catshark**
Morgi cegddu
*Galeus melastomus*

Nursehound
page 57

Smallspotted Catshark
page 56

## CHANGING FORTUNES

Catsharks used to be considered a nuisance by fishermen – they came up in their hundreds in trawls, it was difficult to extract them from the nets and no-one wanted to buy them anyway. As stocks of other fish declined, catsharks became more popular and were marketed as 'rock salmon' 'rock eel' and 'flake' in fishmongers and fish and chip shops. Today they are far less common than they once were but are one of the few sharks whose population appears to be relatively stable.

# SMALLSPOTTED CATSHARK   Y morgi lleiaf   *Scyliorhinus canicula*

**Other names: Lesser Spotted Dogfish, Common Dogfish, Sandy Dog, Rough Hound**   100cm

**KEY IDENTIFICATION FEATURES** This small shark, often known erroneously as 'dogfish', can be identified in the field with a high degree of certainty provided care is taken to distinguish it from the Nursehound. It has a blunt head and long, tapering body with two small, rounded dorsal fins set far back near the tail. Most are a sandy brown colour and are covered with numerous small, darker brown spots. These are set close together on the back and sides but are more widely spaced on the large pectoral fins. Some fish show a series of darker saddles along the back and scattered white spots.

**SIMILAR SPECIES** The only other similar species in Welsh waters is the Nursehound or Greater Spotted Dogfish. With dead or captured fish, look closely at the underside of the head. In Smallspotted Catsharks the nostrils are connected to the mouth by obvious grooves which form simple nasal flaps. Nursehounds, have similar grooves but these do not reach as far as the mouth and the nasal flaps are more complicated and appear frilly.

**BEHAVIOUR** These fish will often remain motionless if approached quietly when they are resting during the day. They are so dopey that divers have been known to pick them up by their tail but often get a nasty surprise as 'dogfish' are very flexible and can bend round in a circle and bite! When large numbers are landed by trawlers they are often all of a single sex as they tend to school as segregated groups.

**HABITAT** Smallspotted Catsharks live on the seabed, mostly on sediment but also in areas of mixed sand and rock and on rocky reefs. Although occasionally found in deep rock pools on the shore, and in deep water below 100m, they mostly live between about 3–110m.

**DISTRIBUTION** Common throughout Welsh waters and all round the British Isles. These small sharks are also found as far north as northern Norway and south to the Mediterranean and down the west coast of Africa to Senegal.

**NATURAL HISTORY** After mating, females lay pairs of egg cases, depositing them amongst kelp, or seaweed and animal undergrowth, usually in shallow water, though live capsules have been photographed to at least 40m depth. As she lays her eggs the female may swim around her chosen anchorage point, so that the long tendrils at the egg case corners get entangled and prevent the egg cases floating away. Live egg cases can be found at any time of year but most are laid between November to July and hatch between eight or nine months after laying (shortest five months, longest eleven months). These small sharks will actively hunt bottom-living fish such as gurnards and gobies, as well as rooting out buried shellfish and worms and grabbing crabs and other crustaceans.

**SIGHTINGS** Single 'dogfish' are commonly seen by divers resting quietly on the seabed. They are regularly caught by trawlers in relatively large numbers, either as by-catch or in targeted fisheries and are occasionally caught by anglers. They are often kept in public aquaria where they will mate and lay viable eggs under the right conditions.

# NURSEHOUND

**Morgi brych**

*Scyliorhinus stellaris*

**Other names: Greater Spotted Dogfish, Bull Huss** 162cm

**KEY IDENTIFICATION FEATURES** This small bottom-living shark can be identified in the field with a reasonable degree of certainty. It is similar to the Smallspotted Catshark in shape and background colour but grows to a larger size (162cm) and has numerous large black or dark brown spots as well as many smaller ones. Some individuals are decorated with small white spots like tiny stars, scattered between the black ones and it is this that gives them their specific name 'stellaris' although some Smallspotted Catsharks also have white spots.

**SIMILAR SPECIES** Large fish over 1m long with large spots are definitely Nursehounds. Smaller individuals could be mistaken for Smallspotted Catsharks if their spots are unclear. With dead or captured fish, you can check the relative vertical position of the front of the first dorsal fin in relation to the base of the pelvic fins. In the Nursehound the two overlap whereas in the Lesser spotted dogfish the dorsal fin begins just rearward of the pelvic fin base. See Smallspotted Catsharks for differences in the nostrils.

**BEHAVIOUR** Little information appears to be available.

**HABITAT** Nursehounds live on the seabed and prefer rough and rocky areas to sediment areas. Although they are sometimes found just below the shore, they are most common between 20–65m and extend down to at least 125m.

**DISTRIBUTION** Found throughout Welsh waters and all round the British Isles, but is not nearly as common as the Smallspotted Catshark. Elsewhere it has a similar distribution to the Smallspotted Catshark, but is most common in the southern part of its range and may extend further south beyond Senegal.

**NATURAL HISTORY** Nursehounds have a similar life history to Smallspotted Catsharks. After mating, females deposit one or usually two egg cases (one from each oviduct) amongst seaweeds or other undergrowth in spring and summer. The egg cases are quite large at 10–13cm long, compared to 5–7cm long for Smallspotted Catshark but are otherwise similar.

**SIGHTINGS** Most 'dogfish' seen by divers lying around on the seabed, are Smallspotted Catsharks but, as Nursehounds prefer rougher rocky ground, divers do sometimes come across them. Similarly anglers occasionally catch them and they are regularly caught by commercial trawlers though in smaller numbers than the Smallspotted Catsharks.

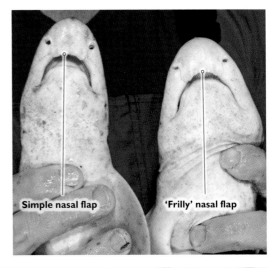

Simple nasal flap    'Frilly' nasal flap

Left: Smallspotted Catshark. Right: Nursehound.

# STARRY SMOOTHHOUND and SMOOTHHOUND     Morgi llyfn
## *Mustelus asterias* and *Mustelus mustelus*

### 150cm

**KEY IDENTIFICATION FEATURES** These two small sharks can be identified in the field with a high degree of certainty provided care is taken to check the dorsal and anal fins. They can sometimes be distinguished from each other by colour pattern when alive or recently dead. Both species of smooth-hounds are slim, elegant fish with a pointed snout, two large almost equal-sized dorsal fins and a single anal fin. Their colour is an unremarkable grey to grey-brown above and cream below. The Starry Smoothhound is speckled with small, even white dots on the sides and back above the lateral line. Some authorities consider that this is not a reliable feature for distinguishing the two species.

**SIMILAR SPECIES** The only other Welsh sharks with white (only) spots are Spurdogs. However, these have an obvious spine in front of each dorsal fin and no anal fin. The two species of smooth-hounds may be difficult to tell apart if the colours have faded in dead specimens. There are some differences in the shape of the tail that may help; the lower lobe in Starry Smoothhounds is more obvious than in Smooth-hounds (described as semi-falcate in shape).

**BEHAVIOUR** Smoothhounds tend to swim rather slowly just above the bottom and divers can sometimes approach them quite closely.

**HABITAT** These small sharks mostly swim near to the seabed in coastal waters and are most common in shallow water down to about 50m. Smoothhounds extend to at least 350m depth

and Starry Smoothhounds to at least 100m. They are sometimes caught in mid-water.

**DISTRIBUTION** Smoothhounds are relatively common throughout Welsh coastal waters and all round the UK, especially in the west and south although the Smoothhound is relatively rare in the North Sea. Further afield they occasionally extend north as far as southern Scandinavia. They are also found throughout the Mediterranean and at least as far south as the Canary Islands. The exact distribution of the two species is unclear since early records did not distinguish between the two.

**NATURAL HISTORY** Smoothhounds feed mainly on crustaceans which is why they are found near the seabed and why they have crushing, plate-like teeth. Both species have between about 5–20 live young but whilst the Smoothhound is truly viviparous the Starry Smoothhound is ovoviviparous, that is, its eggs hatch inside its body.

**SIGHTINGS** Divers tend to come across Starry Smoothhounds more commonly than Smoothhounds. Smoothhounds form an important European fishery and are caught by inshore trawlers, in fixed nets and on lines, whereas Starry Smoothhounds have a low market value and are mainly taken as by-catch. Both species are occasionally taken by anglers. In some parts of their range, Smoothhounds occur in the intertidal and any Welsh shore records would be interesting.

# TOPE SHARK                    Ci glas                    *Galeorhinus galeus*

**Other names: Soupfin Shark**                                    **200cm**

**KEY IDENTIFICATION FEATURES** Although they have no very obvious features Tope can be identified in the field with a high degree of certainty provided they are seen close up or examined carefully if dead. This is another slim 'torpedo-shaped' shark with two dorsal fins and an anal fin, but unlike the similar Smoothhound, the two dorsal fins are of different sizes with the first much larger than the second. Normal adult size is just over a metre long but they can reach 2m.

**SIMILAR SPECIES** Underwater, Tope can easily be confused with Smoothhounds as they are similar in shape, size and colour. The distinguishing feature is the unequal size of the Tope's dorsal fins. With dead fish, the teeth can also help distinguish Tope from Smoothhound as Tope have blade-like cutting teeth in contrast to the low blunt teeth of Smoothhounds.

**BEHAVIOUR** Most Tope form small schools though larger ones may be solitary. The schools usually consist mainly of similar sized individuals and may also be segregated by sex. Schools of females move into sheltered shallow bays and estuaries in the warmer months to give birth. Tope are strong swimmers and some populations from colder waters migrate long distances seasonally. They are active hunters and feed mainly on fish.

**HABITAT** Tope are mostly found over the Continental Shelf from very close inshore out into fairly deep water down the Continental slope to at least 550m, but not out in the open ocean. They spend most of their time near the bottom, mainly over sediment or in areas of mixed sediment and rock. Juveniles remain in inshore nursery grounds for around two years before moving further offshore.

**DISTRIBUTION** Tope are frequent all round the coast of Wales in inshore waters. They are also found all round the British Isles. Elsewhere they have a worldwide distribution in temperate waters though they seem to be absent from eastern parts of both the North Atlantic and North Pacific.

**NATURAL HISTORY** Females give birth to live young (ovoviparous) but not until they are at least ten years old. As is the case with other small sharks, larger females have larger litters with a range from 6–52 pups. Although not as long lived or slow-growing as Spurdog, Tope are thought to live for at least 60 years given the chance.

**SIGHTINGS** Summer is the best time for snorkelers and divers to see Tope, when small ones can be found close inshore, sometimes in less than a metre of water. However, few divers are lucky enough to spot one. They are not an important commercial fish in Wales or within Europe but are a popular sporting fish with anglers. Elsewhere in the world they are heavily fished and are listed in the IUCN Red Data list as 'Vulnerable'. Anglers need to be aware of this and should return mature females to the sea. Pregnant females are likely to be caught in the summer when they come close inshore.

# BLUE SHARK      Morgi glas      *Prionace glauca*

**380cm**

**KEY IDENTIFICATION FEATURES** This shark can be identified in the field with a high degree of certainty and should be unmistakable. It is streamlined and slim with a long snout and large eyes rimmed with white. Like other sharks in this group (requiem sharks) it has two dorsal fins and one anal fin, but the pectoral fins are very long and characteristic. This shark also has a long upper tail lobe. When alive it is characteristic dark blue with a white belly but the blue colour fades to grey in dead fish. The usual size is up to about 2.5m but they can reach 3.8m.

**SIMILAR SPECIES** This shark should not be confused with any other found in Welsh waters.

**BEHAVIOUR** North Atlantic Blue Sharks migrate regularly across the ocean in a clockwise direction riding the ocean currents. Although the details are not clear, it appears that they reach Europe on the Gulf Stream, and then eventually travel south and ride back to the Caribbean on the North Equatorial current. Although they make frequent deep dives they tend to cruise at the surface and the tips of their fins and tail can be seen sticking up out of the water. They feed mainly on small bony fish and squid and have been seen to circle their prey. They will occasionally do this to divers and swimmers and have been known to move in and bite.

**HABITAT** Blue Sharks are pelagic ocean wanderers inhabiting surface waters down to 350m off the edge of the Continental shelf. European populations migrate from the open ocean into coastal waters in the summer but do not usually go close inshore. Occasionally they will venture in as far as the lower edge of the kelp forest.

**DISTRIBUTION** There are confirmed records of this beautiful shark in Welsh coastal waters. In warm summers, Blue Sharks

extend as far north as Norway and down into the North Sea but usually they move north in any numbers only as far as the western English Channel and the Irish Sea. Elsewhere it has a worldwide distribution in temperate and tropical waters and probably the largest range of any shark.

**NATURAL HISTORY** Females give birth to live young (viviparous) in spring and summer in nursery areas that are generally some distance offshore and not as far north as the British Isles. Most Blue Sharks in Welsh waters are immature females or females that have already given birth along with very occasional males. 15–30 young is a normal litter but large females can have over 100. Females are mature between 5–7 years old and pregnancy takes between 9–12 months.

**SIGHTINGS** Blue Sharks are most likely to be seen by divers in summer but usually only on trips designed specifically to find them and other open ocean species. Many are caught on lines by sport fishermen who come specifically to Wales and the south-west in the summer to fish for them. Commercially they are the most heavily fished shark in the world caught mainly for their fins as the meat has a low value. 10 to 20 million Blue Sharks are caught each year, many as by-catch but also on pelagic long lines and trawls. They are listed as 'Near Threatened' in the IUCN Red List and are also listed on Annex I of the 1982 Convention on the Law of the Sea (highly migratory species). There is no specific commercial fishery for Blue Shark around Wales. However they often become tangled in mackerel and pilchard nets and can be seen following fishing boats and feeding on discarded offal. With ocean warming, Blue Sharks may appear in greater numbers around Wales as they move north in the summer and their migration could be earlier.

# RARE AND UNUSUAL SHARKS

## THRESHER SHARK
### Llwynog môr    *Alopias vulpinus*

Thresher sharks have extremely long tails with the upper lobe as long as the shark's body and cannot be mistaken for anything else. There are confirmed records of this shark from around the Welsh coastline especially Pembroke, but they are very rare here. They are more commonly seen off the south Cornish coast and east to the Isle of Wight, especially in the summer when they move closer inshore and more sharks move up into the English Channel from further south. They are essentially oceanic and feed on schools of mackerel and other similar fish. They are occasionally caught by anglers or brought up in commercial gear. One was caught in a fisherman's nets off Pembrokeshire in 2007. Bigeye Thresher Sharks *Alopias superciliosus*, are similar but do not usually extend further north than Spain. However, individuals have very occasionally been recorded from Cornwall.

## SMOOTH HAMMERHEAD SHARK
### Sphyrna zygaena

Hammerhead sharks are mostly found in warm waters and must be the one type of shark all divers can recognise. Smooth Hammerhead Sharks are very rare visitors as far north as the British Isles and probably stray north or over from America accidentally. They have been recorded around south-west Wales as well as the south coasts of Devon and Cornwall but recent records are extremely sparse. In northern European waters including the British Isles, there have been only five records in the 20th century and seven in the 19th century.

## GREAT WHITE SHARK
### Carcharodon carcharias

There are no confirmed sightings of Great Whites in British or Irish waters. However, in September 2008, a fisherman took a photograph with his mobile phone of what he thought was a Great White with its head sticking out of the water, off Caldey Island Pembrokeshire. Unfortunately the photograph is not clear enough for a definitive identification though it is obviously a large shark. Every year there are numerous 'sightings' of Great Whites especially off the south coast of England, many of which can be attributed to sightings of Basking Shark fins. A few records are credible but with no concrete proof. The Shark Trust has investigated many of the supposed sightings and their conclusion is: "Whilst there is no reason why these animals should not be found in British waters there is no concrete proof to support their presence". So keep your eyes open and your camera ready!

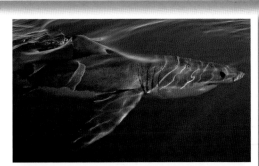

The top photo shows a Great White with just its dorsal fin breaking the surface. In contrast the lower photos shows both a nose and dorsal fin breaking the surface – often the tail fin does too – this is typical of Basking Sharks and is an easy way of identifying them in calm conditions.

# Skates and Rays

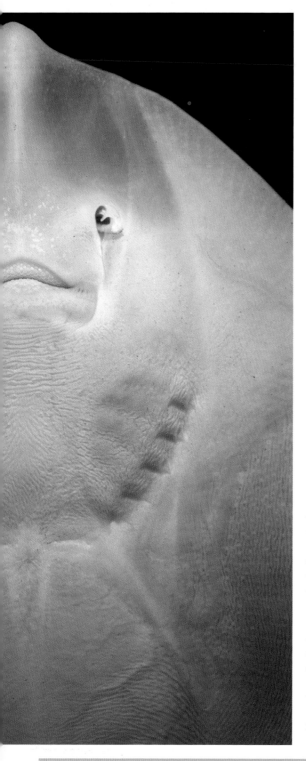

## ORDER  Rajiformes

Like sharks, rays and skates are cartilaginous fish and belong to the group (Class) of fish called Chondrichthyes that have skeletons made principally from cartilage rather than bone. They have flattened bodies with wide pectoral fins which form the 'wings' used for swimming. They have a long, thin tail which, with the exception of electric rays, does not end in a tail fin. Most live on the seabed and their flattened shape is an adaptation to this way of life. With their mouth and gill slits on the underside, rays have well developed spiracles behind the eyes and they draw water in through these rather than the mouth, before passing it over the gills and out again. This prevents their gills getting clogged with sediment.

Most European rays and skates belong to one family, the Rajidae, of which at least 12 species have been recorded in Welsh waters. In general, those with long noses are called 'skate' and those with short noses are called 'ray'. Eight of these are described in detail here with shorter descriptions of the other species. Of these the Bottlenosed or White Skate *Rostroraja alba* and the Starry Ray or Thorny Skate *Amblyraja radiata* are only occasionally encountered in Welsh waters. Starry Ray is a northern cold water species that has been recorded from North Wales and lives offshore in relatively deep water. In Norway it is one of the commonest species and occurs in very shallow water. Bottlenosed Skate is a southern species that strays as far north as the English Channel. There are few records from Welsh waters and its status here is not clear.

One stingray (Dasyatidae) and one electric ray (Torpedinidae) are found in Welsh waters and are described here. Eagle Ray and Devilfish (Myliobatidae) plus a second species of electric ray are rare southern visitors to the British Isles that might occur in Welsh waters but for which there are no confirmed records.

Skates and rays are an important part of mixed demersal fisheries, and are taken as by-catch in beam and otter trawls, and in seine nets. There are also targeted fisheries that use lines and set nets. Up to the present time, all species of rays and skates are landed in Wales and UK under a general category of 'skate and ray'. There is now a move from the Marine Fisheries Agency (MFA) to record all individual species of skates and rays around England and Wales. Fishermen and merchants have been asked to identify and record their landings of the different species, to help build an accurate picture of stocks of skates and rays here. There is currently no EU Minimum Landing Size (MLS) for skate and ray outside a six mile limit. The EU specifies certain mesh sizes for directed skate and ray fisheries. South Wales Sea Fisheries Committee specifies a MLS for skates and rays in general. The North Western and North Wales Sea Fisheries Committees do not currently do so but may follow suit. There is no Total Allowable Catch for skates and rays in the Celtic Sea.

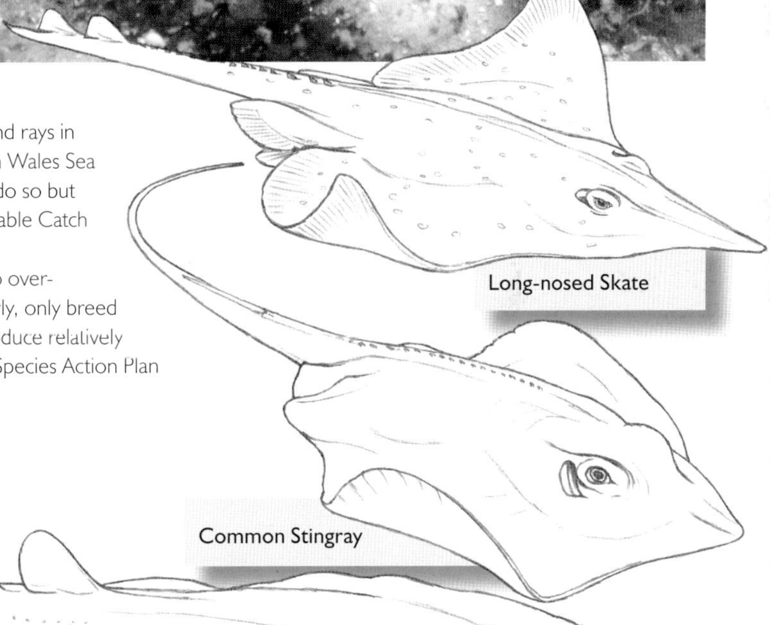

Skates and rays are very vulnerable to over-fishing because most of them grow slowly, only breed when they are several years old and produce relatively few eggs. This group is the subject of a Species Action Plan in UK and Wales, particularly Conwy.

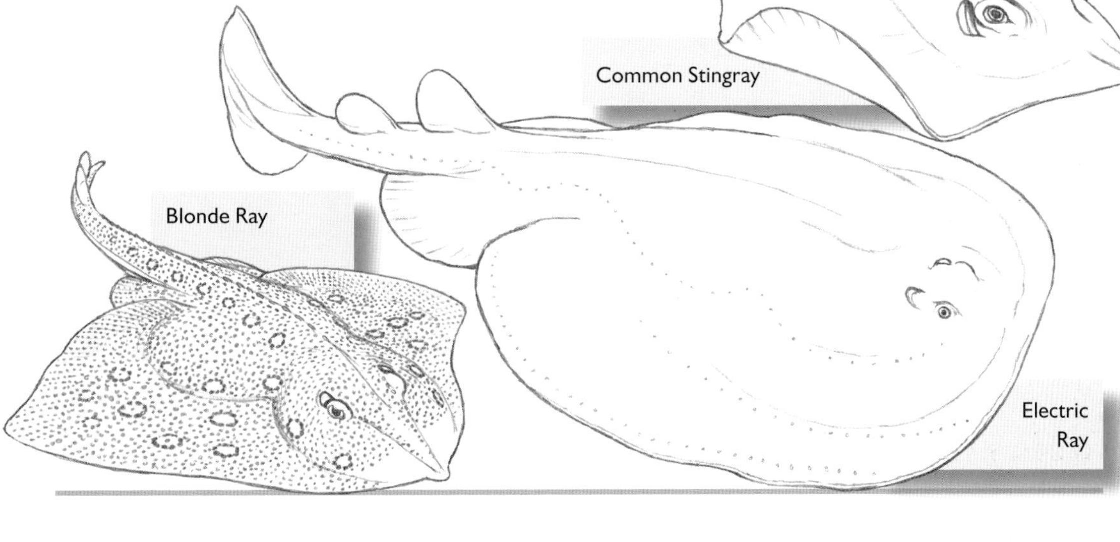

Long-nosed Skate

Common Stingray

Blonde Ray

Electric Ray

# COMMON STINGRAY    Morgath ddu    *Dasyatis pastinaca*

**140cm**

**KEY IDENTIFICATION FEATURES** This ray can be identified in the field with a high degree of certainty. It has wide, rounded wings with straight front edges leading away from a fairly pointed snout. The most obvious feature is its long tapered tail with a single, serrated stinging spine about a third of the way along it. Unlike other Welsh rays, it has no dorsal fins on the tail but it does have folds of skin running along both sides of the tail. Seen from above, it is a uniform dark grey, brown or greenish-brown.

**SIMILAR SPECIES** Pelagic or Blue Rays *Pteroplatytrygon violacea* very occasionally stray north from the Mediterranean but have not yet been recorded in Welsh waters. They have a gently curving smooth head profile.

**BEHAVIOUR** These fish spend most of their time lying partly buried on the seabed. If approached they will often swim away quite fast using their pectoral fins like wings. They are only a danger to people in shallow water where they may be stepped on, but are too rare in Welsh waters to cause any real problem. They also need handling with great care when trawled up. Their barbed, venomous sting can inflict a very painful wound. For treatment see Weeverfish on page 193.

**HABITAT** Like most rays, Common Stingrays live on sediments, and are found mainly on inshore sand and sometimes mud, especially in sheltered bays and outer estuaries. They range from around 5–70m depth.

**DISTRIBUTION** Stingrays have been recorded in all sectors round the west and south coasts of Wales but are relatively uncommon. This is a southern species that extends its range north in summer to the British Isles and can become locally common. In some years it is found as far north as southern Scandinavia. It is relatively common in the Mediterranean and extends at least as far south as Canary Islands.

**NATURAL HISTORY** Stingrays are unusual amongst rays in giving birth to live young (ovoviviparous). They have a short gestation of around four months and produce between three to seven young. They do not breed regularly in Welsh waters as water temperature is not high enough but this could change. They feed on molluscs, crabs and bottom-living fish and unearth their prey using their snout and by wafting sand away with their pectoral fins.

**SIGHTINGS** Divers very occasionally spot stingrays in summer when diving near rocky reefs. Likewise they are sometimes caught by anglers but most sightings are when they are caught incidentally by inshore trawlers. The Welsh rod-caught record was from Aberdovey in 1993 and weighed 31kg. Summer migrations of Common Stingrays into Welsh waters could increase with ocean warming.

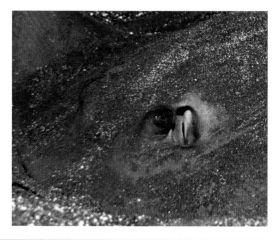

# FLYING VISITORS

**EAGLE RAYS**, Morgath adeiniog, *Myliobatis aquila* are a southern species that occasionally strays as far north as the English Channel and south-western Ireland and even up the west coast to Scotland. There are no confirmed records from Welsh waters but it could easily turn up. It has long pointed wings and a distinct head and swims gracefully through the water often near the surface. **DEVIL FISH**, Morgath gorniog, *Mobula mobular* are an even rarer visitor with only one or two records from around south west Ireland. They are like smaller versions of the tropical Manta Ray.

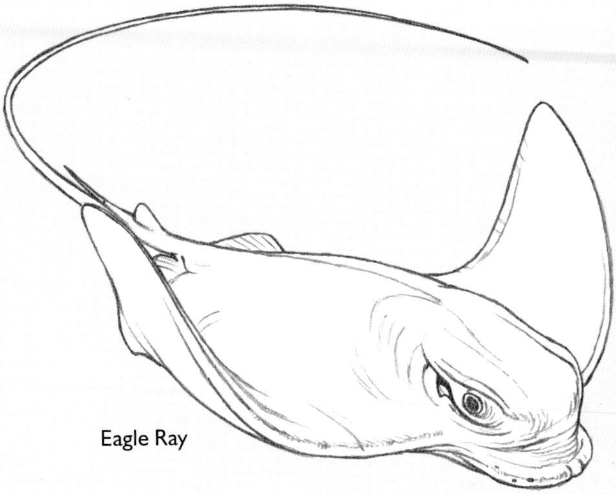

Eagle Ray

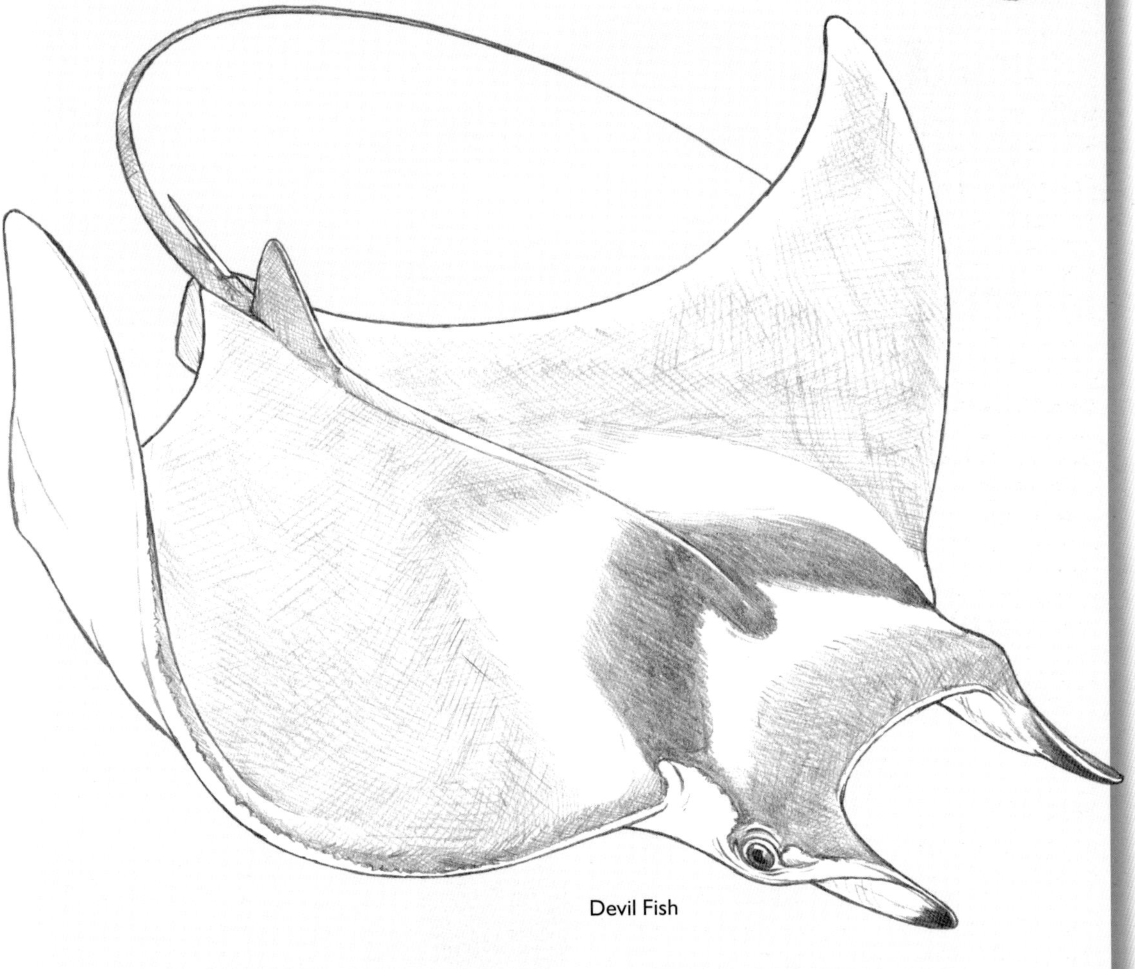

Devil Fish

# BLUE SKATE                    Morgath                    *Dipturus batis*

**Other names:** *Raja batis* (synonym), **Blue Grey Skate, Common Skate**                    285cm

**KEY IDENTIFICATION FEATURES** This fish can be identified in the field with a high degree of certainty. It is the largest of all European skates and rays and females can grow to nearly 3m long though ones this large are now very rare. It has a long pointed snout and pointed wings with distinctly concave front edges as a result of the long snout. Unlike most rays and skates which have a white underside, this species is distinctly bluish underneath and young ones may even be almost black underneath. The upper surface is variable in colour but mostly olive brown to grey brown, often with fairy distinct paler spots, but also darker blotches and marbling.

**SIMILAR SPECIES** Long-nosed Skate is similar but with a much longer snout. See also 'Other skate' on page 67.

**BEHAVIOUR** This is an active hunter that feeds largely on bony fish and can catch them by enveloping them in its huge pectoral fins. It has been suggested that its dark under surface helps conceal it when hunting out in open water.

**HABITAT** When hunting pelagic fish Blue Skate swim up in the water column but otherwise spend their time on the seabed. They can be found in sandy areas and on rough grounds of mixed rock and sediment. In theory they can be found as shallow as 30m but are now mostly restricted to deep water beyond the Continental Shelf, down to around 600m.

**DISTRIBUTION** This huge ray was once very common throughout the Irish Sea but is now very rare and considered effectively extinct there due to over-fishing. It is still very occasionally reported from the Irish Sea and from the Bristol Channel. In the past it has been recorded throughout Welsh coastal and offshore waters. The current range is mainly off the edge of the Continental Shelf and in deepwater off northwest Scotland and in the Celtic Sea. Its wider geographical range extends north to northern Scandinavia and Iceland and south to Senegal and the western Mediterranean but it is now missing from many areas.

**NATURAL HISTORY** This is a long-lived, slow-growing species that can reach 50 years old given the chance. The fish do not breed until they are over ten years old. They lay very large egg capsules in spring and summer which are easy to identify when washed up (see page 75). Aural tradition indicates that this ray was commonly caught and eaten in some localities back in Victorian times but had already become scarce by the mid-twentieth century.

**SIGHTINGS** The best chance of seeing a Blue Skate in Wales is now in an aquarium. They are listed as 'Critically Endangered' in the IUCN Red List. Anglers sometimes fish for this species but most fish caught are released. Around UK, they are landed by trawlers and caught in gill nets targeting other deepwater valuable fish such as Megrim and Hake. It is a biodiversity action plan (BAP) priority species in the UK. Conservation agencies proposed that it be protected under the Wildlife and Countryside Act but this has not yet happened. It is listed by OSPAR as a threatened and declining species. A minimum landing size is specified in South Wales.

# OTHER SKATE *DIPTURUS* SPP. AND *ROSTRORAJA* SP.

**Long-nosed Skate**, Morgath Drwynfain, *D. oxyrhinchus;* **Bottle-nosed or White Skate**, Morgath Wen, *R. alba* **and Norwegian or Black Skate** , Morgath Ddu Norwy, *D. nidarosiensis*

Several skates with long noses and a similar body shape to Blue Skate are found off west coast British Isles and some of these are occasionally caught in Welsh waters.

**LONG-NOSED SKATE**, Morgath Drwynfain, *Dipturus oxyrin-chus* is a deepwater species that has been recorded off Anglesey and extends up the west coast of Ireland, north to Norway. It has a similar shape and colour to Blue Skate but has an exceptionally long snout such that the head forms a steep triangle before the wings spread out sideways. It also has only 4–11 thorns along its tail compared to 12–20 in Blue Skate and is grey underneath. It reaches 150cm long and forms part of the commercial catch of skates and rays.

**BOTTLE-NOSED SKATE** or **WHITE SKATE**, Morgath Wen *Rostroraja alba* is a southern species that strays as far north as the English Channel. There are a few records from Welsh waters but its status here is not clear. It has a moderately long snout and the front edges of the disc are concave overall but with a sinuous outline. Most are grey to brown with numerous lighter spots. Caught fish can be distinguished by looking at the underside which is white but with dark margins to the wings and pelvic fins. It has about 15 thorns along the tail and reaches 230cm long.

**NORWEGIAN SKATE** or **BLACK SKATE**, Morgath Ddu Norwy, *Dipturus nidarosiensis* is a deepwater, northern species found in southern Norway and Iceland and beyond the continental shelf down the west coast of Scotland and Ireland. It has not been recorded from Welsh waters but could conceivably be landed in Wales by boats fishing north of the Irish Sea. It is a uniform dark grey or greyish brown both on top and underneath. It has a row of 42–50 thorns along the tail and reaches 200cm long.

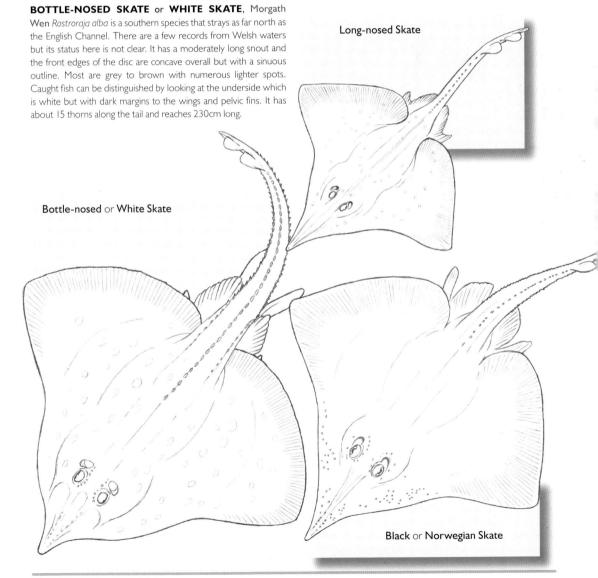

Long-nosed Skate

Bottle-nosed or White Skate

Black or Norwegian Skate

# CUCKOO RAY                    Morgath lygadog                *Leucoraja naevus*

**Other names:** *Raja naevus* (synonym), Butterfly Skate                    **70cm**

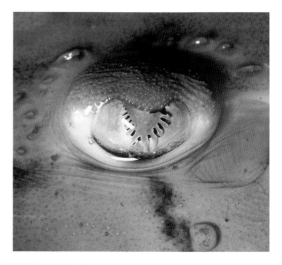

**KEY IDENTIFICATION FEATURES**  This striking ray can be identified in the field with a high degree of certainty from its distinctive colour pattern. In the middle of each wing there is a large black eye spot filled with yellow squiggly blotches. This ray has a short snout and rounded wings. It has a double row of spines running the length of the tail and some way onto the body, which can be seen and felt in dead fish. Small young rays have an additional mid-line row. The underside is white with some darker marks.

**SIMILAR SPECIES**  Occasional Blue Skate and other rays may have similar eye spots but not so well defined, and Blue Skate are a very different shape.

**BEHAVIOUR**  As these rays are not often seen by divers, there are few observations on their behaviour.

**HABITAT**  Cuckoo Ray are a coastal and Continental Shelf species living on sediment, from around 20–150m depth and sometimes deeper.

**DISTRIBUTION**  This ray is found throughout Welsh waters and is one of the more common species. It is also found all round the British Isles but there are fewer records from the eastern English Channel and North Sea. It only extends north to the southern tip of Scandinavia (Kattegat) but is found south to Senegal and throughout the western Mediterranean.

**NATURAL HISTORY**  Females lay 50–170 eggs each year, throughout the year and first breed when about four years old and 50–60cm long.

**SIGHTINGS**  Divers occasionally see this ray but it tends to live mostly below normal diving depths. Anglers also sometimes catch them and they are displayed in public aquaria. It is an important component of the commercial skate and ray catch and is taken in trawls and on long-lines, landed under the general category of 'skate and ray'. Cuckoo Ray are thought to be one of the few species of rays that are being fished sustainably in the North Atlantic. Records and observations from divers would be welcome as little is known of Cuckoo Ray behaviour in the wild.

# DEEPWATER *LEUCORAJA*

**Shagreen Ray** Morgath gribog, *Leucoraja fullonica* **and Sandy Ray** Morgath gron, *Leucoraja circularis*

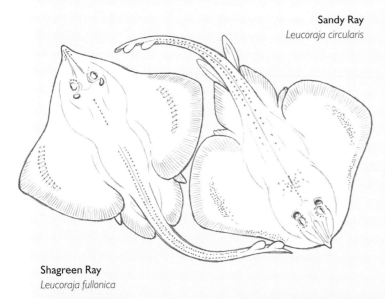

Sandy Ray
*Leucoraja circularis*

Shagreen Ray
*Leucoraja fullonica*

**SHAGREEN RAY** *Leucoraja fullonica* and **SANDY RAY** *Leucoraja circularis* are two other rays that are in the same genus as Cuckoo Ray but live in deeper water and are most common between 100–200m depth. Divers are unlikely to see these rays but they are caught in deepwater trawls and so may be encountered in mixed skate and ray hauls. There are confirmed records of Shagreen Ray throughout Welsh waters in suitable depths, but hardly any records of Sandy Ray. These two rays have a similar shape to Cuckoo Rays. Sandy Rays have four to six black-edged cream spots symmetrically arranged on each wing. Shagreen Ray are a uniform grey to brown but juveniles have wide, dark stripes running from wingtip to wingtip. Length: Both 120cm maximum.

# STARRY RAY        Morgath bigog        *Amblyraja radiata*

**Other names: Starry Skate, Thorny Skate**      **100cm**

**KEY IDENTIFICATION FEATURES** Starry Ray can be difficult to identify as it lacks a distinct pattern, but it always appears very spiny. In captured fish and good photographs the characteristic spine arrangement can be seen. A central row of 12–19 large spines with very broad bases runs down the midline of the back and along the tail. On the tail these are flanked by two other rows of smaller spines. Other large and small spines are scattered over the back. The colour is a fairly uniform greyish to chestnut brown with indistinct patches of dark and cream spots. This ray has a tendency to roll up into a 'basket' shape when disturbed.

**HABITAT AND DISTRIBUTION** The British Isles are at the southern limits of Starry Ray distribution. Starry Rays are sometimes landed from deepwater off the Welsh coastline and live mostly below 50m and down to 1000m on a variety of sediments.

**SIGHTINGS** Mixed trawls of skate and ray sometimes turn up this species in Wales but many more are caught in the north of its range. It is rarely seen by divers but has been photographed underwater at St. Abbs marine reserve off the Scottish east coast.

A trawled specimen caught in the North Sea at about 100m, as part of a scientific survey, and photographed along with a ray egg case probably from this species.

# BLONDE and SPOTTED RAYS Morgath felen gwta & Morgath fannog
## *Raja brachyura* and *Raja montagui*

**Blonde Ray 125cm and Spotted Ray 80cm**

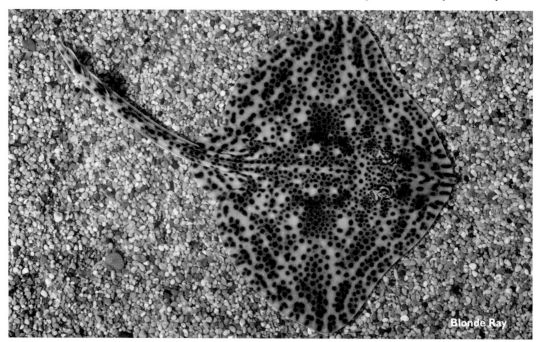

Blonde Ray

**KEY IDENTIFICATION FEATURES** These two rays are difficult to tell apart in the field especially when diving. They can be distinguished from any other rays with a reasonable degree of certainty. Large individuals over 80cm should be Blonde Rays. Spotted Ray are brown with numerous black spots that do not extend to the edge of the wings. Blonde Ray are light brown with similar spots but these extend all the way to the wing edges. In some Spotted Rays this is obvious as they have a wide edge without spots but in others it is much narrower. Blonde Rays also often have scattered rings of spots surrounding a pale centre. Spotted Rays may have these but often only a pair, one on each wing. The photographs shown in many guide books and web sites often confuse these two species.

**SIMILAR SPECIES** Thornback Ray are highly variable in colour and some have many dark spots as well as rings of spots. However they usually also have a variety of other paler markings and a clearly banded tail. They also have distinctive spines (see page 71).

**BEHAVIOUR** No specific behaviours have been recorded.

**HABITAT** Both species live on sandy or muddy sediment from about 60–120m. Young fish can be found in shallower water from about 20m down, possibly even less. Both species can be found considerably deeper in parts of their range to the south of the British Isles. Spotted ray can also be caught in areas of mixed sand and rock but Blonde rays prefer sand.

**DISTRIBUTION** These rays are fairly common and found throughout Welsh waters, though there are more records from south Wales especially from Milford Haven. Both species extend north all round Ireland to Scotland and south to the Mediterranean but are absent from much of the North Sea.

**NATURAL HISTORY** Spotted Ray mature when they are around 55cm long and aged three to eight years old. The larger Blonde Ray matures when about 90cm long, aged five or six years. Female Spotted Rays lay 24–60 egg cases per year which hatch after about four or five months. Blonde Rays lay about 30 per year and they hatch after about seven months.

**SIGHTINGS** Divers are only likely to see juveniles, which makes telling them apart even more difficult especially as the size difference between the two species will not be obvious. Both these rays form an important component of the 'skate and ray' landed by commercial trawlers. The larger Blonde Ray grows more slowly and matures later than the Spotted Ray and so is more impacted by fisheries.

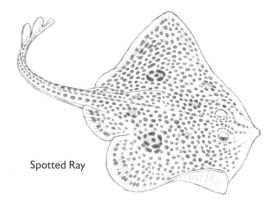

Spotted Ray

# THORNBACK RAY     Morgath ddreiniog     *Raja clavata*

**Other names: Roker**       **120cm**

**KEY IDENTIFICATION FEATURES** This ray can be identified in the field with a high degree of certainty but underwater, the very varied colour patterns may cause confusion. First look at the tail which has a series of alternating dark and light bars along its length. The general colour runs from brown to grey with light patches and lines and numerous dark spots. This ray also has characteristic large, broad-based thorns (like rose thorns) running along the midline from part way along the body up to the first dorsal fin on the tail. Other similar spines are scattered on the wings and tail, along with many smaller spines, making this a very prickly fish. This is really obvious in dead fish which must be handled with care!

**SIMILAR SPECIES** Thornbacks without many white patches and lots of dark spots might be mistaken underwater for Spotted or Blonde Ray. Sometimes some of the white patches are surrounded by dark spots forming oscelli and some Spotted and Blonde Rays sport similar marks.

**BEHAVIOUR** There is a general movement of Thornbacks from offshore into shallow water in the spring, with the females arriving before the males. This is a breeding migration.

**HABITAT** This is an unfussy ray found on almost all types of sediment and sometimes on rough ground and in sediment areas between rocky reefs. It is commonest between about 10–60m but can be found from just below the shoreline down to around 300m, deeper in some parts of the Mediterranean.

**DISTRIBUTION** Thornback Rays are found throughout Welsh waters and are one of the commonest species of ray and skate. This ray has a wide distribution extending all round the British Isles, north to Iceland and Norway and south to Namibia. It extends throughout the Mediterranean and Black Sea.

**NATURAL HISTORY** Thornback Rays do not breed until they are between five to ten years old and around 60–85cm long. Females lay 50–180 egg cases during the summer and the eggs take about five months to hatch. Empty egg cases are frequently washed up on shore and the majority of 'mermaid's purses' as they are known, are from Thornback Rays (see page 75). They feed on bottom-living invertebrates especially crabs and other crustaceans.

**SIGHTINGS** This is the ray that divers are most likely to see. Thornbacks are one of several species landed under the category of 'skate and rays' and are an important component as they are large and relatively common. This species is caught mainly by small inshore trawlers. It is regularly caught by anglers using rod and line. It is listed as 'Near Threatened' in the IUCN Red Data List but populations in the Irish Sea and Bristol Channel are considered sustainable at the moment. It does well in public aquaria and is one of the rays almost always on show.

# SMALL-EYED RAY     Morgath lygaid bach     *Raja micoocellata*

**Other names: Painted Ray, Owl Ray**      **86cm**

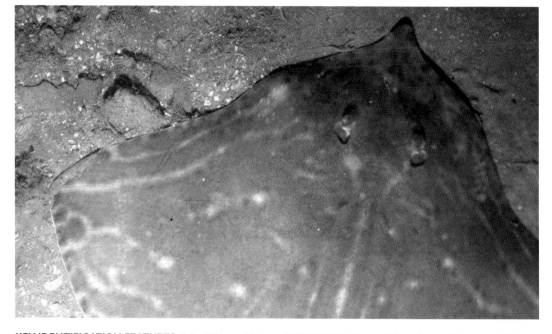

**KEY IDENTIFICATION FEATURES** It should be possible to identify this ray in the field with a reasonable degree of certainty, as long as the colour pattern is clear. If this is not the case then identification will be more uncertain. This is a pale to yellow brown ray with a pattern of slightly wavy whitish stripes that run parallel to the front and back edges of the wings and scattered white blotches. The pattern may be obvious but in some fish can be quite faint and so difficult to see underwater. In juveniles the pattern may be only white blotches. With dead fish measure the length of the eye plus spiracle. It should be less than half the distance between the eyes (hence the common name). A row of densely packed (about 50) thorns runs along the midline of the disc and onto the tail. These are bent back at a right angle.

**SIMILAR SPECIES** Both this ray and the Undulate Ray are referred to as 'painted rays' because of their patterns. The Undulate Ray has much more clearly defined lines edged with white spots (see page 73).

**BEHAVIOUR** Little specific information is available.

**HABITAT** Found in sandy areas, bays and outer estuaries and seems to be particular about its habitat. It lives close inshore down to around 100m depth.

**DISTRIBUTION** This pretty ray has been recorded all round the Welsh coastline but not far north of Anglesey. It is most common in the Bristol Channel. Compared to most other Welsh rays it has a rather restricted wider distribution and Wales and the west coast of Ireland are about its northern limit. It extends south to Western Sahara but not into the Mediterranean.

**NATURAL HISTORY** Relatively little is known of the life history of this ray. They mature at 45–60cm long but age of maturity is not known. Females lay around 50–60 egg capsules per year.

**SIGHTINGS** Divers might easily see this ray particularly on shore dives out through sandy bays. As it is not very common around Wales, it does not contribute much to commercial fisheries but does come up in trawl nets. It is only occasionally caught by anglers. It is often kept in public aquaria, perhaps because of its relatively small size and is usually labelled 'Painted ray'. Stocks in the Celtic Sea and especially the Bristol Channel are thought to be stable. They are listed as 'Near Threatened' in the IUCN Red List.

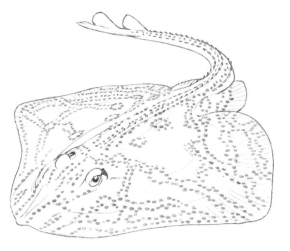

# UNDULATE RAY　　　Morgath donnog　　　*Raja undulata*

**Other names: Painted Ray**　　　　　　　　　　　　　　　　100cm

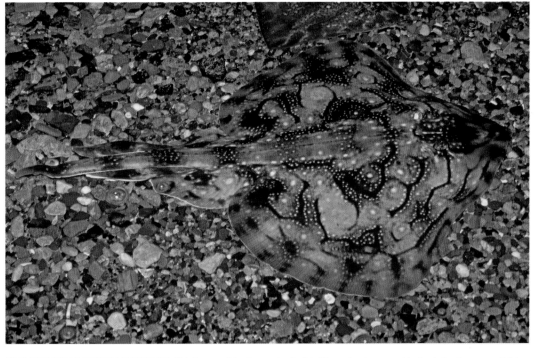

**KEY IDENTIFICATION FEATURES** This is one of the few rays that should be instantly recognisable in the field and can be identified with a very high degree of certainty. It has a distinctive pattern of dark, wavy lines, each edged with rows of small white spots. Larger white blotches are interspersed between the lines. The pectoral fins have rounded tips and the two dorsal fins on the tail have a wide space between them.

**SIMILAR SPECIES** Both this and the Small-eyed Ray are referred to as 'painted rays' because of their patterns. However, the lines in Small-eyed Rays are pale and are not edged with white spots and are arranged in a distinctive pattern

**BEHAVIOUR** There are few observations of this ray in its natural habitat.

**HABITAT** Mainly found in inshore sandy areas from about 10m downwards, but most often below about 45m depth. It is commonest down to 100m but extends down to at least 200m.

**DISTRIBUTION** Undulate Rays have been recorded round south and west coasts of Wales but not off Anglesey and further north. It is predominantly a southern species and mid-Wales and southern Ireland are about its northern limit and it is not a ray that is seen very often around Wales. It is common off Portugal and it extends south to Senegal and into the western Mediterranean and possibly eastern Mediterranean as well.

**NATURAL HISTORY** This ray is estimated to mature when it is between 50–60cm long and aged five or six years though some work on Portuguese populations suggests even later maturity. It can live to at least 13 years old. Egg capsules are laid in late summer in the English Channel and presumably at a similar time around Wales, if it breeds at all this far north. It eats flatfish and other bottom-living fish, crustaceans and squid.

**SIGHTINGS** Divers occasionally see Undulate Rays but they live mostly below normal diving depths. It is sometimes caught by anglers around the coasts of south and west Wales but more commonly further south, such as around the Channel Islands. Public aquaria often keep this species because it is so colourful and seems to do well in captivity. This ray is landed along with many others as 'skate and ray' and the status of its stocks in the Irish and Celtic Sea is uncertain. However, it seems to be susceptible to local over-exploitation.

# ATLANTIC TORPEDO     Morgath drydan     *Torpedo nobiliana*

**Other names: Electric Ray, Crampfish**                    180cm

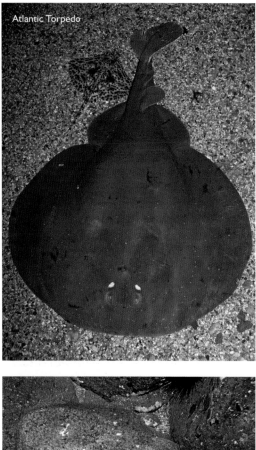

Atlantic Torpedo

Spotted Torpedo

**KEY IDENTIFICATION FEATURES**: This fish can be identified in the field with a very high degree of certainty. Its rounded, disc-like shape is completely different to true rays with their pointed wings. It has a thick fleshy tail with two dorsal fins, the first larger than the second and a normal fish-shaped tail fin. It has no spines and the skin feels smooth to the touch (care! see below). In colour it is a uniform dark brown, dark grey or almost black.

**SIMILAR SPECIES**: One other electric ray, the Marbled Electric Ray or Spotted Torpedo *Torpedo marmorata* is found in European waters and occasionally moves north to the English Channel and southern North Sea. There are no confirmed records from Welsh waters. This ray has a pattern of darker marbling over a brown background. The spiracles behind its eyes look frilly as they are edged with small skin lobes. Atlantic Torpedo have smooth-edged spiracles. This species seems to live only on the seabed.

**BEHAVIOUR**: There are some reports that Atlantic Torpedo may migrate long distances. As these fish do not normally breed around the British Isles but can be found as far north as Scotland in summer and autumn, they must be reasonably capable swimmers. They are mainly nocturnal.

**HABITAT**: Young fish live on coastal seabed on mud, sand and gravel and can be found amongst seagrass and sometimes in areas of mixed sediment and rock as shallow as 10m depth. Adults rest on the seabed but also make forays up into the water column where they may remain hunting for fish and squid for some time. 150m is the normal depth limit but these rays can be found as deep as 350m.

**DISTRIBUTION**: This is an uncommon fish in Welsh waters. There are confirmed records from north, west and south coasts of Wales and it is relatively frequent along southern and western coasts of the British Isles. It extends north to Scotland, is found throughout the Mediterranean and extends further south to the Gulf of Guinea and South Africa. In the western Atlantic it occurs off parts of the North American and South American coasts.

**NATURAL HISTORY**: Atlantic Torpedo Rays give birth to live young producing between 5–30 or so pups after a gestation of ten months. However, currently they do not seem to breed this far north. They feed on bottom-living and free-swimming fish and use their electrical abilities to stun their prey – see below.

**SIGHTINGS**: Divers do occasionally come across young Atlantic Torpedo but most sightings are from fish trawled up as bycatch. They are also kept in public aquaria.

## STUNNING FISH

Both Atlantic and Spotted Torpedo are capable of emitting a strong electric shock, from electric organs at the base of their pectoral fins. The voltage depends on the size and resting condition of the fish – voltages of up to 220 volts have been measured. Simply by stalking and wrapping its wings around its prey, an electric ray can stun large fish. It must then build up its stored charge again before it can hunt effectively. Although sluggish and unaggressive, these fish, especially adults, should only be handled with great care. In the past they have supposedly been used to numb the pain of childbirth and operations.

# SKATE AND RAY EGGCASES 'MERMAID'S PURSES'

To be technically and biologically correct, rays give birth to live young whilst skates lay egg cases. Historically however, the common names have not reflected this and the terms 'ray' and 'skate' are more often used to distinguish between those with short noses (rays) and those with long noses (skates) though even this is not entirely adhered to. Skates (and many species called rays) produce tough eggcases, inside which the egg is protected, develops and finally hatches, a process which can take between six and nine months. Like catshark eggcases (see page 54) these cases are known as 'mermaid's purses'.

Very little is known about where many skates actually lay their eggcases and research (some involving amateur divers) is currently ongoing to try to find out where these eggcases are laid and in what sort of habitat and substrate. Few photographs have been taken of skate eggcases *in situ*, and those that have seem to show them either fastened in place (effectively 'glued' down) or posted (wedged perhaps) in crevices between rocks.

Some species of ray have shown dramatic declines in numbers – the Blue Skate also referred to rather inaccurately as the 'Common' Skate is now very rare in the Irish Sea and considered to be virtually extinct, so any information on how this or other skates reproduce is important in understanding why they are not surviving.

Top. Blue Skate eggcase.
Middle. Live Thornback Ray eggcase.
Bottom. Live Thornback Ray eggcase covered in epiphytes.

This eggcase is empty and seems to have been washed onto sand so not all eggcases found underwater are 'alive' or *in situ*!

# Chimaeras

## ORDER Chimaeriformes

Like sharks and rays, Chimaeras are cartilaginous fish but are sufficiently different to be grouped separately from them. There are only about 34 known species in three families worldwide and most are deepwater fish. These fish have flabby bodies, no scales, large heads and long tails. Like many sharks, they have two dorsal fins but unlike sharks they can raise and lower the first fin. All chimaeras have a venomous spine in front of the first dorsal fin. Three species are found around the British Isles in deep water below 200m but there are no confirmed records of chimaeras from Welsh waters as these waters are relatively shallow. However, in sheltered Norwegian fjords, Rabbit fish *Chimaera monstrosa* extend up into diving depths.

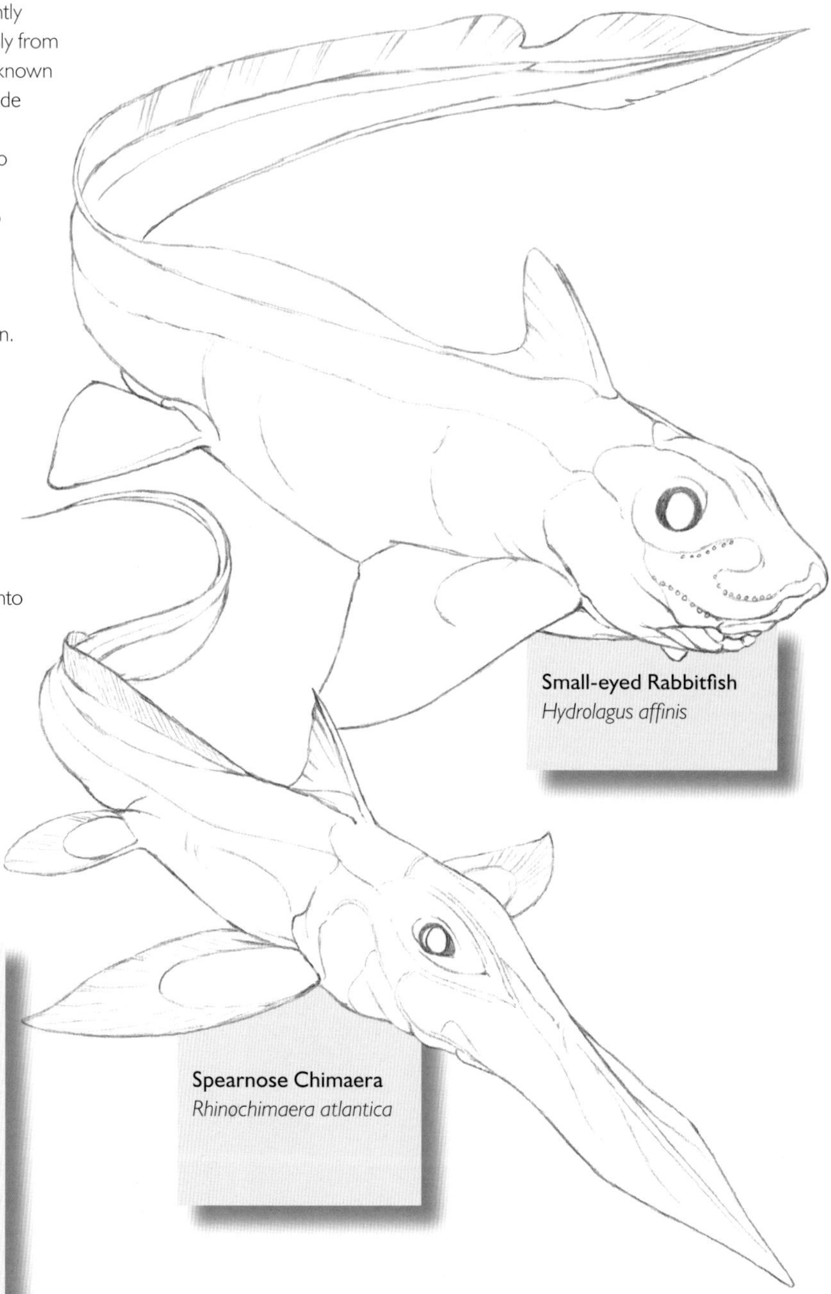

**Small-eyed Rabbitfish**
*Hydrolagus affinis*

**Spearnose Chimaera**
*Rhinochimaera atlantica*

**SIGHTINGS** In the northern North Sea and Skaggerak, Rabbit fish are a common by-catch in shrimp trawls. In Wales, the greatest likelihood of a sighting would be from deepwater trawlers fishing in the Celtic Sea. These fish are not of commercial interest and their venomous spine can rip fishing nets and give a painful wound to fishermen.

# RABBIT FISH          Cwningen          *Chimaera monstrosa*

**Other names: Chimaera, Rat-fish**          150cm

**KEY IDENTIFICATION FEATURES** Chimaeras can readily be identified as such in the field and Rabbit Fish have a distinctive pattern of wavy brown and white lines when live or freshly dead. This species has a rounded snout and head with winding rows of sensory pores. The first dorsal fin is triangular followed immediately by a long, low second dorsal fin. The pectoral fins are very large and the tail ends in a thin filament, rather like a rat's tail from which its other common name of Rat-fish is derived.

**SIMILAR SPECIES** Two other deepwater chimaeras are found around the British Isles.

**BEHAVIOUR** Rabbit Fish are slow-moving sluggish fish that spend their time hunting for molluscs, crustaceans and bottom-living fish. They crunch these up with paired plate-like teeth from which they get their common name.

**HABITAT** This is a deepwater fish that lives on the edge of the Continental slope and in deeper water, usually between 300–500m depth. Its depth range extends up to 40m and down to at least 1000m. Records from above 100m are mostly from the north of its range including Scotland and Norway. It spends most of its time near to the seabed.

**DISTRIBUTION** So far there are no confirmed records of this fish in Welsh waters. Off the west coast of Ireland this species makes up around 15% of discards from deepwater trawlers and so it is not a rare fish. Its distribution extends from Morocco and the western Mediterranean northwards up to Cornwall and the west coast of Ireland to Scotland, Iceland and northern Norway.

**NATURAL HISTORY** Females lay large tadpole-shaped egg cases following pairing and mating.

**SIGHTINGS** In the northern North Sea and Skaggerak, Rabbit Fish are a common by-catch in shrimp trawls. In Wales, the greatest likelihood of a sighting would be from deepwater trawlers fishing in the Celtic Sea. These fish are not of commercial interest and their venomous spine can rip fishing nets and give a painful wound to fishermen.

# Introduction to Bony Fish

Bony fish belong to a group (Class) of fish called Osteichthyes and, as is easy to guess, they all have an internal skeleton made of hard bone rather than the cartilage seen in sharks and rays (Chondrichthyes). As anyone who has handled or eaten bony fish knows the skeleton extends into the fins as articulating sharp spines and soft rays. The relative numbers of these in the dorsal and anal fins is often used as an aid to identification, though usually only when dealing with dead fish.

In most bony fish the mouth is at the end of the head rather than underneath as in sharks and the gills are hidden by a bony flap called the operculum. This structure along with the scales and the ear bones (ossicles) can all be used to estimate the age of temperate water fish by counting annual growth rings, because the fish stops growing or grows more slowly in winter.

Whilst most (not all) sharks are of a similar shape with 'standard' fins, bony fish have evolved a huge variety of different body shapes to suit their particular environment and way of life. Thanks to the possession of a buoyancy aid in the form of a gas-filled swim bladder, bony fish have been able to develop and use their fins for purposes other than swimming, such as defensive spines, display and attachment suckers. The general shape of both the body and fins of bony fish is therefore often the first clue as to a fish's identity.

In contrast to the relatively small number of cartilaginous fish species (sharks, rays, chimaeras) found in the world's oceans, bony fish are incredibly numerous and thus the task of identifying them is much greater.

Above. Bony fish have well-developed eyes of a similar design to other vertebrates. Those of the Anglerfish are a beautiful blue and green.

Below. Bony fish have an internal skeleton made of hard bone. This extends into the fins as hard spines and flexible rays. The number of these in the dorsal and anal fins is a useful identification feature.

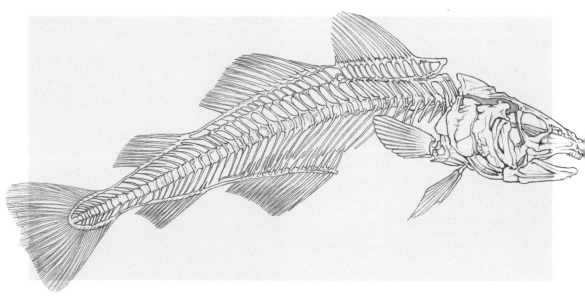

# Eels

Almost everyone will be familiar with the long, sinuous shape of an eel and 'eel-like' is used to describe many other animals and objects. Eels have no scales or pelvic fins and one long fin runs along the back, tail and belly.

True eels form a group (Order) of fish (Anguilliformes) that range from tiny to huge, shallow to deep and fresh to salt water. Moray eels (Muraenidae) predominate in shallow warm and tropical waters where there are many different species. Only two species are represented in Welsh waters, Conger Eel (Congridae) and European Eel (Anguillidae). Mediterranean Moray (Muraenidae) is a rare visitor as far north as the English Channel. Two deepwater snipe eels (Nemichthyidae) are the only other eels found around the British Isles.

## ORDER Anguilliformes

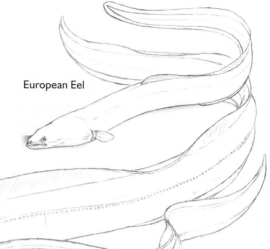

European Eel

Conger Eel

### WARM WATER VISITOR

Mediterranean or Marbled Moray Eel *Muraena helena*, is a common fish south of the Bay of Biscay and throughout the Mediterranean. It has never been recorded in Welsh waters but is a rare visitor to the English Channel and might extend its range north with ocean warming. It is instantly separated from Conger or European Eels by its distinctive marbled yellow pattern on a dark background and lack of pectoral fins. It can reach 150cm and lives in shallow rocky areas including shore pools.

A Conger Eel peers out from its daytime lair.

# EUROPEAN EEL     Llyswen     *Anguilla anguilla*

**Other names: Common Eel**     100cm

**KEY IDENTIFICATION FEATURES** European Eels can be identified in the field with a high degree of certainty. Adults have a small head with the lower jaw slightly longer than the upper. A single, long fin starts some way down the body and runs all the way round the tail and onto the belly so that the dorsal, anal and tail fin are all merged. This eel has small, rounded pectoral fins. Adults are dark greenish brown often with a yellowish tinge especially on the sides and a pale belly, or are silvery grey when ready to breed.

**SIMILAR SPECIES** European Eel are much smaller than Conger Eel but could be mistaken for young Conger, especially if only the head can be seen. Look carefully at the jaws which are equal in length in Conger Eels. The shape of the pectoral fins and position where the dorsal fin starts will also help.

**BEHAVIOUR** In shallow water this eel can be found hiding in rock crevices with just its head showing in a similar manner to Conger Eels. However they spend more time out in the open, but hiding amongst seaweed and often align themselves with tall seaweeds for camouflage.

**HABITAT** Although essentially a freshwater fish, European Eels are commonly found on the shore and in shallow water amongst seaweeds and under boulders. They are also frequently found in estuaries and in low salinity saltmarsh pools and other pools. They have been caught as deep as 700m.

**DISTRIBUTION** European Eels are common throughout Welsh coastal waters although their numbers are declining. They are found all round the British Isles, north to Iceland and Norway, and throughout the low salinity Baltic. To the south they extend to Morocco and throughout the Mediterranean

**NATURAL HISTORY** European Eels have a complex and still incompletely known life history involving several changes in body shape and size. Adults approaching maturity change to a pale silvery grey, and embark on a migration out to deep Atlantic waters in the Sargasso Sea. Here they are thought to spawn and die. The eggs hatch into a transparent leaf-shaped larvae (known as a leptocephalus). The larvae drift back into coastal waters on the Gulf Stream, and change into elvers – miniature transparent eels, otherwise known as glass eels. They swim and wriggle their way up estuaries and into rivers, lakes and ponds in their thousands.

**SIGHTINGS** European Eels can be spotted almost anywhere by anyone although they are becoming increasingly rare due to over exploitation and deterioration of river habitats. They can move from pool to pool over the shore and overland in damp conditions. They are caught in river estuaries in baited fyke nets, traps and dip nets and by anglers on the coast and on rivers. Glass eels and elvers are fished especially in the tidal reaches of the River Severn and south Wales rivers draining into the Bristol Channel. Inshore trawlers may also bring some eels up. Along the coast adults are an important food source for otters, whilst elvers sustain waders and herons.

# EUROPEAN CONGER     Congren     *Conger conger*

**Other names: Conger**        **200cm**

**KEY IDENTIFICATION FEATURES** This eel can be identified in the field with a high degree of certainty. It is the largest eel or eel-like fish found in Welsh waters and exceptionally can reach 3m long. Divers will mostly see this fish with just its head sticking out of its refuge. Look carefully at the mouth (especially in small ones) – the jaws are equal in length or the upper jaw is slightly longer than the lower. Like European eel it has a fin that runs all the way from its back round onto its belly. This fin starts close behind the head. Pectoral fins are pointed but with rounded tips.

**SIMILAR SPECIES** See under European Eel.

**BEHAVIOUR** Conger Eels are nocturnal and stay in their hidey holes during the day. At night they emerge and swim freely searching amongst rocks and seaweeds for hidden fish, crabs, lobster, octopus and other bottom-living animals. Although not normally aggressive, they can inflict a nasty bite and should be treated with respect. In tropical waters, other fish 'shadow' hunt moray eels to share in their kill. It is possible that this happens with Congers as well and any observations would be very interesting.

**HABITAT** This eel is found mainly in rugged, rocky areas where there are plenty of holes, crevices and caves for it to hide in. Congers up to about a metre in length, live close inshore and small ones can be found in deep rock pools low down on the shore especially amongst kelp. Larger ones live in deeper water down to around 500m (even deeper in the Mediterranean). Congers are also common in man-made habitats such as shipwrecks, artificial reefs and harbour structures. In deep water they can be found in sandy areas.

**DISTRIBUTION** Conger Eels are common throughout Welsh waters. They are found all round the British Isles, north to Iceland and Norway, south to Senegal and throughout the Mediterranean.

**NATURAL HISTORY** A Conger Eel lives nearly its whole life as an immature fish. When it does finally mature aged somewhere between about 5–15 years old, it will spawn once and then die. When they are ready to spawn, these fish swim many miles out into the deep Atlantic to specific spawning grounds, the number and location of which are unknown except for an area between Gibraltar and the Azores and some in the Mediterranean. Eggs hatch into leaf-shaped leptocephali larvae which drift back inshore over one to two years and metamorphose into young eels.

**SIGHTINGS** A Conger Eel with its head sticking out of a rocky crevice or wreck is a familiar sight to divers. Both this eel and European eels can be seen and caught with a push net in deep rock pools. Congers can be caught on rod and line and is a good angling fish, taken from shore or boat. It is also taken as by-catch from various bottom-fishing equipment including deep trawls. It is good to eat but is easily over-fished as it reproduces only once. They are often kept in public aquaria.

## Poor to rich, rich to poor

Eels have provided an abundant and cheap food item for European peoples for hundreds of years. Populations have been declining since the 1960s and the rate of decline has increased sharply since the 1980s. Eels are now an expensive luxury food item. European Eel were assessed in 2008 and are now listed as Critically Endangered on the IUCN Red List, as a result of over exploitation, hydroelectric dams blocking migration routes and river pollution. Various restrictions in international trade will come into force in 2009. This and other management plans will take many years before they have a significant effect.

# Herrings

The herring family (Clupeidae) is a large one with over 200 species worldwide. In Welsh waters it includes the familiar Atlantic Herring, Atlantic Sprat, and Pilchard (Sardine). Anchovies (Engraulidae) are similar and closely related. It also includes, the less familiar shads, fish that spend part of their life in freshwater rivers. These fish are all quite similar with a relatively thin body that in the species described here is compressed from side to side and is intensely silvery. However, this silver sheen is quickly lost out of water as their large scales rub off easily. Members of this order have a single dorsal fin near the middle of the back and the pelvic fins on the belly are set far back, more or less under the dorsal fin base. The tail fin is forked and there is no obvious lateral line.

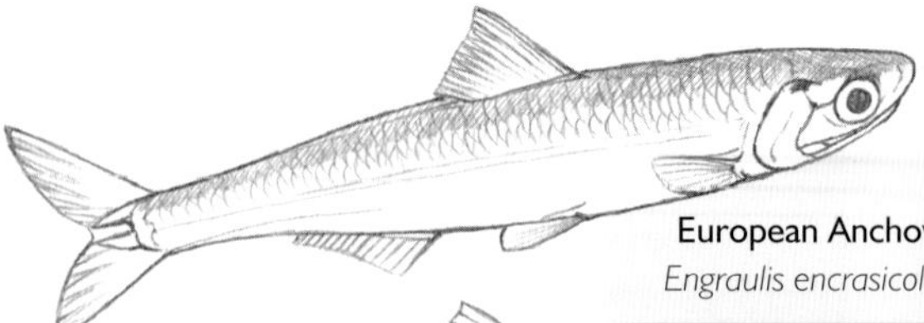

**European Anchov**
*Engraulis encrasicolu*

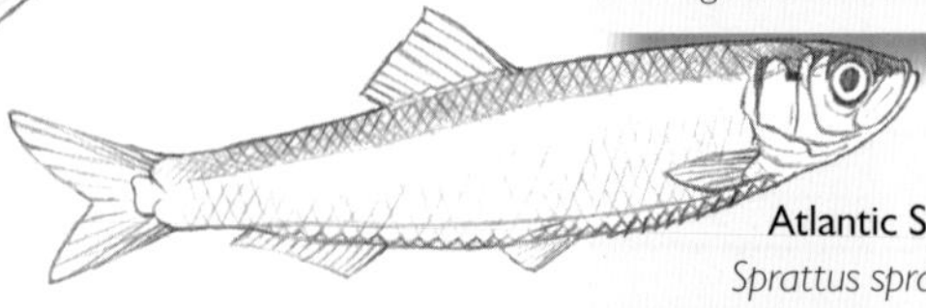

**Atlantic Spra**
*Sprattus sprattu*

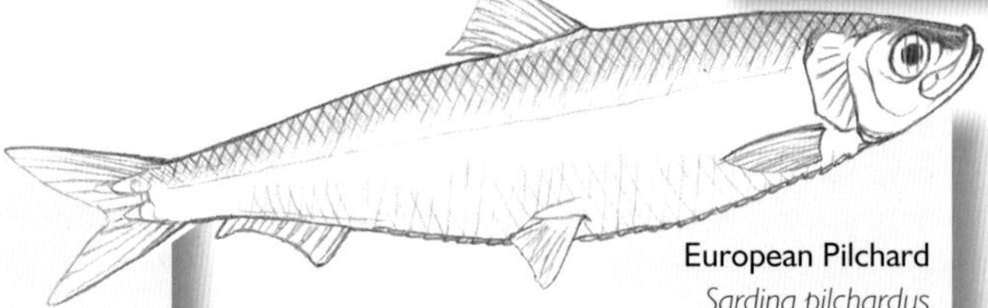

## TESTING HERRINGS

Notch in upper lip: Twaite and Allis Shad
Dusky blotch on gill cover: Twaite and Allis Shad
Radiating ridges on operculum: European Pilchard, Twaite and Allis Shad
Belly with sharp keel: Twaite Shad, Allis Shad, Atlantic Sprat, Atlantic Herring (young)
Rounded belly: European Pilchard, Atlantic Herring (adults)
Upper jaw much longer than lower: Anchovy
Longer than 25cm: Atlantic Herring, Twaite and Allis Shad

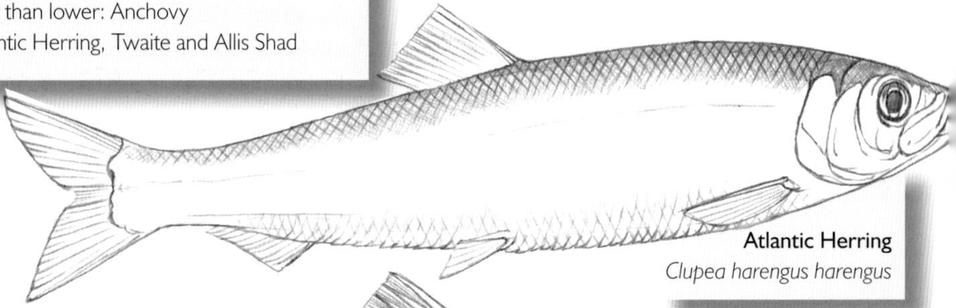

**European Pilchard**
*Sardina pilchardus*

**Atlantic Herring**
*Clupea harengus harengus*

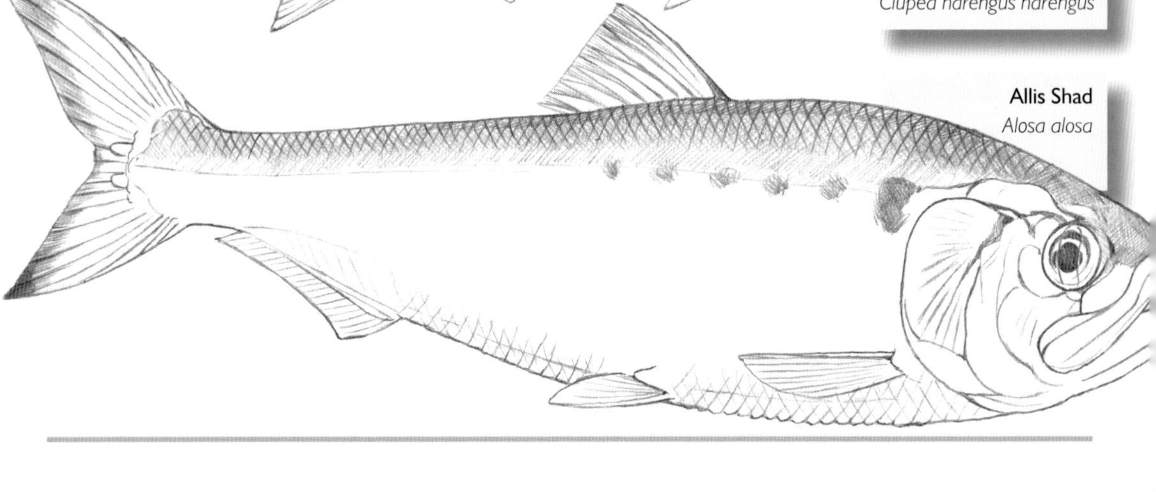

**Allis Shad**
*Alosa alosa*

# ALLIS SHAD and TWAITE SHAD

## Herlyn & Gwangen
### *Alosa alosa* and *Alosa fallax fallax*

**Other names: Mayfish (*A. alosa*)**                                    60–80cm

**KEY IDENTIFICATION FEATURES** These fish are difficult to identify in the field and it is unlikely they would be recognised underwater. With dead fish it should be possible to distinguish shad from other members of the herring family. Shad are deep-bodied and larger than Herring. Viewed head on, a notch in the mid-line of the upper jaw should be visible. Both species have a large dark spot behind the gill cover but this is sometimes absent. Telling the two species of shad apart is difficult. Most (but not all) Twaite Shad have a row of seven or eight small dark spots along the flank. Allis Shad usually lack these but occasionally have one or two spots. In the laboratory, scale and gill raker counts can be made.

**SIMILAR SPECIES** Other members of the herring family.

**BEHAVIOUR** These are schooling fish that feed in open water on plankton and small fish.

**HABITAT** Schools in shallow coastal waters and estuaries and enters rivers to spawn.

**DISTRIBUTION** There are records of both shad species from all round the Welsh coastline but these fish are rare in Welsh waters. Twaite Shad are known to spawn in rivers that empty into the Severn estuary such as the Severn, Usk, and Wye. Allis Shad may now only spawn in a few French rivers. Elsewhere these fish are locally distributed with a range north from the British Isles to Iceland, Norway and the Baltic and south to Morocco and the Mediterranean. Allis Shad is common in France.

**NATURAL HISTORY** Adults move from the sea up into rivers to spawn, in spring and early summer, possibly into the river where they were hatched. After spawning the adults move back downriver into the sea. Juveniles spend the summer in the river before swimming out to sea in the autumn. Twaite Shad only run up into the tidal reaches of rivers. The main reasons for the decline of these once common fish are pollution, river and estuary barriers, over-fishing and destruction of river breeding habitat.

**SIGHTINGS** Anglers fishing for salmon and trout sometimes catch shad. They are no longer exploited commercially in Wales or the UK but might be caught at sea in coastal pelagic trawl nets and purse seines. These fish are listed in the Bern Convention; the rarer Allis Shad is strictly protected (Appendix II) and Twaite Shad is protected (Appendix III). Both are on Annexes II and V of the EC Habitats Directive. They are also the subjects of UK Biological Action Plans (BAPs). Although still locally rare, both species are now listed in the IUCN Red List as 'Least Concern' in a worldwide context due to current low, but stable populations.

# HERRING              Pennog                    *Clupea harengus*

**Other names:** *Clupea harengus harengus* (Atlantic race)                    45cm

**KEY IDENTIFICATION FEATURES** Telling the difference between Herring, Sprat and Pilchard (Sardine) underwater is rarely possible except that Herring grow much larger than the other two. With dead fish and some practise, the adults can be separated but young fish are a problem in the field. Feel the belly – although the scales form a keel this is quite rounded compared to the sharp, serrated keel in Atlantic Sprat. Look at the fish sideways and draw an imaginary line vertically down from the start (origin) of the dorsal fin. This line should fall clearly in front of the pelvic fin.

**SIMILAR SPECIES** See Sprat and Pilchard.

**BEHAVIOUR** Atlantic Herring feed on zooplankton such as copepods, picking them from the water as they swim along.

**HABITAT** Lives in large shoals in coastal open water, from the surface down to at least 200m

**DISTRIBUTION** Atlantic Herring are a northern species, common throughout Welsh waters, though their numbers everywhere are considerably reduced from what they once were. Atlantic herring have a wide distribution on both sides of the North Atlantic extending from the Bay of Biscay north to northern Scandinavia, the Baltic, Iceland, and southern Greenland and down the east coast of North America.

**NATURAL HISTORY** Herring spawn in extensive offshore areas over gravelly banks and in many smaller coastal areas. The eggs stick to the gravel but after hatching, many larvae drift into inshore, sheltered nursery areas. There are no important spawning or nursery areas in Welsh waters, though the whole of Liverpool Bay along the coast from North Wales to Solway Firth acts as a nursery area. Shoals of young Herring in North Wales mostly come from autumn/winter spawning stocks. There is (or was) a small summer spawning stock in Milford Haven.

**SIGHTINGS** Atlantic Herring are rarely seen by divers as they live in open water, though shoals of young might be spotted in sheltered bays. On the shore, young fish can occasionally be caught in sandy or muddy pools especially in estuaries. These fish are caught in purse seines and pelagic trawls. The state of the Irish Sea stock is unknown but thought to be stable. There is a minimum landing size for herring in EU waters.

# EUROPEAN PILCHARD    Pennog Mair    *Sardina pilchardus*

**Other names: Sardine (when half-grown)**    **25cm**

**KEY IDENTIFICATION FEATURES**    European Pilchard appear very similar to Atlantic Herring but do not reach as large a size and the remarks made under Atlantic Herring identification apply. With dead fish, look at the gill cover, which in European Pilchard has a series of clear ridges radiating from a point just behind the eye. The belly is rounded with only a very slight keel.

**SIMILAR SPECIES**    Twaite and Allis Shad also have ridges on the gill cover.

**BEHAVIOUR**    Schools of Pilchard migrate northwards in summer after spawning and so more are found around our coasts at this time. In winter they retreat southwards and into deeper water.

**HABITAT**    Pilchard live in shoals in open water, near to the coast, usually at depths between about 25–100m but nearer the surface at night.

**DISTRIBUTION**    Pilchard have been recorded around most of the Welsh coastline but this is essentially a southern species that reaches the northern limit of its distribution around the British Isles. It is much commoner in the Mediterranean and south to Senegal.

**NATURAL HISTORY**    Like Sprat, Pilchard spawn in spring and summer out at sea and after hatching, the larvae drift inshore. Young Pilchard can be found close inshore during their first season.

**SIGHTINGS**    These fish are caught in the same way as Sprat but again there is no directed fishery in Welsh waters. Further south in Portugal and Spain, they are of vital importance.

# ATLANTIC SPRAT    Corbennog    *Sprattus sprattus*

**Other names: Brisling**    **17cm**

**KEY IDENTIFICATION FEATURES**    Sprat closely resemble small Atlantic Herring and the remarks made in the Herring entry apply. The best way to tell them apart is to feel the belly, which in Atlantic Sprat has scales that form a sharp keel like a miniature saw blade. Look at the fish sideways and draw an imaginary line vertically down from the start (origin) of the dorsal fin. This line should fall onto or behind the base of the pelvic fin.

**SIMILAR SPECIES**    Atlantic Herring and Pilchard

**BEHAVIOUR**    Schools of Sprat migrate between winter feeding grounds and summer spawning grounds. Like Atlantic Herring they feed on planktonic crustaceans. The schools stay in deeper water during the day and migrate nearer the surface at night.

**HABITAT**    Sprat live in shoals in open water in inshore areas and estuaries down to about 150m depth.

**DISTRIBUTION**    Sprat are found all round the Welsh coastline and the British Isles, north to Norway and in the Baltic, Mediterranean and Black Sea.

**NATURAL HISTORY**    Sprat spawn out at sea and the eggs and larvae float in the plankton. Young fish are found close inshore sometimes forming schools with young Herring.

**SIGHTINGS**    Sprat are caught using pelagic trawls (and other methods in other countries) but the main fisheries are in the Baltic and North Sea and there are no directed fisheries in Welsh waters. Young fish can be caught in push nets at low tide on sandy and muddy shores especially in estuaries.

# EUROPEAN ANCHOVY     Brwyniad     *Engraulis encrasicolus*

**Other names: Southern Anchovy**                                  **20cm**

**KEY IDENTIFICATION FEATURES** Anchovy are sufficiently different from members of the herring family described here, that although similar in size and colour, they can be identified in the field with a high degree of certainty. However, again it may be difficult to distinguish them from other schooling silvery fish underwater, especially as the shoals veer off when approached. This is a slender, rounded fish without a keel on the belly, but it is the head that gives it away. It has a very protuberant snout because the lower jaw is much shorter than the upper jaw. Most are under 12cm long. Netted fish tend to lose all their scales which are large and very easily detached.

**SIMILAR SPECIES** Similar in colour to Atlantic Herring and Sprat, but the mouth is distinctive. Sand Smelt *Antherina presbyter* are superficially similar but have two dorsal fins.

**BEHAVIOUR** Under the right conditions, European Anchovy congregate in huge shoals in plankton-rich areas.

**HABITAT** This too is an open water schooling fish, found near the coast and often near the surface, though it extends down to 300m. In summer it moves close inshore and into sheltered bays and estuaries. They can withstand very low salinity

**DISTRIBUTION** European Anchovy have been recorded round most of the Welsh coastline, but are not common and have a similar, essentially southern distribution to European Pilchard.

**NATURAL HISTORY** In contrast to the similar sized Atlantic Sprat which can live to six years, this is a short-lived species that only reaches three years old. It spawns inshore in summer and the eggs and larvae float in the plankton but most spawning in northern Europe is off the Dutch coastline.

**SIGHTINGS** Anchovy are not fished for around British Isles but are caught further south in pelagic trawls and purse seines. Stocks in the Bay of Biscay are so low that the fishery has been closed. Sightings in Welsh waters are likely to be from incidental catches taken along with Herring, Sprat and Pilchard.

Shoals of small, shoaling, silvery fishes move quickly and are difficult and often impossible to identify even when photographed as their highly reflective bodies reveal little detail useful for identification when they are small in the image.

# Salmon, Smelt and Argentine

ORDERS Salmoniformes and Osmeriformes

**SALMON** are a large family of fish (Salmonidae) found throughout the northern hemisphere but widely introduced elsewhere. Designed for fast swimming, they have a torpedo-shaped body, powerful tail and a large mouth and eyes. A single dorsal fin on the back is followed by a small adipose (fatty) fin that looks like a slightly curved, fleshy growth. The pelvic fins are set well back on the belly.

Atlantic Salmon *Salmo salar* are famous for their migratory runs up rivers when they use their powerful body and tail to leap up waterfalls and other obstacles. Only this species and Sea Trout are native to Welsh marine waters. Rainbow Trout *Oncorhynchus mykiss*, native to the eastern Pacific Ocean and bordering rivers, have been widely introduced into the UK and worldwide. Individuals from the sea going race (Steelheads) are occasionally caught in British waters as as well as very occasional Pink Salmon *Oncorhynchus gorbushcha* and Coho Salmon *Oncorhynchus kisutch*.

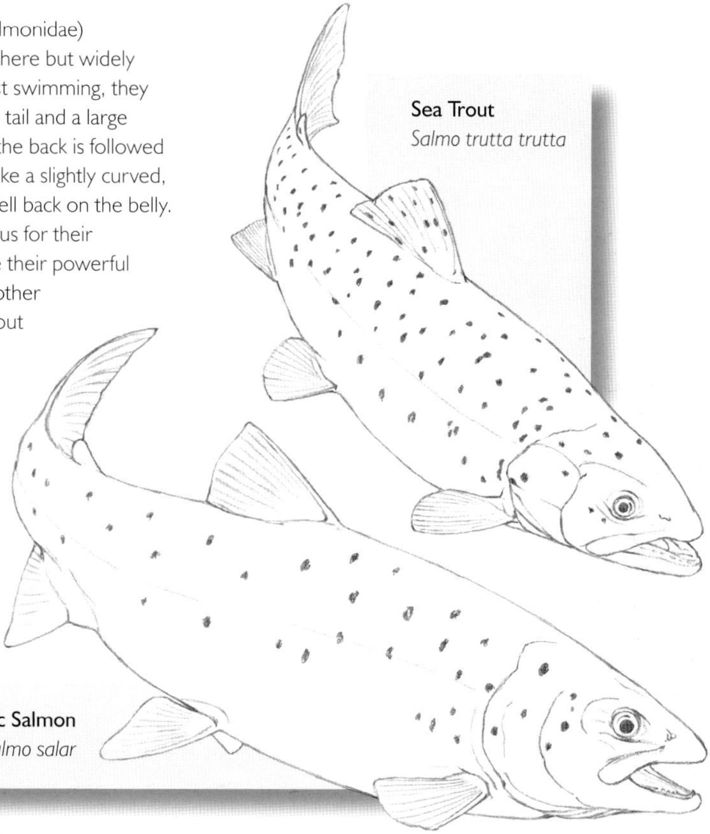

Sea Trout
*Salmo trutta trutta*

Atlantic Salmon
*Salmo salar*

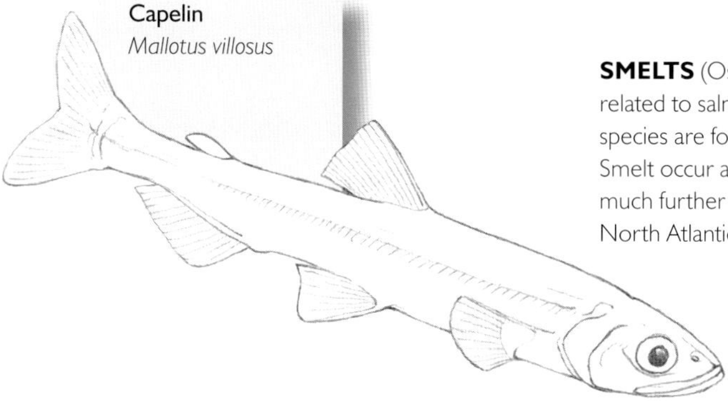

Capelin
*Mallotus villosus*

**SMELTS** (Osmeridae) are a small family of fish, closely related to salmon but in general much smaller. Only two species are found in northern European waters and only Smelt occur around Wales. Capelin *Mallotus villosus*, live much further north and are common in Arctic parts of the North Atlantic.

**ARGENTINES** (Argentinidae) are sometimes called herring smelts and are a small family with only two species found in northern European waters and only one found (rarely) in Welsh waters. They are slim silvery fish with very large eyes.

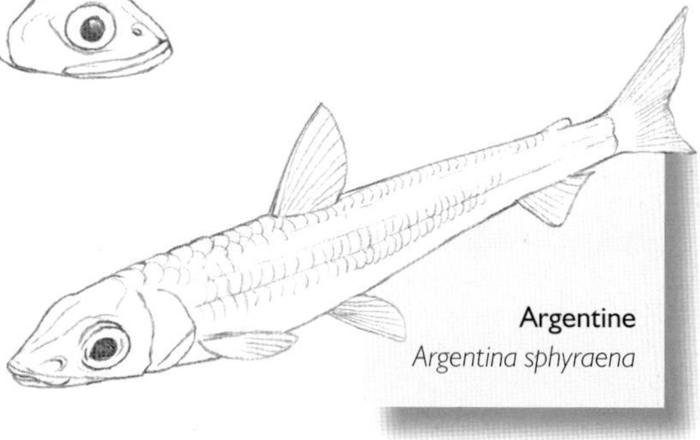

Argentine
*Argentina sphyraena*

# ATLANTIC SALMON            Eog                    *Salmo salar*

**Other names: Black Salmon**                              150cm

**KEY IDENTIFICATION FEATURES**   Sea going Atlantic Salmon can be identified with a high degree of certainty although on the rare occasions when one is seen underwater there may be confusion with large Sea Trout. This is a large, torpedo-shaped fish, typically silvery at sea, with a darker back and many small black spots most of which are on the head and above the lateral line. Spawning and spent fish in freshwater darken and lose their silver colour. Young fish in freshwater (parr) have distinctive thumbprint marks along the flanks. Look for the small adipose fin near the tail, found in all members of the salmon family.

**SIMILAR SPECIES**  Out at sea, large Sea Trout can be difficult to distinguish from Atlantic Salmon as they are very similar in colour. A close look at the mouth will distinguish them. Salmon have a relatively small mouth in which the upper jaw does not extend beyond the eye, whilst in Sea Trout it does. The tail stalk (caudal peduncle) in Atlantic Salmon is narrow whilst in Sea Trout it is wide.

**BEHAVIOUR**  Sea going Atlantic salmon often migrate large distances to reach good feeding grounds such as those off Greenland.

**HABITAT**  At sea adult fish live in open water from the surface to around 200m depth.

**DISTRIBUTION**  Atlantic Salmon are found throughout Welsh waters but are now a rare sight. Scotland, Ireland, Norway and Iceland support the majority of the population. The wider distribution is right across the northern part of the North Atlantic.

**NATURAL HISTORY**  Atlantic Salmon mature at about three years old and return from the sea in autumn and early winter to 'run' up the rivers where they were born and lay their eggs far upstream in fast flowing gravel areas. Many die after spawning but some return to the sea and may spawn again. Young fish spend two or three years in the river before changing colour and physiology and migrating out to sea.

**SIGHTINGS**  Wild Atlantic Salmon are becoming increasingly rare and many people only ever see farmed fish. Atlantic Salmon are caught by drift netting at sea and along the coast as they return to spawn. Illegal fixed gill netting especially in estuaries, has contributed to their decline. Stock recovery programmes are strengthening some stocks. They are a magnificent sport fish both at sea and in rivers. They are protected under Appendix III of the Bern Convention, but not when at sea and are listed by OSPAR as a threatened and declining species.

# SEA TROUT                  Sewin                *Salmo trutta trutta*

140cm

Sea Trout are very similar in looks and life history to Atlantic Salmon and like them, mature fish swim up rivers to spawn and the young spend some time in freshwater before migrating down to the sea. However, this species also has a non-migratory race that never leaves freshwater – the familiar Brown Trout favoured by fly fishermen in rivers and streams. Mature Sea Trout are silvery with a dark back and tend to have fewer but larger spots than Atlantic Salmon and these do extend below the lateral line. Other more reliable differences are described under Atlantic Salmon. To protect dwindling stocks of wild Sea Trout there is a regionally based closed season in the UK and other restrictions for anglers.

# EUROPEAN SMELT    Brwyniad Conwy    *Osmerus eperlanus*

**Other names: Sparling**    45cm

**KEY IDENTIFICATION FEATURES** European Smelt can be identified in the field with a high degree of certainty. They look a bit like a cross between a herring and a small trout. As well as a single dorsal fin in the middle of the back, these fish have a small adipose (fatty) fin near the tail. They have a large mouth with reaches well back past the eye (so do trout). They are a silvery fish with a greenish back and almost translucent skin. Caught fish have a strong smell often described as like cucumber.

**SIMILAR SPECIES** Salmon, trout and Argentine also have an adipose fin but differences in colour and habitat should prevent confusion.

**BEHAVIOUR** Young European Smelt feed up in the water column on plankton, mainly crustaceans, progressing later to small fish including young herring and bottom-living fish such as gobies.

**HABITAT** This is essentially a coastal species that remains close inshore in the vicinity of river mouths and within estuaries.

**DISTRIBUTION** European Smelt are an uncommon fish in Welsh waters but have been recorded around the coast of North Wales and Cardigan Bay and in the Severn Estuary. A stock in the Conwy Estuary used to be fished commercially. They have rather a localised distribution around the British Isles but are common in some estuaries such as the Wash. They extend north to the White Sea, throughout the shallow Baltic and south to the west coast of France.

**NATURAL HISTORY** Like salmon and trout, European Smelt move from the sea into rivers to spawn. Mature fish gather near river mouths and in estuaries in winter and run up the rivers to the tidal limit in spring. Eggs are laid amongst gravel, sand and weed and the adults return to the sea after spawning. Young Smelt often remain in estuaries until they mature at an age of about three or four years. They can live for ten years.

**SIGHTINGS** These fish are most often caught by inshore pelagic trawlers fishing in large estuaries for whitefish. They are occasionally caught by anglers but are too small to provide any great sport, although they make good eating. They can also be caught in fixed and drift nets. European Smelt populations have declined in some areas due to pollution in estuaries and obstruction of their river spawning migrations. However, they are currently (2008) categorised as 'Least concern' in the IUCN red List as the total population is abundant.

# ARGENTINE    Pysgodyn arian bach    *Argentina sphyraena*

**Other names: Lesser Argentine, Lesser Silver Smelt**    35cm

**KEY IDENTIFICATION FEATURES** This will be an unfamiliar fish to many people but it should be possible to identify it in the field with a reasonable degree of certainty. This is a slim fish with a pointed head, small mouth and large eyes, which in life has large silvery scales that glitter green on the back and sometimes blue on the sides. However, trawled fish often have most of the scales missing. At first sight it seems that this fish has only a single dorsal fin near the midline but a careful look will show an additional small adipose (fatty) fin near the tail.

**SIMILAR SPECIES** Similar in size to Smelt but these have a much larger mouth extending well back past the eye and are found inshore and in estuaries. A second species the Greater Argentine *Argentina silus* is a northern species not found in Welsh waters. The similarly coloured Sand Smelt has two normal dorsal fins.

**BEHAVIOUR** This fish has been shown to feed both on bottom-living and pelagic invertebrates and small fish and is therefore thought to spend some time near the seabed but to forage up into mid-water.

**HABITAT** This is predominantly a deepwater fish found over muddy sediment from 50–500m (deeper in the Mediterranean) but commonest down to 200m and occasionally found as shallow as 20m.

**DISTRIBUTION** This is an uncommon fish in Welsh waters and confirmed records are mostly from the Severn Estuary. It occurs all round Great Britain, north to Norway and Iceland and south into the western Mediterranean.

**NATURAL HISTORY** Around the British Isles spawning peaks in April with the season extending from March through July. The eggs and young are pelagic and float in the plankton. The oldest largest fish tend to be found at the deeper depths of its range.

**SIGHTINGS** This fish is most likely to be brought up in offshore trawls though much more commonly off Atlantic west coasts than in Welsh and adjacent waters. They have been photographed underwater in Norwegian fjords.

# Codfish

As well as the Cod, and other familiar fish such as Pollack all of which belong to one family (Gadidae) this large Order of fish includes Hake (Merlucciidae), Rocklings and Ling (Lotidae), Forkbeard (Phycidae) and Grenadiers or Rat-tails (Macrouridae). The latter are not included here as they are deepwater fish found on the Continental slope and not recorded from Welsh waters. Ten species of gadoid fish (Gadidae) are found in Welsh waters and are described here. Of these Blue Whiting and Norway Pout are encountered less often as they live in relatively deep water. One further species, Silvery Pout *Gadiculus argenteus*, which includes two subspecies, is also found around UK but has not been recorded in Welsh waters.

In all these fish the pelvic fins are found just behind the operculum (gill cover) and in front of the pectoral fins. Cod and all others in the cod family (Gadidae) have three dorsal fins and two anal fins. This makes it easy to recognise this family of fish. Hake, Rocklings, Ling and Forkbeard have only two dorsal fins, the first short and the second long.

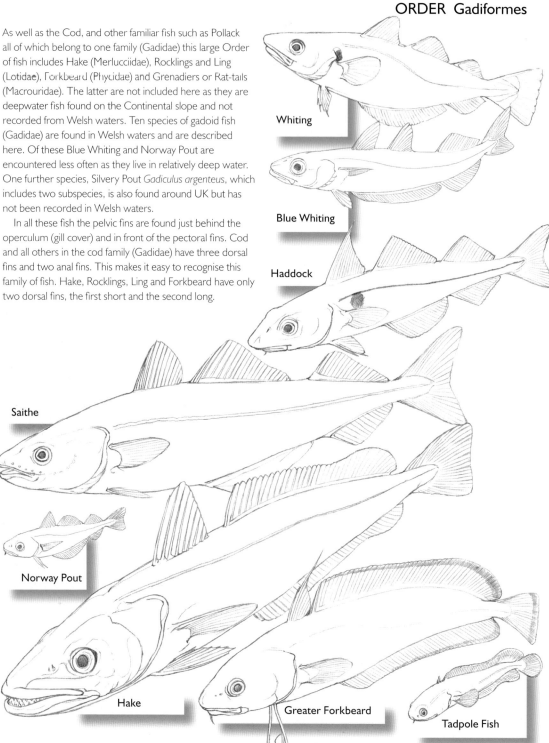

Whiting

Blue Whiting

Haddock

Saithe

Norway Pout

Hake

Greater Forkbeard

Tadpole Fish

# ATLANTIC COD    **Penfras**    *Gadus morhua*

**Other names: Codling**    **200cm**

**KEY IDENTIFICATION FEATURES** With the exception of young fish, Cod can be identified in the field with a high degree of certainty. The most useful identification feature is the large head which has an overhanging upper jaw and a long barbel on the lower jaw. Adult fish have a distinctive white lateral line that is clearly visible underwater and usually persists in dead fish. Most have numerous brown mottles and flecks on a paler background giving an overall impression of brown or sometimes reddish colour. Young fish often lack the white colouring of the lateral line and are an orange brown with chequered paler markings.

**SIMILAR SPECIES** The most likely confusion is with young fish especially Pollack which are a similar colour to young Cod but have a protruding lower jaw. Poor Cod, which only grow to around 20cm, could also be mistaken for young Cod.

**BEHAVIOUR** Most cod live in large shoals which makes them especially vulnerable to modern computerised tracking and fishing methods. The shoals tend to break up at dusk when the fish are feeding and reform at dawn. They are omnivorous and will take almost any bottom-living fish and invertebrates as well as open water fish such as herring.

**HABITAT** Cod are an adaptable species that live in a variety of habitats and spend much of their time swimming above but within reach of the seabed, usually between about 30–80m above it in water 150–200m deep. However, large shoals also swim and hunt in mid-water and up to the surface and cod can be found down to at least 600m depth. Young fish mostly live close inshore.

**DISTRIBUTION** Cod are found throughout Welsh waters, all round the British Isles south to Bay of Biscay and north to the Barents Sea. They are also found around Iceland, southern Greenland and northern parts of North America.

**NATURAL HISTORY** Cod concentrate their spawning efforts into relatively well-defined areas none of which are in Welsh waters. Most spawn between February to April and the fish tend to concentrate into these areas in winter, migrating further afield in summer. The eggs and larva float in the plankton and young fish start to live near the seabed when they are around six months old. Cod can live for 60 years but large, old fish are now rare.

**SIGHTINGS** Divers may come across young fish especially in kelp forests and sometimes lone adults around wrecks and rocky reefs. Cod are one of the most valuable targeted commercial fish and are caught mostly by trawling. They have been heavily over-fished and stocks in the Irish Sea (as well as elsewhere) are badly depleted. Cod are also caught on long lines and by anglers. They are listed as 'Vulnerable' in the IUCN Red Data List. There is a minimum landing size in EU waters but this is below the size at which 50% of females first spawn. Some Cod are now farmed though not yet in Wales.

Juvenile Atlantic Cod.

# HADDOCK                    Hadog                    *Melanogrammus aeglefinus*

**70–100cm**

**KEY IDENTIFICATION FEATURES**  Haddock can be identified in the field with a high degree of certainty. The most reliable feature is the first of the three dorsal fins, which is tall and pointed giving it a high triangle shape. Another reliable feature is a thumbprint-sized black mark on each side on or just below the lateral line behind the pectoral fin. This usually persists after death, but may fade over time and is not always clear in fish photographed underwater at night. As with Cod, the upper jaw overhangs the lower, but Haddock only have a short chin barbel. The largest Haddock on record was 112cm long but fish this large are now rare.

**SIMILAR SPECIES**  Fish without the characteristic black mark could be mistaken for Bib or even Cod but a careful look at the dorsal fin, lateral line and barbel should sort them out.

**BEHAVIOUR**  Although solitary fish are sometimes seen, Haddock mostly live and feed in schools, taking bottom-living worms, molluscs, crustaceans and brittlestars. Some populations, especially in the far north, migrate considerable distances between feeding and spawning grounds. Winter and summer inshore and offshore migrations also occur but vary with latitude in response to water temperature.

**HABITAT**  Like Cod, Haddock spend much of their time near the seabed mostly in water between about 80–200m deep and over shell grounds, gravel, sediment and sometimes rock. They have been recorded from as shallow as 10m down to 450m in their wider range. At certain times such as when migrating, shoals can also be found in mid-water.

**DISTRIBUTION**  Records of Haddock in Welsh waters are patchy possibly because they are not often seen underwater, tend to form local populations and live mostly offshore. It extends all round the British Isles and its wider range is very similar to Cod.

**NATURAL HISTORY**  Haddock is a northern, cold water species that does not usually spawn in Welsh waters. The main spawning grounds are in the north including Iceland, Faroes and to the west of Orkney and Ireland and east of Shetland. The eggs are spawned in spring and float in the plankton. Young Haddock move down to the seabed when they are a few centimetres long. They can live for 20 years.

**SIGHTINGS**  In summer Haddock are sometimes seen by divers in shallow water but only in places where the water does not warm up too much. This is a very important commercial fish and most Haddock are caught by trawling along with Cod, as part of a mixed demersal fishery. It can also be caught on long lines and by anglers. There is a minimum landing size in EU waters. It is currently listed as 'Vulnerable' in the IUCN Red Data List but has not been assessed since 1996. Fishing pressure is intense but just how well the Irish Sea stock is holding up is uncertain.

# WHITING     Gwyniad môr chwitlyn gwyn     *Merlangius merlangus*

**70cm**

**KEY IDENTIFICATION FEATURES** Whiting can be identified in the field with a reasonable degree of certainty, although more from a lack of features found in other codfish than by any one distinctive feature. This is a slim grey-blue fish with silvery sides (when alive) and as in Haddock and Cod, the upper jaw is longer than the lower. However adults have no chin barbel though young fish have a minute one, only easily seen with a hand lens and not usually visible to divers. Live fish have distinct white edges to the anal fins, but this fades when the fish dies. Look also for a black mark near the top of the base of each pectoral fin and a square-cut tail. Most adults reach only 30–40cm long.

**SIMILAR SPECIES** The lack of a chin barbel distinguishes Whiting from most other codfish except Blue Whiting, Pollack and Saithe. The most likely confusion in dead fish is with Saithe. In this case, draw an imaginary line vertically down from the rear of the first dorsal fin. The line should fall some distance after the start of the first anal fin. In Saithe it falls in front of this fin.

**BEHAVIOUR** The most interesting behaviour is that of young Whiting that shelter amongst the tentacles of stinging jellyfish (see page 238). Whilst Whiting spend a lot of time feeding on bottom-living invertebrates, older ones also feed in mid-water up to the surface on young Herring, sand eels, other small fish and shrimp.

**HABITAT** Most Whiting live in shallow inshore waters from 25–100m over sand and mud. They are occasionally caught as deep as 200m. Young fish live close inshore up to the surf zone.

**DISTRIBUTION** Whiting are common throughout Welsh waters and are also found all round the British Isles over the Continental Shelf. This species is especially common in the North Sea, extends north to northern Scandinavia, and Iceland and south to northern coasts of the Mediterranean and in the Black Sea.

**NATURAL HISTORY** Many spawning grounds are known for Whiting all round the British Isles including areas round Wales, but especially in the North Sea. Juveniles are commonest inshore in sheltered bays and estuaries.

**SIGHTINGS** Young fish can be caught using push nets at low tide off sandy shores and are occasionally stranded in sandy pools. Divers sometimes see young fish but not commonly and they can also be seen in public aquaria. Whiting are frequently caught by small inshore trawl boats. Many are taken in mixed demersal trawls for whitefish or in bottom trawls for *Nephrops*, flatfish and shrimp. This species is relatively low in value and bycatch is sometimes discarded though to a lesser extend nowadays. It forms an important link in the food chain as it is widely eaten by larger fish such as Cod. Anglers regularly take Whiting.

# POLLACK and SAITHE

**Morlas & Chwitlyn glas**
*Pollachius pollachius* and *P. virens*

**Other names: Coalfish, Coley *P. virens*, Lythe *P. pollachius***    130cm (both)

Pollack

**KEY IDENTIFICATION FEATURES** These two codfish can both be identified in the field with a high degree of certainty. Both are large silvery fish with a dark greenish back, but whilst Pollack has a protruding lower jaw, in Saithe the jaws are equal or at most the lower jaw is slightly longer then the upper. The lateral line can also be used to tell these two fish apart; in Pollack the line is dark and curves sharply down below the first of the three dorsal fins, whilst in Saithe it is pale and runs straight along the body. Neither fish has a chin barbel though young Saithe may have a minute one. Young Pollack have a distinctive chequered orange red pattern, still visible in the fish shown here.

**SIMILAR SPECIES** Whiting also lack a chin barbel but their gently curved lateral line and long upper jaw should avoid confusion even if colour patterns have faded.

**BEHAVIOUR** Adult Pollack are often solitary but may form schools prior to spawning. Saithe usually live and migrate in schools and have been seen to act together to trap shoals of small fish. Saithe may make long migrations between different feeding areas and to spawning areas.

**HABITAT** Pollack are inshore fish generally found near the seabed in water down to around 100m though extending to at least 200m depth. Adults are commonly found over rocky and rough ground and in kelp forests. Saithe are found both inshore and offshore to over 300m both near the seabed and in shoals right up to the surface. Young Pollack (especially first year) and Saithe range into shallow water and even into estuaries. Juvenile Saithe (less than about 6cm long) are common in rock pools in the north of their range such as in Scotland.

**DISTRIBUTION** Both species are common all round the Welsh coastline and all round the British Isles. Both extend north to Norway (Saithe to Barents Sea) and Iceland. Saithe are also found around southern Greenland and north eastern North America but extend south only to Biscay. Pollack extend much further south into northern parts of the western Mediterranean.

**NATURAL HISTORY** Both species spawn between January to April and young fish drift inshore into coastal waters where they spend the first year or two of their lives. Young Pollack largely eat shrimp and other crustaceans progressing to sand eels and other small fish as they grow. Saithe have a similar diet but large adults mainly eat herring, cod and other fish caught in mid-water. Saithe can live for at least 25 years whilst Pollack appear only to reach eight years or so.

**SIGHTINGS** Divers are most likely to see Pollack in rocky areas and around wrecks and anglers catch large ones in similar habitats. Although taken as bycatch Pollack are not targeted commercially. In contrast, adult Saithe are rarely seen by divers but are an important commercial species caught by trawl, purse seine nets, on longlines and by anglers. However, the main stocks are in the north and in Wales it does not form an important fishery. There is a minimum landing size for Saithe and Pollack in EU waters. Records of young Saithe in rock pools around Wales would be interesting as Saithe do not usually come onshore this far south.

Saithe

# POUTING

## Codyn llwyd

### *Trisopterus luscus*

**Other names: Bib**

**45cm**

**KEY IDENTIFICATION FEATURES** Large Pouting can be identified in the field with a high degree of certainty but smaller ones can easily be confused with Poor Cod. This fish has a deep body, giving it a shape like two cones placed with their bases together. The first of the three dorsal fins is tall and triangular. The upper jaw is longer than the lower jaw and the latter has a long chin barbel. Most adult fish are a coppery colour with three or four light vertical bands. However, large fish often lack these bands and can be very dark. There is a black mark at the base of the pectoral fins (also in Poor Cod and Whiting).

**SIMILAR SPECIES** The most likely confusion is with Poor Cod which have a very similar head and colour. With dead fish or a good photograph, draw an imaginary line up from the start of the first anal fin. In Poor Cod this line should fall in the space between the first and second dorsal fin or just forward of it. In Pouting it will fall in the middle of the first dorsal fin.

**BEHAVIOUR** Divers often find that Pouting are relatively easy to approach and photograph as the shoals tend to stay in the dark recesses of wrecks or in the shelter of rocks during the day.

**HABITAT** This is a predominantly coastal species though larger, older fish extend offshore down to at least 300m. Shoals are common over rocky reefs and around wrecks. Young fish often frequent sheltered sandy areas extending almost up to the shoreline.

**DISTRIBUTION** Pouting is a common species all round the Welsh coastline and all round the British Isles in suitable habitats. It only extends as far north as southern Norway but reaches the western Mediterranean in the south.

**NATURAL HISTORY** Fish living offshore move into relatively shallow water (around 50–70m) to spawn mainly between March and April. Young fish grow fairly rapidly and are mature by about a year old. They are known to live for at least four years and some may reach six to eight years old. They feed mainly on bottom-living crustaceans including shrimp and larger ones also catch small fish and squid. During the winter the shoals move offshore into deeper warmer water.

**SIGHTINGS** This is one of the codfish most often seen by divers, especially in the vicinity of wrecks. Pouting is not commercially fished but is taken as bycatch in trawls for other whitefish. It is also taken by anglers and is frequently exhibited in public aquaria.

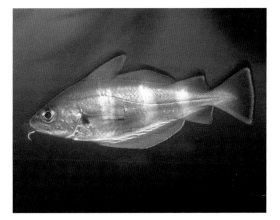

# POOR COD                    Codyn Ebrill              *Trisopterus minutus*

**30cm**

**KEY IDENTIFICATION FEATURES**    Poor Cod can be identified in the field with a reasonable degree of certainty, though could be confused with small Pouting. Overall this is a slimmer, smaller fish that rarely exceeds 20cm and has large eyes. Otherwise it is very similar to Pouting, with a long chin barbel, overhanging upper jaw and a similar coppery colour. Although some fish exhibit faint pale vertical bands, most are uniform in colour and they never appear truly striped as Pouting often do. Like Pouting there is a black mark at the base of each pectoral fin.

**SIMILAR SPECIES**  The most likely confusion is with small Pouting – see page 95 for differences in where the first anal fin begins.

**BEHAVIOUR**: Schools of Poor Cod can be found hunting for crustaceans and small fish over the seabed and in mid-water. In the daytime, divers often see them lurking in the dim recesses of overhangs and between large rocks and boulders. They are relatively easy to approach especially at night.

**HABITAT**  Poor Cod are found in large numbers in coastal waters and further offshore down to about 300m. Unlike Pouting whose young frequent very shallow water, Poor Cod are usually found below about 10m depth around rocky reefs, on boulder slopes and over sediment.

**DISTRIBUTION**  Poor Cod are common all round the Welsh coastline and all round the British Isles though less so in the southern North Sea. This species is similar to Pouting in its wider distribution.

**NATURAL HISTORY**  Like Pouting, Poor Cod spawn in spring when the water has warmed up to at least 8°C at depths between about 50–100m. They feed mainly on a variety of small crustaceans such as mysid shrimps but will take other invertebrates and small fish. They can live for at least five years.

**SIGHTINGS**  Divers often see Poor Cod around rocky reefs and wrecks though they are not as common as Pouting within diving depths. They are too small for commercial fisheries but are caught in trawls and used as an industrial fish to make fishmeal. They are important as a food fish for valuable commercial species such as Cod.

The chin barbel in this Poor Cod is not obvious but the small black spot at the base of the pectoral fin is.

# NORWAY POUT          Swtan Norwy          *Trisopterus esmarkii*

**25cm**

**KEY IDENTIFICATION FEATURES**  A diver might find difficulty telling this fish from Poor Cod underwater but with a good photograph or a close look at a fish in the hand, a positive identification can be achieved. The differences are principally a shorter chin barbel and the lower jaw slightly longer than the upper. A very close look will show small spaces between the three dorsal fins – in Poor Cod these fins touch or are very close.

**HABITAT AND BEHAVIOUR**  Mainly offshore between 80–200m, often in large schools, over soft sediments and in mid-water shoals.

**DISTRIBUTION**  There are relatively few confirmed records in Welsh waters as it is an offshore, northern species which extends to the Barents Sea and Iceland, with its southern limit in the English Channel. It is very common in the north of its range.

**NATURAL HISTORY**  Known spawning grounds are mainly in the northern North Sea where the fish spawn in deep water mainly between March and May.

**SIGHTINGS**  Divers are not likely to see this species in Welsh waters though it enters diving depths in Norwegian fjords. This small codfish is caught in mid-water nets in large numbers for processing into fishmeal and fish oil especially in the North Sea. It is not targeted in Wales but may be caught along with other whitefish. It is an important food fish for larger commercial codfish and flatfish such as Halibut.

# BLUE WHITING          Swtan glas          *Micromesistius poutassou*

**50cm**

**KEY IDENTIFICATION FEATURES**  Although this codfish is one of the more unfamiliar ones, identification of dead fish in the field should be straightforward. This is a slim, blue-grey codfish in which the three dorsal fins are all separated by large gaps. The first anal fin is very long. It does not have a chin barbel but has a large mouth with a slightly protruding lower jaw.

**HABITAT AND BEHAVIOUR**  An oceanic species that lives in huge shoals in mid-water and is most abundant around 100–300m where the depth is 1000m or more.

**DISTRIBUTION**  Confirmed records of this species in Welsh waters are mainly of immature fish caught in inshore waters. Adults are uncommon and within the British Isles, mainly restricted to areas beyond the Continental Shelf edge to the west of Ireland and Scotland. It occurs from the Barents Sea and Iceland, south to the western Mediterranean and off north eastern coasts of North America.

**SIGHTINGS**  Blue Whiting are mainly caught by deep water trawlers fishing for other species but as it forms such big shoals large numbers can be taken and like Norway Pout, the catch is mainly processed for fishmeal. It is rarely caught in any numbers in Welsh waters.

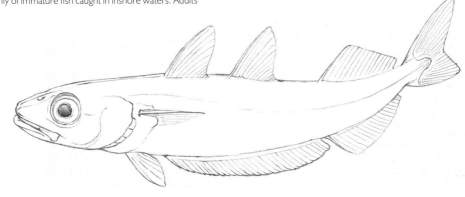

# TADPOLE FISH     Penbwl môr     *Raniceps raninus*

**Other names: Lesser Forkbeard**     **30cm**

**KEY IDENTIFICATION FEATURES** This fish can be identified in the field with a high degree of certainty. It has a broad, thick head with a large mouth, thick lips and a single chin barbel. The head tapers to a long, but stout body ending in a rounded tailfin. It has two dorsal fins but the first is tiny and very difficult to see. The second dorsal and the single anal fin are long and often have pale edges. Tadpole Fish have startlingly white inner parts to their lips which show up against the dark brown to almost black body. This is usually obvious, but if the lips are not pushed forward, the white does not always show because the outside of the lips is brown.

**SIMILAR SPECIES** Other elongated, similar-sized fish that stick their heads out of holes are rocklings, Ling and Conger Eel. The latter has no chin barbel, rocklings all have more than one barbel and Ling has a much flatter head. Forkbeard are superficially similar but live in deep water over sediment.

**BEHAVIOUR** This is a shy fish that is rarely seen out in the open during the day but has been seen by divers out in the open at night. They do not move far from their home territories and the same fish have been spotted living in the same place for several years (Steve Porter pers. comm.). They are mostly solitary but several fish may occupy one good hidey hole.

**HABITAT** This secretive fish prefers to live hidden away in crevices in rocky reefs or hiding amongst stones, seaweeds and animal undergrowths from just below the shore to about 100m with a preference for the shallower depths. It has also been caught from sandy and muddy areas.

**DISTRIBUTION** There are records of Tadpole Fish round most of the coastline of Wales though predominantly from the south. It is probably under-recorded because of its preference for living in rocky crevices. It occurs all round the British Isles, north to Norway and south to Biscay.

**NATURAL HISTORY** There are conflicting reports about when and at what depth these fish spawn but it seems to be above either 50m or 70m and between May or July and September and temperature is probably the important factor (not below 10°C). The eggs are broadcast over the substratum. Observations of young and spawning activities around Wales would be very useful.

**SIGHTINGS** Divers only rarely record this fish but it is not rare, just difficult to spot. Peering into rocky crevices and holes is the best way to find them. They are sometimes caught from piers, rocks and boats by anglers and are occasionally dredged or trawled up from sediment areas. As there are few Welsh records, all sightings would be of interest.

# EUROPEAN HAKE          Cegddu          *Merluccius merluccius*

**Other names: Cornish Salmon**                                    **140-180cm**

**KEY IDENTIFICATION FEATURES**  This codfish can be identified in the field with a high degree of certainty. It is a long, slender fish with a large head and jaws full of long, pointed teeth, the lower jaw protruding slightly. There are two dorsal fins, the first short and pointed and the second long. The tail fin is square cut. It has a straight lateral line. Hake are a silvery bluish grey often with brown blotches.

**SIMILAR SPECIES**  The body shape and dorsal fins are similar to Ling and Forkbeard but these two fish both have a chin barbel.

**BEHAVIOUR**  Hake spend most of the time near the seabed, foraging for fish in mid-water at night. Moen & Svensen (2004) report seeing Hake on the seabed throwing sand over their backs with their fins.

**HABITAT**  Hake live in moderately deep water mostly between 70–400m but in their wider range they have been found as shallow as 25m (especially in summer) to 1000m.

**DISTRIBUTION**  Hake have been recorded round most of the Welsh coastline (mostly juveniles) and occur all round the British Isles. Their wider distribution extends north to Norway and Iceland and south to Mauritania and the Mediterranean.

**NATURAL HISTORY**  Hake mature late at an age of between five to seven years. They spawn in spring and summer depending on latitude at around 150–200m (deeper in the Mediterranean). The eggs float in the plankton and the young fish live in deep water over muddy bottoms. They move further inshore after they reach about three years old.

**SIGHTINGS**  Divers are unlikely to see Hake in Welsh waters as they live mainly below normal diving depths. However, they have been photographed underwater at night in Norwegian fjords. They are a valuable commercial fish that has been heavily overexploited in the past. Hake are caught in demersal and pelagic trawls and to a lesser extent on longlines. The northern stock, which includes the Irish Sea stock, is currently harvested sustainably following the implementation of a recovery plan. The main fishing areas are to the west of Ireland and Scotland. There is an EU minimum landing size for Hake.

# LINGS

## Family Lotidae

Like their close relatives rocklings, lings have a long, sinuous eel-like body and the chin barbel that is a ubiquitous feature of fish in this family (Lotidae). Three species are found in Northern Europe but only the Ling in Welsh waters. **Blue Ling** *Molva dypterygia* is a deepwater, northern species that extends down west coast British Isles; **Spanish Ling** *Molva macrophthalma* is a southern species that extends north up west coast British Isles.

Top. The barbels on the upper jaw as well as the chin, help distinguish this young rockling from a young Ling.

Bottom. The mottled colour of this Ling is typical of the young fish seen inshore by divers.

# LING                        Honos                        *Molva molva*

**Other names: European Ling**                                                    **200cm**

**KEY IDENTIFICATION FEATURES**   This fish can be identified in the field with a high degree of certainty. It is a long, slim, elegant fish with a large, rounded tail fin and two dorsal fins, the first short and the second long. There is a single, long barbel on the chin. The young fish seen by divers are usually a greeny-brown marbled with paler camouflage markings and the dorsal, anal and tail fins have a pale edge. There is a dark blotch on the rear part of the first dorsal fin although this seems to be less obvious in larger, older fish.

**SIMILAR SPECIES**   A Ling sticking its head out of a hole could be mistaken for a Common Eel or Conger Eel but the barbel on its chin will soon dispel that notion plus the fact that these fish prop themselves up on their pelvic fins, something eels do not have. See also rocklings (page 102). The Spanish Ling *Molva macrophthalma* is a southern species found in the Mediterranean and offshore along west coast British Isles and has so far not been recorded from Welsh waters. It is a slimmer fish than a Ling and has a shorter chin barbel.

**BEHAVIOUR**   Divers often see ling peering out from the safety of a rocky lair or hidey hole in a shipwreck. They are wary fish and usually remain within a short distance of a safe refuge. However, divers have found that in some areas at least, these fish are curious and can be lured out of their hiding places.

**HABITAT**   Adults are found in deep water most commonly between 100–300m. Smaller, younger fish live inshore as shallow as 10m depth, in rocky areas on exposed coasts, where they can lurk safely under overhangs, in fissures and in shipwrecks. They will also hide amongst seaweeds.

**DISTRIBUTION**   Ling are found throughout Welsh waters and round most of the British Isles, though not in the southern North Sea. Further afield they extend north to the Barents Sea and Iceland and south to Morocco and a short distance into the Mediterranean. They are also found off southern Greenland and Canada.

**NATURAL HISTORY**   These fish spawn mainly in a few specific offshore areas, none of which are in Welsh waters. The main spawning grounds are off southern Iceland and Faroes, and Continental slope off western British Isles to Bay of Biscay. The eggs float up into the plankton and the developing young fish mainly settle inshore, where they stay in relatively shallow water for two or three years.

**SIGHTINGS**   Divers are most likely to see young fish, up to about 1m long, in rocky reef areas below about 20m depth, sometimes less. Large fish are caught offshore in trawls and on lines and this is a valuable commercial fish. Anglers sometimes catch this fish but usually from boats over rocky areas rather than from the shore. There is a minimum landing size for this fish in EU waters.

# ROCKLINGS

**FAMILY** Lotidae

Rocklings have long, sinuous bodies and at a quick glance, as they slither rapidly out of sight, could be mistaken for an eel. They are actually related to cod and are often included with them in the family Gadidae. Modern classifications now group them in their own family (Lotidae) along with Ling and Deepwater Torsk and Forkbeard. Like Cod, they all have a chin barbel and rocklings also have other barbels on their head, the number and arrangement of which is useful in identification. Five species are found in Welsh waters and are described here. A sixth species, the Big-eyed Rockling *Gaidropsaurus macrophthalmus* is found offshore in deep water down west coast British Isles. All these fish live on or near the seabed.

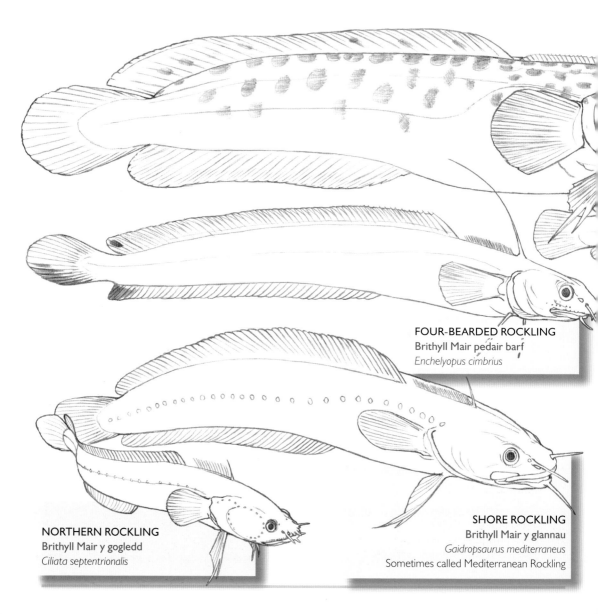

**FOUR-BEARDED ROCKLING**
Brithyll Mair pedair barf
*Enchelyopus cimbrius*

**NORTHERN ROCKLING**
Brithyll Mair y gogledd
*Ciliata septentrionalis*

**SHORE ROCKLING**
Brithyll Mair y glannau
*Gaidropsaurus mediterraneus*
Sometimes called Mediterranean Rockling

## KEY IDENTIFICATION FEATURES

Rocklings can be identified as such in the field with a high degree of certainty. They have two dorsal fins but the first one is difficult to see as it consists of a fringe of very short rays preceded by one longer ray. The second dorsal fin and the anal fin are both long and the tail fin is rounded. Identification of different species in the field is usually possible but a close look at the head and a note of the habitat are vital. The Northern Rockling is the smallest reaching only 15cm long whilst the Three-bearded is the largest at 50cm. The others grow to between 25–40cm.

**Three barbels:** Shore Rockling and Three-bearded Rockling. Whilst the shore rockling is usually a rather uniform brown colour, the Three-bearded Rockling is much paler and marked with unmistakable bold, dark blotches. Some Shore Rockling are a paler reddish brown.

**Four barbels:** Four-bearded Rockling. The first ray of the first dorsal fin is very long. Dusky to pale brown colour.

**Five barbels:** Five-bearded Rockling and Northern Rockling. The Northern Rockling has small skin lobes hanging down over the upper lip and a large mouth that reaches back behind the eyes. Both are usually a dark brownish colour.

Three-bearded Rockling

Shore Rockling

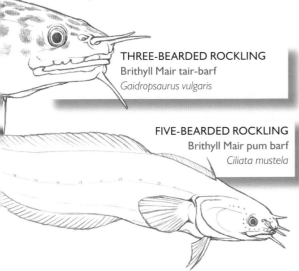

### THREE-BEARDED ROCKLING
Brithyll Mair tair-barf
*Gaidropsaurus vulgaris*

### FIVE-BEARDED ROCKLING
Brithyll Mair pum barf
*Ciliata mustela*

Five-bearded Rockling

## KEY FIELD IDENTIFICATION SUMMARY:

**Bold dark blotches plus three barbel:** Three-bearded Rockling

**Dark brown plus five barbels**: Five-bearded or Northern Rockling

**Dark brown plus three barbels:** Shore Rockling

**Light brown plus three barbels**: Shore Rockling

**Light brown plus four barbels:** Four-bearded Rockling.

## SIMILAR SPECIES

At first glance a large pale coloured rockling could be confused with a Ling *Molva molva* but ling have only a single chin barbel and two normal dorsal fins.

Northern Rockling

Young rocklings are called 'mackerel midge' and have metallic bluish or greenish backs. They are an important food item for tern and Puffin chicks.

## BEHAVIOUR

Rocklings tend to hide away amongst seaweeds and in crevices and are not that easy to observe. The best time to see them out and about is at dusk or on a night dive. When lying quietly on the seabed, these fish vibrate the hair-like rays of their first dorsal fin with a rapid rippling motion. This creates a current of water which brings with it the scent of food.

## HABITAT

**(1) Shore:** Only the Shore Rockling and the Five-bearded Rockling are normally found on the shore around the Welsh coast. They are both relatively common and the Five-bearded Rockling can be locally abundant. Both prefer rock pools with dense seaweed or lurk under weed-covered boulders. Northern Rockling can be found in shore pools on north eastern coasts of the British Isles but not (so far) around Wales.

**(2) Shallow rocky areas:** All the rocklings described here, with the exception of the Four-bearded Rockling, can be found amongst seaweed or animal undergrowth down to about 30m depth. Three-bearded and Northern Rocklings also range down to 100–150m depth and are both uncommon.

**(3) Deep rock and sediment:** Four-bearded Rockling are usually found only below about 50m depth in Welsh waters, down to at least 550m. In northern parts of their range they can be found in shallower water. They are an uncommon fish.

## DISTRIBUTION

These five rocklings are found all round the Welsh coast and all round the British Isles except that the shore rockling is apparently absent from east coast Britain. All also extend north to varying degrees, at least as far as Norway. Only shore and Three-bearded Rocklings extend as far south as the Mediterranean.

## NATURAL HISTORY

Rocklings move away from the shore to spawn at various times of the year depending on the species and the water temperature. The eggs float in the plankton and hatch into tiny 'mackerel midge' larvae. Sometimes dense shoals of these tiny fish can be seen near the surface. Those that survive swim down to the seabed after some weeks or months of development.

## SIGHTINGS

Rock poolers are most likely to find Five-bearded Rocklings (five barbels) and less often, Shore Rocklings (3 barbels). Divers might find any of the five species described here but Four-bearded Rocklings mostly live below diving depths. Three-bearded and Four-bearded Rockling are sometimes brought up in trawls and seine nets as they can both be found in deep sediment areas.

Five-bearded Rockling

# PHYCID HAKES

Family Phycidae

## GREATER FORKBEARD    Swtan barfog    *Phycis blennoides*

**Other names: Forked Hake**    100cm

**KEY IDENTIFICATION FEATURES** This fish can be identified in the field with a high degree of certainty. The most obvious identification feature is the pair of long thin, thread-like pelvic fins which reach back to at least the start of the anal fin. Each of these consists of a single forked ray – hence the common name of 'forkbeard'. It has a long body, similar in general shape to ling or rockling, but it is fairly stout. Like them it has a single chin barbel. The first dorsal fin is short and triangular whilst the second dorsal fin and the anal fin are both long and even. Most forkbeards are greyish brown in colour whilst the dorsal, anal and tail fins are edged in black with a very thin pale outermost edge. The maximum length is just over 1m but most of those caught are smaller than this.

**SIMILAR SPECIES** Young fish hiding in holes could be mistaken for a number of other species such as ling and other codfishes, that have chin barbels, but as long as the pelvic fins can be seen then identification is certain. The related Forkbeard *Phycis phycis* is a very similar southern species found as far north as the Bay of Biscay.

**BEHAVIOUR** Schools near the seabed and feeds mainly on sediment-living crustaceans such as *Nephrops*. Some observations suggest the young fish may be nocturnal and hide amongst rocks during the day.

**HABITAT** This is an offshore codfish usually found over muddy and sandy bottoms from about 100–350m depth, and down to at least 1000m. Young fish can be found inshore, occasionally as shallow as 10m depth and apparently mainly in rocky areas – or at least this is where divers have photographed them.

**DISTRIBUTION** Around Wales there are confirmed records from North Wales, Anglesey and the Severn estuary. This offshore fish is relatively common around the whole of the British Isles and extends north to Iceland and Norway, and south to Morocco and the Mediterranean. It is most abundant in the south of its range.

**NATURAL HISTORY** Greater Forkbeard spawn in spring and early summer around the British Isles, earlier in the Mediterranean.

**SIGHTINGS** Young fish extend up into diving depths but are only rarely seen and photographed. Any such records around Wales would be of interest. These fish are caught by bottom trawlers, especially those fishing for Hake. They are extensively fished in the Mediterranean.

# Anglerfishes

### ORDER Lophiformes

Anglerfishes have the first ray of their dorsal fin modified to form a fishing lure called an illicium, huge mouths and flabby bodies. Three families are found in northern European waters. Two of these (Himantolophidae and Ceratiidae) are families of deep-sea fishes. Only shallow water anglers (Lophiidae) are found in Welsh waters.

## ANGLER                    Cythraul môr                    *Lophius piscatorius*

**Other names: Monkfish; Goosefish**                                          **200cm**

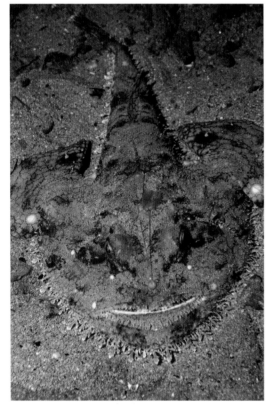

**SIMILAR SPECIES** Fish caught in deeper water (below about 100m) could also be Black-bellied Angler *Lophius budegassa*. This species is very similar but is confined to deep water on Atlantic coasts around the British Isles and has not been recorded in Welsh waters.

**BEHAVIOUR** This is the archetypal ambush predator that lures its prey, usually fish, within reach of its cavernous jaws by flicking its 'fishing lure' back and forth. Thanks to its camouflage and habit of partly burying itself in sediment, it is a successful hunter and can engulf its prey in a fraction of a second. Large fish in shallow water have even been known to lunge up to the surface to take seabirds, although this is an often cited but almost certainly extremely rare event! The fish is so confident in its camouflage that divers can often get really close.

**HABITAT** Anglers are bottom-living fish found mostly on sand, gravel and shell but also on mud and in rocky areas. They occur from just below the shoreline down to 1000m but are most common below 20m and above 500m.

**DISTRIBUTION** Anglers are found throughout Welsh waters. They have an extensive wider distribution, from the Barents Sea and Iceland in the north to Mauritania and the Mediterranean in the south.

**NATURAL HISTORY** Eggs are spawned in the form of an 'egg veil', a floating gelatinous ribbon, over deep water in spring and early summer. These can be as much as 3m wide and 9m long. The larvae float and are helped to do so by having very long fin rays. Young fish settle on the seabed when about 8cm long and Angler can live for up to 24 years.

**SIGHTINGS** Divers mostly see these fish lying on sediment patches amongst rocky reefs or in kelp forests. In spite of its bizarre appearance this is valuable fish and is caught commercially in bottom trawls. Angler and Black-bellied angler are not distinguished in landings but the majority of the catch is of immature Angler. Recently the EU introduced a minimum weight of 500g (with its bizarre shape, minimum size is not appropriate).

**KEY IDENTIFICATION FEATURES** There should be no mistaking this fish. Often described as one of the ugliest in the ocean, it can be identified in the field with a high degree of certainty. It has a broad, flattened head tapering gradually to a stout tail. Large fan-shaped pectoral fins flare out where the tail starts. Anglers have a huge mouth that extends right across the front of the head and is filled with needle-sharp teeth. The first dorsal fin consists of separate individual rays along the back. The first of these is very mobile and is used as a 'fishing lure'. Fringed lobes of skin all round the head and body provide camouflage, along with a variable blotchy brownish to reddish colour. It is white underneath.

## CRUSTACEAN IMITATION

Angler flesh looks and tastes similar to 'Scampi' *Nephrops norvegicus* when deep fried – so beware!

# Dory and Boarfishes

## ORDER Zeiformes

John Dory and Boarfish are the only representatives in Welsh (and British) shallow seas of two families Zeidae and Caproidae both of which belong in the order Zeiformes. Although very different in size and colour, these two fish have many similarities in shape and fin structure and Boarfish almost look like miniature John Dory.

| JOHN DORY | Pysgodyn darn arian | *Zeus faber* |
|---|---|---|

**Other names: Dory; Atlantic John Dory** 90cm

**KEY IDENTIFICATION FEATURES** It would be very hard to confuse a John Dory with any other fish and it can be identified in the field with complete confidence. Hovering upright in the water, it resembles a dinner plate on edge. It has a large head and mouth and heavy jaws that can be shot forwards. The first part of the dorsal fin consists of nine or ten long, sharp spines with the fin membrane between them elongated into long elegant filaments. The anal fin has a similar structure with three or four shorter spines. In the middle of each side of the fish is a conspicuous black spot, as large as the eye and ringed with yellow.

**SIMILAR SPECIES** None in Welsh waters. Silvery John Dory *Zenopsis conchifer* occur further south from Bay of Biscay to South Africa, Indian Ocean and western Atlantic.

**BEHAVIOUR** Adults are generally solitary though small groups can sometimes be seen. They are stealthy hunters and often stalk their prey head on so that they are practically invisible to their prey. Once within striking distance the fish shoots out its jaws and engulfs its dinner, usually a small fish. Although wary of divers, they can often be approached quite closely with patient stalking.

**HABITAT** An inshore fish generally found near the bottom between 10–150m depth. It sometimes comes right inshore into harbours and bays and can also be found as deep as 400m.

**DISTRIBUTION** Found all round the Welsh coastline, this strange fish has a very wide world distribution. It is found in the eastern Atlantic, Mediterranean, Black Sea, western and southwestern Pacific and Indian Ocean.

**NATURAL HISTORY** John Dory spawn in June to August around southern England. How much further north they breed is not known and any Welsh observations would be interesting. The eggs and larvae float in the plankton

**SIGHTINGS** Divers can spot these elegant fish over rocky reefs, in stands of tall seaweeds and over sand, especially in sheltered bays. Very occasionally they can be spotted from boats and jetties. It makes excellent eating but there is no directed fishery in Wales or around the UK and it is generally trawled up as by-catch from sediment areas. Anglers occasionally land them.

# BOARFISH
## Baedd môr
### *Capros aper*

**30cm**

**KEY IDENTIFICATION FEATURES**   This fish can be identified in the field with a high degree of certainty. It is similar in shape to its larger relative the John Dory, but is much smaller, usually only up to 10cm long. It has a small pointed head and large eyes. The first part of the dorsal fin consists of long, sharp spines, the anal fin is preceded by three short spines and the pelvic fins by one long one. The colour varies from almost completely red, through orange with yellow markings to silvery with orange tipped fins.

**SIMILAR SPECIES**   Other similar boarfish *Antigonia* spp. occur south of the British Isles but none have been recorded from Welsh waters.

**BEHAVIOUR**   In the Azores shoals of Boarfish have been photographed underwater by divers. It feeds mainly on small crustaceans using its highly protrusible mouth.

**HABITAT**   This little fish lives mostly close to the seabed in water 100–400m deep. It is sometimes found further inshore, at least as shallow as 40m, and on occasion even in rock-pools, possibly brought there following upwelling from rocky areas offshore. It also extends down to 600m (700m in the Ionian Sea). It may associate with deepwater soft corals in rocky areas but has also been trawled up from sandy areas. There is no information available on its habitat in Welsh waters and it may simply be a stray here.

**DISTRIBUTION**   There are only a few confirmed records of Boarfish in Welsh waters. The most recent record is of a stranded fish from the north Pembrokeshire coast. Other records are from Swansea Bay and the north coast of Wales. Its main distribution is from western Norway, down the Atlantic coasts of the British Isles, south to Senegal and the western Mediterranean.

**NATURAL HISTORY**   The British Isles are at the northern limit for spawning of this species. It spawns in summer and the eggs and larvae float and drift in the plankton.

**SIGHTINGS**   Although divers in Wales are unlikely to see this pretty little fish it is always a possibility. In some years it is common in the western English Channel and could possibly turn up in deepwater trawls in Welsh waters. Stranded fish are sometimes found on Welsh shores.

# Opahs

## ORDER Lampriformes

Opah belong in a tiny family of fish the Lampridae with only two members. Six other small families make up the order Lampri-formes and this order contains a fascinating array of rather bizarre fish none of which are likely to turn up in Welsh waters.

## OPAH                              Opa                              *Lampris guttatus*

**Other names: Jerusalem Haddock**                                              **200cm**

**KEY IDENTIFICATION FEATURES** Although rarely seen, this fish is unmistakable and can be identified in the field with certainty from its colour alone. It has bright red fins which stand out from its deep metallic blue back and silvery grey, green or pinkish sides. It is covered with large silvery white spots and the fins are sometimes edged with yellow. It has a similarly deep body to John Dory and Boarfish with a very rounded belly. The first part of the dorsal fin is tall and curved backwards as are the pelvic and pectoral fins.

**SIMILAR SPECIES** None in Welsh or European waters. The Southern opah, which only occurs in the southern hemisphere, is the only other species in this family.

**BEHAVIOUR** Little information is available. It is known to feed on squid, crustaceans and fish such as Blue Whiting found in its open water habitat. It swims mainly by flapping its pectoral fins in much the same manner as wrasse.

**HABITAT** Opah is an oceanic fish living in mid-water from around 100–400m deep, but sometimes near the surface.

**DISTRIBUTION** This is a rare fish in Welsh waters and it is uncommon in British and Irish waters. It has a worldwide distribution in tropical to temperate waters.

**NATURAL HISTORY** The Opah's life history is largely unknown.

**SIGHTINGS** Most sightings of this beautiful fish are of stranded specimens. It is very occasionally caught in mid-water trawl nets and even by anglers. In warmer waters it is sometimes caught along with tuna. It makes good eating but is too rare for commercial fishing in northern European waters.

## SEA SERPENT

The Oarfish *Regalecus glesne* is a relative of the Opah (in the same Order) and at 11m is the longest bony fish known. Its long flattened body has given rise to many tales of sea serpents when it has occasionally appeared at the surface. It has never been recorded in Welsh waters but has a world wide distribution so if you see one you may not be dreaming!

# Clingfish

## ORDER Gobiesociformes

Clingfish are small shore and shallow water fish that have a strong sucker disc on the underside formed from a modification and joining of the pelvic fins. This allows them to cling firmly to rocks and so survive in wave-battered environments. Their rather flattened shape, smooth almost triangular head and scaleless skin help to give them a low profile. There are four well established species found in northern European waters and in Welsh waters, but fish identified as Small-headed Clingfish are now recognised by some authorities as belonging to two different species *Apletodon dentatus dentatus* and *Apletodon microcephalus*. Little information is easily available on the differences between these two species and it is difficult to be certain which species is being described in the various texts. However, they certainly cannot be told apart in the field. As all clingfish are both difficult to spot and often difficult to identify in the field, their abundance and distribution in Welsh waters is still unclear.

Two-spotted Clingfish

A Shore Clingfish with eggs.

# SMALL-HEADED CLINGFISH

## Glynwr danheddog

### *Apletodon dentatus dentatus* and *A. microcephalus*

**4cm**

**KEY IDENTIFICATION FEATURES**  These two almost identical clingfish cannot be told apart in the field nor can they be distinguished from female Two-spotted Clingfish. They are the same shape, have the same fin arrangement and are similar in their variable colour to each other and to Two-spotted Clingfish. The ones shown here are examples of the colour range, which is typically reddish brown with lighter patches, blotches and spots.

**SIMILAR SPECIES**  See section on 'Similar species' under Two-spotted Clingfish.

**BEHAVIOUR**  Little specific information is available.

**HABITAT**  Found almost entirely below the shoreline down to around 25m depth but occasionally in pools on the shore near low water mark. These fish are frequently found sheltering in spaces within kelp holdfasts (*Laminaria* spp. and *Sacchoriza polyschides*) and holdfasts of other large seaweeds, where they also lay their eggs.

**DISTRIBUTION**  There are only a few confirmed records of Small-headed Clingfish *A. dentatus dentatus* around the Welsh coastline and none have been recorded as *A. microcephalus*. As they are difficult to spot and can be confused with Two-spotted Clingfish, they may be under-recorded. They also occur from Scotland down the Atlantic coasts of the British Isles south to the western Mediterranean.

**NATURAL HISTORY**  These fish have been observed to lay their eggs within the holdfasts of kelp and other seaweeds in spring and summer. The larvae are planktonic and young fish have been found living amongst seaweeds in autumn. Otherwise little is known of their biology.

**SIGHTINGS**  As for Two-spotted Clingfish. Breaking open kelp holdfasts at extreme low water may turn up specimens.

# TWO-SPOTTED CLINGFISH

**Glynwr deusmotiog**
*Diplecogaster bimaculata bimaculata*

**Other names:** *Lepadogaster bimaculatus* (synonym)                              6cm

**KEY IDENTIFICATION FEATURES** This little clingfish is difficult to distinguish from Small-headed Clingfish in the field. Males have two purple spots outlined with yellow on the sides behind the pectoral fins and if these are visible then identification is certain. These are quite low down and a close look may be needed to see them. This (and Small-headed Clingfish) have their single short dorsal fin set well back near the tail which distinguishes them from Shore and Connemara Clingfish. Individual fish vary in colour but many are a blotchy red with blue and brown spots.

**SIMILAR SPECIES** It is not possible to distinguish female Two-spotted Clingfish from Small-headed Clingfish in the field. Both are similar in size, shape and colour. In the laboratory, differences in fin ray counts, head size in relation to body size, and teeth help identification.

**BEHAVIOUR** These small fish tend to be rather secretive – their small size makes them a target for predatory fish – but if exposed by turning over stones for example, they often stay still, clinging on to the remains of their hidey hole.

**HABITAT** This clingfish lives mainly below the shore down to at least 55m, possibly 100m, but is sometimes found in rock pools near low water. It seems to prefer stony areas rather than bedrock and is also found on sediment where it hides in or under shells and stones. It has also been found in beds of bivalves such as horse mussels.

**DISTRIBUTION** Two-spotted Clingfish can be found all round the Welsh coastline, though they are not especially common or at least are not often seen. This is the only clingfish to extend as far north as Norway. It extends south round the British Isles and down into the western Mediterranean.

**NATURAL HISTORY** Females attach their yellow eggs in spring and summer (time depending on latitude) in or on the underside of old mollusc shells and stones. They are guarded by one of the parents until they hatch and the larvae join the plankton.

**SIGHTINGS** Sharp-eyed divers are most likely to see this clingfish although they may also turn up with a careful search in lower shore pools. It is quite common in scientific dredge samples from coarse ground. All Welsh records would be of interest.

# SHORE CLINGFISH        Glynwr        *Lepadogaster purpurea*
# CONNEMARA CLINGFISH  Glynwr Connemara  *Lepadogster candollei*

**Other names: Cornish Sucker (Shore) & *L. l. purpurea* (Shore)      6.5cm (Shore)  8cm (Connemara)**

Connemara Clingfish

**KEY IDENTIFICATION FEATURES**  Provided a good clear view can be had of the whole fish, then these two species can be identified in the field with a reasonable degree of certainty. These clingfish have a long flattened snout that is reminiscent of a miniature duck's bill when viewed from above. They have one dorsal and one anal fin which are quite long. Although difficult to see underwater, these two fins are joined to the tail fin in Shore Clingfish and not in Connemara Clingfish. Both are variable in overall colour but Shore clingfish have a pair of blue spots just behind the head, surrounded by a brown ring, outlined in blue. In some fish these look like a pair of dark glasses whilst in others they are quite faint. Shore clingfish are often patterned with irregular brown spots. Large adult Connemara Clingfish often have a few red spots along the base of the dorsal fin and other red spots on the head but many fish (perhaps females and juveniles) lack these.

**SIMILAR SPECIES**  *L. lepadogaster* occurs from Galiza southwards. It has a single blue indented shape instead of two ocelli often with two small blue marks in it. This species was previously considered a subspecies *Lepadogaster lepadogaster purpurea*.

**BEHAVIOUR**  As their name suggests, clingfish spend much of their time hanging onto the sides and undersides of rocks, and try to be as inconspicuous as possible.

**HABITAT**  Shore and Connemara Clingfish live on shores and in very shallow water, especially where there are plenty of small boulders for them to cling to. They can also be found attached to kelp holdfasts and other large seaweeds.

**DISTRIBUTION**  Both species have been recorded occasionally close inshore around the Welsh coastline. They extend from Scotland down the west coast of the British Isles, south to the Canary Isles and Mediterranean.

**NATURAL HISTORY**  Clingfish attach their eggs to the undersides of stones or boulders in summer and one of the parents guards them until they hatch. The larvae join the plankton for a short time before settling down on the seabed.

**SIGHTINGS**  Shore Clingfish can be found by carefully turning over boulders in the lower parts of the shore (and turning them back again). Snorkelers and divers in shallow water might also find them with some careful searching but Connemara Clingfish are only rarely spotted. Take photographs of Shore Clingfish heads to determine whether the southern *L. lepadogaster* occurs here.

Shore Clingfish have a fringed flap by each nostril.

# PERCOMORPHA

# Sand Smelts

ORDER Atheriniformes

**SAND SMELT**    **Pysgody ystlys arian**    *Atherina presbyter*

**20cm**

**KEY IDENTIFICATION FEATURES** Sand Smelt can be identified in the field with reasonable certainty although they cannot be distinguished from Big-scale Sand Smelt, very occasionally found in brackish Welsh waters. Sand Smelt is a small, slender fish with big eyes, a forked tail and two widely separated dorsal fins. The first dorsal fin is spiny whilst the second is soft. Perhaps the most obvious feature is an intense silvery line running along the sides. This stripe is still visible even in dead fish and some preserved specimens though the silvery sheen is lost.

**SIMILAR SPECIES** Big-scale Sand Smelt differ from Sand Smelt only in details such as the number of scales along the mid-line, and the relative sizes of the head and eye. They grow only to 9cm whilst Sand Smelt can reach 15cm and sometimes 20cm long. Underwater, Sand Smelt could be mistaken for other small silvery fish such as sprat and a close view is needed to see its two dorsal fins and silvery stripe. The similarly named Smelt *Osmerus eperlanus* is unrelated.

**BEHAVIOUR** Schools of these fish tend to be rather sedate and move slowly away from divers. Individual fish are easiest to photograph at night when they remain transfixed by a diver's torch. Southern fish are believed to migrate northwards in summer, swelling the numbers found around Wales and southern Britain.

**HABITAT** An inshore schooling, fish found mostly near the surface over muddy and sandy bottoms but also down to around 20m depth. It is also found in estuaries and occasionally in rock and saltmarsh pools.

**DISTRIBUTION** This little fish is found all round the Welsh coastline and can be common at times especially in summer. It occurs all round the British Isles but no further north and is commonest in the southern half. It is also found from Denmark (Kattegat), where it is rare, south to Mauritania and the western Mediterranean.

**NATURAL HISTORY** Sand Smelt spawn close inshore and onshore in summer in areas where there is plenty of seaweed. The eggs have a sticky filament at one end and quickly become attached to seaweeds and seagrass. When the eggs hatch the young fish stay in the pools or sheltered areas in which they were laid until they are a few centimetres long.

**SIGHTINGS** Small schools of juveniles can occasionally be found in shore pools and in this case, may well have hatched from eggs laid there. They can be caught using push nets or more usually beach seine nets at low tide off sediment shores. Shore divers may see shoals of these fish in sandy bays. They are not caught by directed commercial fisheries due to their small size but when they are caught they are used as 'whitebait'. They are also an important food item for seabirds such as terns that feed by plunge diving.

## SOUTHERN RELATIVE

Big-scale Sand Smelt *Atherina boyeri* is a southern species common in the Mediterranean but rare in southern Britain and around Wales. Welsh records are of fish collected from a few warm and low salinity habitats including Hinckley Point Power station in the Severn Estuary, Aberthaw lagoon (South Glamorgan) and Swansea Docks where it is known to have spawned.

# Grey Mullets

## KEY IDENTIFICATION FEATURES

Although grey mullets are easy to identify as such, it is not usually possible to distinguish the three species in the field. Grey mullets can be recognised by their torpedo-shaped body, two widely spaced, equal sized dorsal fins and faint, longitudinal grey stripes. The first dorsal fin has four spines and the scales are large and easily visible. A close-up view or photo of a grey mullet's head will show that the lips are notched in the middle, rather than smoothly curved.

Most mullet seen in Welsh waters are likely to be Thicklip Grey Mullet. This species has a very broad upper lip with coarse papillae covering the lower part. In dead fish or in a close-up photograph, the depth of this lip can be measured and should be more than half the eye diameter. Thinlip Grey Mullet and Golden Grey Mullet have a thinner upper lip with a depth less than half the eye diameter. Golden Grey Mullet usually have a yellow patch on the top of the gill cover but this fades in dead and aquarium fish. Thinlip Grey Mullet have a dark spot at the start of the pectoral fins. In dead fish fold one of the pectoral fins forward; in a Thinlip Grey Mullet it will not reach the eye whereas in a Golden Grey Mullet and Thicklip Grey Mullet, it will partly cover the eye.

## SIMILAR SPECIES

Bass are also silvery grey with two dorsal fins but the latter are longer and closer together and these fish have a large mouth and no stripes.

**GOLDEN GREY MULLET**
**Hyrddyn aur**
*Liza aurata*          60cm

Grey mullet are difficult to tell apart especially when seen from above swimming in shallow water, such as a harbour at low tide, but seen here in an aquarium pool.

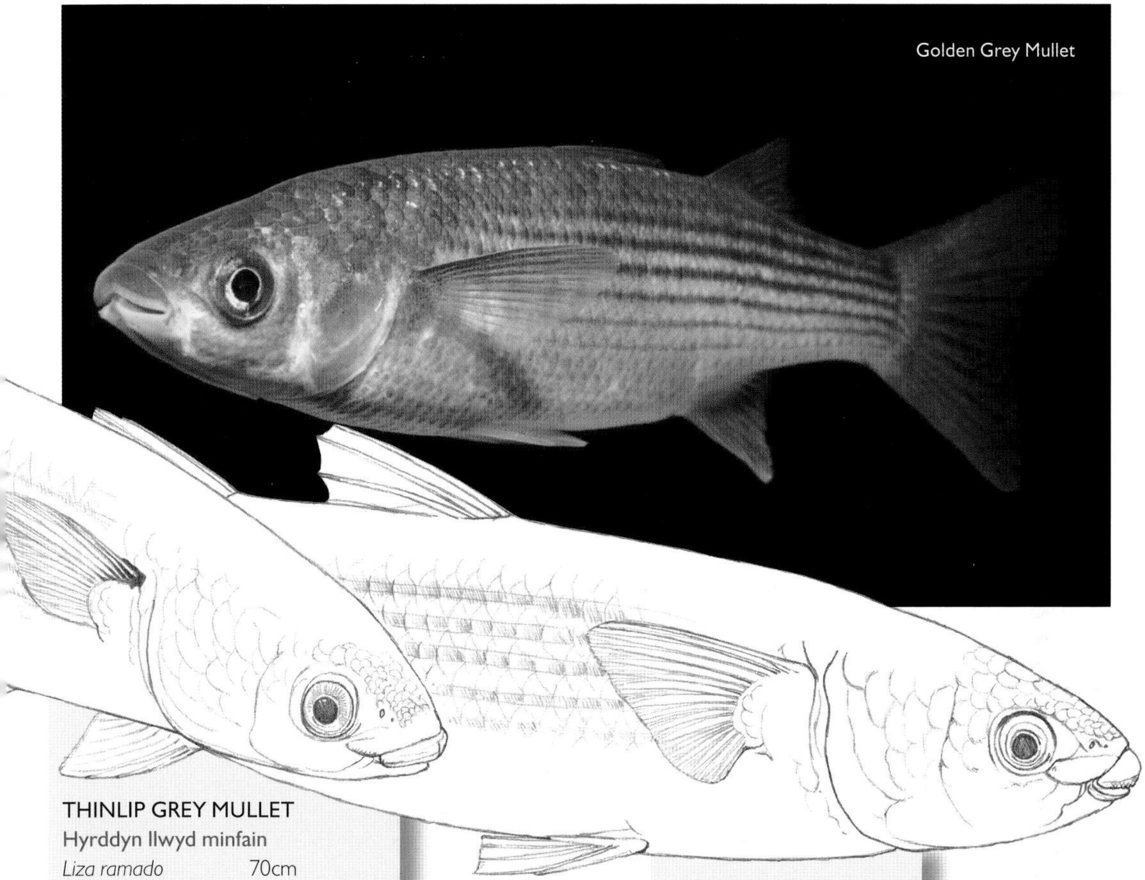

Golden Grey Mullet

## THINLIP GREY MULLET
Hyrddyn llwyd minfain
*Liza ramado*          70cm
Other name: *Liza ramada* (misspelling)

## THICKLIP GREY MULLET
Hyrddyn llwyd gweflog
*Chelon labrosus*     75cm

### BEHAVIOUR
Grey mullets are one of the vacuum cleaners of the marine world. They shovel in mouthfuls of mud, swallow anything edible including general detritus, worms, crustaceans and plant material and eject as much inedible material as they can through their gills. They will also take floating surface material and suck and scrape slimy algae off any hard surface.

### HABITAT
The three species of grey mullet are all tolerant of brackish water and are found close inshore in sheltered bays, estuaries and lagoons. Thinlip Grey Mullet are the most tolerant and will swim up into freshwater rivers. They live and feed mainly near the seabed but also swim at the surface.

### DISTRIBUTION
These three grey mullet species are found throughout Welsh waters but only the Thicklip mullet is common. Golden Grey Mullet are probably under-recorded due to their similarity to Thinlip Grey Mullet. At times they are common in the English Channel but this species probably does not breed this far north. Thinlip Grey Mullet is the most southerly species and is predominantly a summertime visitor to Welsh waters. It is rare north of the English Channel. All three species extend south into the Mediterranean and north to southern Norway.

### NATURAL HISTORY
Thicklip Grey Mullet spawn in summer in Welsh waters close inshore and the eggs and larvae float in the plankton. Young fish stay close inshore in sheltered bays and estuaries. The other two species may not breed as far north as Welsh waters but little information is available.

### SIGHTINGS
Grey mullets can often be seen from harbour walls and marina pontoons milling around at the surface. Divers are most likely to see them in sheltered sandy bays. Juvenile Thicklip Grey Mullet up to about 10cm long can be found in large shore pools in the south and southwest of England and Ireland and may well occur in Welsh pools. Thicklip Grey Mullet are also caught by anglers and this is a good sport fish. Angling clubs encourage 'catch and release' because this is a long-lived species. Local byelaws specify minimum landing sizes in parts of the area covered in this book. They are sometimes caught as by-catch in seine and gill nets especially in estuaries.

# GARFISH                    Cornbig môr-nodwydd                    *Belone belone*

**Other names: Garpike**                                                    94cm

**KEY IDENTIFICATION FEATURES** These fish can be identified in the field with a high degree of certainty although underwater it would be difficult to tell small ones apart from Atlantic Saury. In shape it resembles a slim cigar, tipped by long thin jaws filled with needle-sharp teeth. Its slimline shape is interrupted only by a single small dorsal and anal fin both set well back near the tail, and a pair of small pelvic fins on the belly near the midline. Seen from above, this fish looks dark greenish blue, whilst from the side and below it is burnished silver. This 'counter-shading' provides good camouflage in open water. Small fish have unequal jaws as the lower one grows faster than the upper.

Garfish

**SIMILAR SPECIES** Atlantic Saury or Skipper Sgipiwr, *Scomberesox saurus saurus* are very similar but have a deeper body and a row of finlets between the dorsal and anal fins and the tail. This is a widespread species in warm temperate and tropical seas, that is rarely recorded in Welsh waters but does sometimes come this far and further north. A second garfish species, *Belone svetovidovi*, very occasionally turns up in southwest Britain and Ireland but has not (yet) been recorded from Welsh waters.

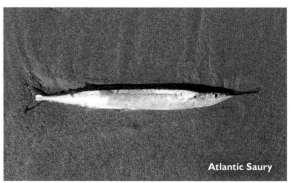

Atlantic Saury

**BEHAVIOUR** Garfish often leap clear out of the water when caught by anglers and when being chased by larger predatory fish. They are extremely fast swimmers and hunt small surface-living fish by grabbing them with their needle-sharp teeth. They migrate northwards and inshore in summer in response to rising water temperatures.

**HABITAT** This fish lives and hunts near the water surface, spending most of the time offshore but moving inshore in the summer months, sometimes even into estuaries.

**DISTRIBUTION** Garfish can be found all round the Welsh coastline but are only common inshore in summer. They also occur all round the British Isles. Although Garfish extend north to Norway and Iceland they are much rarer in the north. In the south, subspecies extend into the Mediterranean and to Madeira and the Canaries.

**NATURAL HISTORY** The fish spawn inshore in early summer, releasing their eggs in the open sea where they drift with the currents. However, the eggs have trailing filaments and become entangled and attached to floating debris, seaweed and even to rocks in shallow water.

**SIGHTINGS** Divers and snorkelers sometimes see Garfish hanging just below the water surface in sheltered bays. They are caught by anglers and on mackerel lines and lures trailed from boats and make good eating, in spite of off-putting green bones. They are also trapped in floating gill nets but have little commercial value. Look out also for Atlantic Saury in Welsh waters as their numbers could increase with ocean warming.

Photographic evidence from Cardigan Bay shows that dolphins do catch Garfish in Welsh waters although this may be the young practicing their fishing technique.

# MEDITERRANEAN FLYINGFISH

## Pysgodyn hedegog
### Cheilopogon heterurus

**Other names: Atlantic Flyingfish**                                40cm

**KEY IDENTIFICATION FEATURES**   Although other fish sometimes leap clear of the water surface, only flyingfish can glide for long distances. The Mediterranean Flyingfish is a slim cigar-shaped fish with very large pectoral and pelvic fins, the latter set well back on the belly. The lower lobe of the forked tail fin is longer than the upper, which helps it to 'take off'. In colour it is a dark iridescent blue shading to white on the belly.

**SIMILAR SPECIES** Blackwing Flyingfish *Hirundichthyes rondeletii* occasionally reach the English Channel. The differences between these two species are small and a specimen or close-up photograph sent to an expert would be needed to tell the difference.

**BEHAVIOUR** When threatened by predators or scared by boat engines, these fish propel themselves up out of the water, open their pectoral and pelvic fins like wings and glide over the surface.

**DISTRIBUTION AND HABITAT**   Whilst a common sight in tropical waters, flyingfishes are rare in northern European waters and especially as far north as the British Isles. Although not yet reported from Welsh waters, they have been recorded from the southern North Sea and from southern Norway to the Mediterranean. Subspecies are found in the tropics. They live and feed in coastal surface waters.

**SIGHTINGS**   Most likely to be seen when disturbed by boat engines in the warmer summer and autumn months. It is very occasionally caught in pelagic nets.

# Pipefishes and Seahorses

**ORDER** Syngnathiformes

**FAMILY** Syngnathidae

## PIPEFISHES

### KEY IDENTIFICATION FEATURES

Pipefish can be identified in the field with a high degree of certainty. All six species found in the British Isles are long thin fish closely related to seahorses. They swim stiffly because they are encased in armour made of rigid bony plates. In the four larger species this gives an angular cross-section to the body (not obvious in the Snake Pipefish). All pipefish have a tubular snout with a small mouth at the end. To distinguish the four larger species of pipefish, look carefully at the head. The Broad-nosed Pipefish is relatively easy to identify as its snout is almost as deep as the rest of its head, and is flattened from side to side. The Greater Pipefish has a humped head, especially noticeable in large individuals and a long snout. The Snake Pipefish has a smooth profile and can easily be recognised from its colour pattern. Nilsson's Pipefish is perhaps the most difficult to recognise and resembles a small Greater Pipefish. However it has a short snout and although the head is knobbly it has no distinct hump. The two remaining species, the Worm Pipefish and the Straight-nosed Pipefish are both very slender, smooth, and rounded in cross-section. The Worm Pipefish has an upturned snout, whilst, not surprisingly, the Straight-nosed Pipefish does not. These two species are both variable in colour but usually dark. The Straight-nosed Pipefish sometimes has distinct blue markings along the sides.

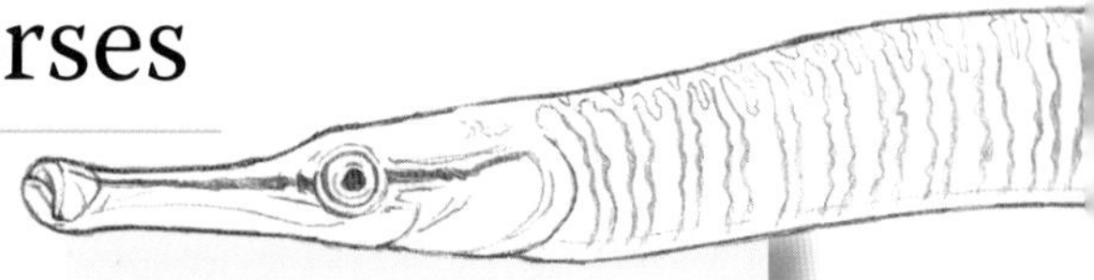

**SNAKE PIPEFISH** Pibell fôr hir
*Entelurus aequoreus* ♀ 60cm; ♂ 40cm

**GREATER PIPEFISH** Pibell fôr fawr
*Syngnathus acus* 50cm
Other names: Common Pipefish

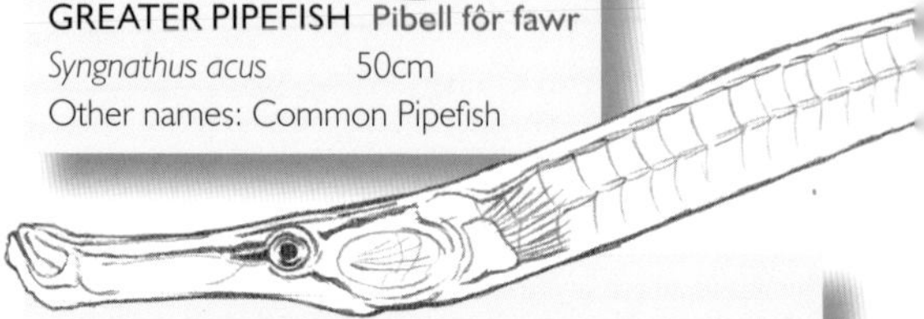

**BROAD-NOSED PIPEFISH** Pibell fôr drwynllydan
*Syngnathus typhle* 35cm
Other names: Common Pipefish

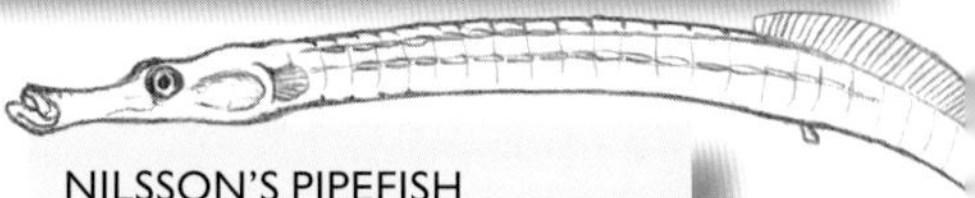

**NILSSON'S PIPEFISH**
Pibell fôr Nilsson
*Syngnathus rostellatus* 17cm
Other names: Lesser Pipefish

A Snake Pipefish demonstrates superb camouflage both in colour and behaviour as it sways in rhythm with and amongst the seaweed *Halidrys siliquosa*.

Heads of the four pipefish most commonly encountered by divers, from top to bottom:

**Snake Pipefish**, *Entelurus aequoreus*. Head profile straight with a reddish longitudinal band from tip of snout, through eye to gill cover.

**Greater Pipefish**, *Syngnathus acus*. Head profile concave, snout long, more than half head length.

**Broad-nosed Pipefish**, *Syngnathus typhle*. Head profile very straight, snout deep and laterally compressed.

**Nilsson's Pipefish**, *Syngnathus rostellatus*. Snout short, less than half head length.

**STRAIGHT-NOSED PIPEFISH**
Pibell Fôr Drwynsyth
*Nerophis ophidion*    30cm

**WORM PIPEFISH**
Pibell fôr leiaf
*Nerophis lumbriciformes*
17cm

**SIMILAR SPECIES** At first glance pipefish, especially Worm and Straight-nosed Pipefish, could be confused with small eels.

**BEHAVIOUR** Pipefish live in shallow water and prefer to hide amongst dense seaweed or seagrass. Look carefully as they often lie along the seaweed and allow themselves to sway in rhythm with it. Some pipefish seem to react to noise, such as a diver shouting, so to observe them you may need to be quiet and breathe gently.

**HABITAT** Pipefish are inshore, coastal species found within scuba diving depths and even in rock pools though this is rare for Straight-nosed and Snake Pipefish. They are found in both rocky and sediment areas wherever there is a dense cover of seaweeds or seagrass.

**DISTRIBUTION** These pipefish are all found round the coastline of Wales and the British Isles, but the Worm Pipefish is less common on Britain's east coast as it prefers rocky shores. The Straight-nosed Pipefish is less often seen and has not been recorded from northern Scotland though as it occurs in southern Norway, this may be due to lack of surveys. Until recently, the Snake Pipefish was rarely seen by divers but since 2003 divers and fishermen have reported seeing increasing numbers round our coasts. A dedicated 'Seasearch' survey in 2007 showed large numbers along the east coast of the British Isles from Moray Firth to North Norfolk. In Wales they still appear to be occasional to rare. All six species of pipefish extend at least as far north as Norway and south to Spain. Greater, Broad-nosed and Straight-nosed Pipefish extend into the Mediterranean.

**NATURAL HISTORY** If you manage to catch a pipefish during the summer, perhaps in a rock pool, gently turn it over and see if it is carrying eggs. If it is, then it is a male as the female lays her eggs in a special pouch or groove on the male's belly. Here they remain safe until they hatch out and disperse.

**SIGHTINGS** Rock pool visitors, snorkelers and divers will all come across pipefish. The worm pipefish is common on the shore amongst brown seaweeds, whilst Broad-nosed and Nilsson's can be caught in push nets over sand especially in estuaries. Snake and Greater Pipefish often come up in shrimp trawls.

**Worm Pipefish**, *Nerophis lumbriciformes*.
Snout short with the end tilted up.

**Straight-nosed  Pipefish**,
*Nerophis ophidion.*
Snout short but straight.

# SEAHORSES

## LONG- & SHORT-SNOUTED SEAHORSES
### Morfarch

### *Hippocampus guttulatus* and *Hippocampus hippocampus*

**Other names:** *H. ramulosus* (synonym *H. guttulatus*); Spiny Seahorse *H. guttulatus*    16cm

**KEY IDENTIFICATION FEATURES**  Seahorses have such an unusual and characteristic shape that it should be virtually impossible to mistake them for anything else. However, telling the two species so far recorded from British and Irish waters apart, is trickier. As with pipefish, the head is the key. The Short-snouted Seahorse has a short, slightly curved snout whilst (logically) the Long-snouted Seahorse has a longer, straight snout. The Long-snouted Seahorse often grows tassels and filaments, but these are not present in all individuals. The colour of both species is highly variable.

**SIMILAR SPECIES**  None.

**BEHAVIOUR**  Both species of seahorse have been shown to be resident all year round (British Seahorse Survey), not just summer visitors from further south. Seahorses use their prehensile tails to cling onto seaweeds and seagrasses and can often be approached quite closely by divers as they rely on their camouflage for protection. Close-up photographs are therefore a possibility to help with later identification.

**HABITAT**  Shallow inshore water, usually amongst seaweeds and seagrass.

**DISTRIBUTION**: Only the Long-snouted Seahorse has so far been recorded from the Welsh coastline. The Short-snouted Seahorse appears to be restricted to the south and southwest coasts of Britain and Ireland but is relatively common in the nearby Channel Island of Jersey. It extends south to the Gulf of Guinea and the Mediterranean. The Long-snouted Seahorse, although uncommon, is relatively widespread. It has been recorded from the entire south coast of Britain and Wales, the south coast of Ireland and as far north as Orkney and Shetland (but not yet in between). In the south it reaches Morocco and the Mediterranean.

**NATURAL HISTORY**: Seahorses are famous for their parental skills, with the male carrying the eggs in a special belly pouch that seals over after the female has deposited her eggs there. The eggs hatch into well-developed young. The Long-snouted Seahorse breeds in our waters, probably throughout its range. Short-snouted Seahorses breed in the Channel Islands but there is little data from elsewhere over their range.

**SIGHTINGS**: Usually spotted by sharp-eyed divers searching amongst seaweed. All records are of interest. These fish may extend their range northward if sea temperatures continue to rise.

Above. Short-snouted Seahorse, *Hippocampus hippocampus*. Snout is one third or less of total head length with a concave top.
Below. Long-snouted Seahorse, *Hippocampus guttulatus*. Snout is more than one third of total head length and is straight.

# Sticklebacks

## ORDER  Gasterosteiformes

Although small in size, sticklebacks are well-known fish, caught in pools and streams by children, used in laboratory behavioural experiments and kept in aquaria. Along their backs they have a series of separate sharp spines followed by a normal dorsal fin. The pelvic fins are reduced to a single spine and one or two soft rays and there is another spine in front of the anal fin. They have no scales but a series of bony plates along both sides. Three species are found in Wales. The Sea or Fifteen-spined Stickleback is common in shallow coastal waters. The familiar Three-spined Stickleback occurs in freshwater streams and rivers as well as the sea. Nine-spined Sticklebacks are found in freshwater and only occasionally in slightly salty water and this species is not described here.

Sea Stickleback

Sea Stickleback

### What's in a name?

In old Anglo Saxon, a sticel was a goad or prickle. In Latin *spina* means thorn or spine, so both scientific and common names refer to this stickleback's spiny back.

# SEA STICKLEBACK      Crothell dri phigyn    *Spinachia spinachia*

**Other names: Fifteen-spined Stickleback**          **20cm**

**KEY IDENTIFICATION FEATURES** This fish can be identified in the field with a high degree of certainty. Shaped like a slim torpedo, it has a long thin tail stalk ending in a small, fan-shaped tail fin. Most fish have 15 spines along the back but the range is 14–17, though it is not usually possible to count these underwater. Look for a characteristic brown stripe that runs from the snout through the eye. The maximum size is around 20cm long.

**SIMILAR SPECIES** At first sight, hidden amongst seaweed, this fish could be confused with a pipefish, especially the Snake Pipefish which has a similar dark band running through the eye, but a close look will soon show its true identity.

**BEHAVIOUR** This fish is often difficult to spot because it spends much of its time hanging motionless amongst seaweeds. Relying on its camouflage, it will often allow a diver to approach quite closely.

**HABITAT** A thorough search of weed-filled shore pools below around mid-tide level may reveal this stickleback, but with the exception of shores in the north west and Scotland, it is more commonly found in shallow water down to about 10m depth. It prefers dense stands of seaweeds such as the podweed *Halidrys siliquosa* in rocky areas and hides amongst seagrass in sediment areas. It can also be found in seaweed fringes hanging from boats and man-made structures such as piers.

**DISTRIBUTION** Found all around the Welsh coast but not very common and easily overlooked. It also extends all around the British Isles, north to Norway, in the Baltic and south to the Bay of Biscay.

**NATURAL HISTORY** In spring and summer males build a substantial nest by pulling together seaweed fronds and sticking them with kidney secretions. The male selects a single female and entices her to lay her eggs inside the nest. He then guards and fans the eggs until they hatch two to four weeks later. Both parents die, the female after spawning and the male after egg hatching.

**SIGHTINGS** This well-camouflaged fish will usually only be spotted by a careful search of shore pools or by divers patiently searching through curtains of weed. In autumn large numbers of young are sometimes dredged up along with dense seaweed in the mouths of estuaries. Any records are of interest, especially of nests and all records from Welsh shores. Look also for dead ones washed ashore in late summer.

# THREE-SPINED STICKLEBACK

### Crothell dri phigyn
### *Gasterosteus aculeatus aculeatus*

**10cm**

**KEY IDENTIFICATION FEATURES** This fish can be identified in the field with a high degree of certainty. It is a small, slender fish that is flattened from side to side and so appears rather thin. It has two large spines and one small one on its back followed by a normal dorsal fin. The spines are not always easy to see as the fish often folds them down. Seen sideways on, a series of silvery bony plates shows up along the flanks. These provide some protection as the fish has no scales. Males develop a bright red throat and blue eyes in the breeding season. Grows to a maximum of about 10cm long.

**SIMILAR SPECIES** From a distance Three-spined Sticklebacks can look like any number of other small silvery fish. At close quarters the spines and bony plates along the flanks make it easy to recognise, although the spines are often laid flat along the back.

**BEHAVIOUR** When nesting, males will try to drive away rival males, egg stealers and even divers and it is at this time that they are easiest to approach. Anything red is considered to be a rival male stickleback! Out of the breeding season, these fish often live in schools and in Scandinavia, Denmark and the Baltic have at least in the past been sufficiently abundant for commercial exploitation for fishmeal and fertilizer.

**HABITAT** Around Wales and the southern parts of its range, three-spined sticklebacks are most commonly found in brackish lagoons (e.g. The Fleet in Dorset) and estuaries. From around the Isle of Man northwards they are commonly caught in shore pools and are also found in shallow, weedy coastal areas. This fish is usually confined to shallow coastal waters but there are some records from several miles offshore.

**DISTRIBUTION** Found all round the Welsh coast. Elsewhere

it has a circumpolar distribution throughout most coastal waters of the North Atlantic and in coastal Pacific waters of North America and north of Japan.

**NATURAL HISTORY** The intricate courtship and nesting habits of this fish are very well known and extensively documented. Coastal Sticklebacks move close inshore in the spring and spawn in shallow water, tidal pools and estuaries. The male builds a tunnel-like nest on the seabed, from seaweed and debris and courts a series of females, enticing each in turn into the nest to lay their eggs. He then takes sole charge guarding the eggs assiduously and fanning them to provide plenty of oxygen until they hatch and the fry are a few days old.

**SIGHTINGS** Like the Sea Stickleback, this little fish needs a careful search in shore pools to find it. Divers need to look in shallow, seaweed areas and seagrass beds especially in sheltered bays and saline lagoons. It can also be trawled up from weedy areas and there are some reports of Three-spined Sticklebacks caught several miles offshore. Any records from shore pools and offshore areas around Wales would be especially useful.

## What's in a name?

*Gasterosteus* is derived from the Greek, *gaster*: belly and *osteon*: bone which together create 'bony-belly' in reference to the bony processes under this fish's abdomen. Latin for prickle is *aculeus*, referring to the spines.

# Scorpaeniformes

## ORDER Scorpaeniformes

This Order includes the well-known Sea scorpions (Cottidae) and Scorpionfish (Scorpaenidae) but also Redfish (Sebastidae), Gurnards (Triglidae), Flying gurnard (Dactylopteridae), Hooknose (Agonidae), Lumpsucker (Cyclopteridae) and Sea snails (Liparidae). All these fish have large, often spiny heads, most have spiny dorsal fins and many are heavily armoured.

Sea scorpions are also sometimes known as sculpins or bullheads and belong to the family Cottidae. These tough, spiny, bottom-living fish with a big head and tapering body are familiar to many children from rock pools and Bullheads are also found in freshwater. They have large, bulging eyes almost on top of the head, which allows them to spot danger as they lie hidden on the seabed. If this fails and a predator tries to eat one, the sharp, backward-pointing spines on their gill covers often means that they are quickly spat out. The first of

their two, separate dorsal fins, is also sharply spiny whilst the second is soft. These fish have no scales and instead are protected by bony plates embedded in the skin, which makes them appear rather stiff especially when they move. Two species are common in Welsh waters and are described here, whilst a third, the Norway Bullhead *Micrenophrys lilljeborgi* is a northern species that is known to extend south to around the Isle of Man and so it is possible that it might just occur in north Welsh waters.

Scorpionfish (Scorpaenidae), have a similar body shape and are equally spiny. Although these are predominantly warm-water fish and are more familiar from the Mediterranean and the tropics, two species extend north to the British Isles and are described here. They have a single, long, dorsal fin consisting of sharp, venomous spines with a short soft rear portion.

Even in a small Long-spined Sea Scorpion, the mouth barbels show up clearly.

# LONG-SPINED SEA SCORPION Sgorpion môr hirddreiniog penlletwad
### *Taurulus bubalis*

**Other names: Long-spined Bullhead**                                    **25cm**

**KEY IDENTIFICATION FEATURES** These two fish can both be identified in the field with a high degree of certainty. The best way to tell them apart is to look for a small barbel at both corners of the mouth. Only the Long-spined Sea Scorpion has these and although small, they are usually fairly obvious. The length of the cheek spines is also diagnostic but difficult to see underwater. As its name suggests, the Long-spined Sea Scorpion has one long cheek spine as well as shorter ones whilst they are all much the same length in the Short-spined. Colour is of little use in identification as the Long-spined species is an expert at matching its colour to the background. A small fish caught in a rock pool will almost certainly be a Long-spined Sea Scorpion, whilst a large fish trawled up is likely to be a Short-spined. Short-spined sea scorpions usually grow to a maximum of 30cm in the south of their range but up to 90cm in the north. Long-spined Sea Scorpions are smaller at 15cm but sometimes grow up to as much as 25cm.

**SIMILAR SPECIES** The Norway Bullhead *Micrenophrys lillje-borgii* (see page 130) looks like a small Long-spined Sea Scorpion but, although it too has mouth barbels, these are very small. It also has rows of spines in its skin above the lateral line but this can be difficult to see underwater but may be visible in photos. Although it has not yet been recorded in Welsh waters it has been from the Isle of Man.

**BEHAVIOUR** Long-spined Sea Scorpions will wriggle out of rock pools that become too hot or low in oxygen and can survive for some time under damp weed. They tend to have a home pool to which they return as the tide goes out. Underwater, both species of sea scorpions will often remain perfectly still when approached, relying on their camouflage colours to deceive predators. Fish caught in rock pools can be handled, with care – their spines are not venomous.

# SHORT-SPINED SEA SCORPION

## Sgorpion môr byrddreiniog
### *Myoxocephalus scorpius*

**Other names: Shorthorn Sculpin, Bullhead, Bull-rout, Fatherlasher**                    **30cm**

**HABITAT** Long-spined Sea Scorpions are very common on rocky shores in pools filled with seaweed. They are also found hiding amongst seaweed or plant-like animal growths (such as sponges and hydroids) in rocky areas down to 30m depth, and sometimes deeper. In contrast, the larger Short-spined Sea Scorpion is very rarely found on the shore and is happy both in rocky areas and on sediment down to at least 60m. Look for it also around harbour walls and under piers.

**DISTRIBUTION** Both sea scorpions are common all round the Welsh coastline and around the whole of the British Isles. They extend north to Scandinavia and Iceland and south to the Bay of Biscay. The Long-spined Sea Scorpion reaches further south to Portugal and just into the Mediterranean. The Short-spined Sea Scorpion also occurs along the Atlantic coast of Canada and northern USA.

**NATURAL HISTORY** Both species lay clusters of orange or yellow eggs in rock crevices, under stones or amongst clumps of seaweed in late winter or early spring. Whilst male Short-spined Sea Scorpions are well known for their attentive parental care, there is less information on the Long-spined species. Sea scorpions are accomplished ambush predators and their large mouths allow them to make a meal of sizeable crabs and other invertebrates as well as small bottom-living fish.

**SIGHTINGS** Small Long-spined Sea Scorpions are one of the commonest fish found by people searching in rock pools. Divers will also see these fish in the kelp forest and just below. Short-spined Sea Scorpions are also seen by divers but less often. Large ones are sometimes trawled up from sediment areas. Any records of Short-spined Sea Scorpions on Welsh shores would be interesting as it is usually only intertidal in Scotland and further north.

Above. Norway Bullhead *Micrenophrys lilljeborgii*; the spines above the lateral line are just visible in this photograph.

Long-spined Sea Scorpions are very variable in colour as they can change their pigmentation. Very young fish often have 'stripes' of differing colours when just a few centimeters long.

# BLACK and LARGESCALED SCORPIONFISH

## Pysgodyn dreiniog
### *Scorpaena porcus* and *S. scrofa*

**Other names: Smallscaled Scorpionfish (Black Scorpionfish)**      **25cm and 50cm**

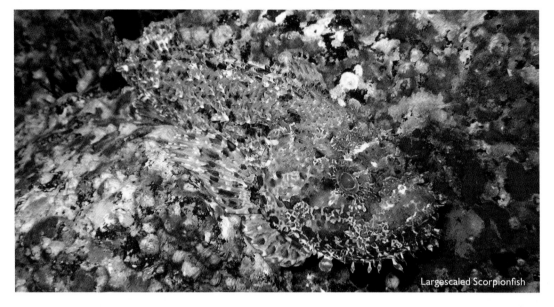

Largescaled Scorpionfish

**KEY IDENTIFICATION FEATURES** Scorpionfish can be identified as such in the field with a high degree of certainty but it is more difficult to tell the species apart underwater. Although similar in shape to sea scorpions, they grow much larger; the Black Scorpionfish to 25cm and the Largescaled Scorpionfish to 50cm. Seen from the front they appear to be all head, with a large, semi-circular mouth that gives them a doleful expression. Both the head and body are covered in irregular skin flaps that help disguise them. The spikey dorsal fin is usually obvious even when partially folded down. The colour is very variable but usually a marbled mix of red, orange, and brown in dark and light shades. If the fish lifts its head it may be possible to see that the Black Scorpionfish has no skin flaps on its chin but large ones above the eyes, whilst the Largescaled species has well-developed chin flaps and only small ones above the eyes.

**SIMILAR SPECIES** It would be difficult to confuse scorpionfish with any other group of fishes but it is possible that the two species themselves have not been reliably distinguished in all the British Isles records.

**BEHAVIOUR** Relying on their camouflage for protection, scorpionfish will remain perfectly still, resting on their large fan-like pectoral fins, even when approached really closely and it is all too easy to miss them. They have venomous spines in the dorsal fins and should not be touched (if you can see them!).

**HABITAT** Most scorpionfish are seen lying motionless on or amongst weed or turf-covered rocks in inshore areas, but they can also occur in deep water on sandy and stony grounds especially *S. crofa*. Small fish may inhabit shallow water but most live below about 20m and down to at least 500m or even deeper.

**DISTRIBUTION** Scorpionfish are rare southern visitors to the British Isles. There is a record of *S. porcus* from North Wales

(Henderson 1994), and an unpublished record of *S. scrofa* from mid-Wales (Sarns) in 1986. Both species have been recorded from the English Channel and *S. scrofa* from scattered points around the British Isles, as far north as Orkney. They are common in the Mediterranean and extend south to Canary Isles, Azores and as far as Senegal.

**NATURAL HISTORY** So far there is no evidence of these fish breeding around the British Isles. In the Mediterranean, the eggs are laid in gelatinous lumps on the seabed

**SIGHTINGS** In the Mediterranean, scorpionfish are regularly caught on rod and line. They have occasionally come up in trawls in the English Channel. They are also very occasionally seen and photographed by divers. Any sightings of scorpionfish from Welsh waters would be of great interest as these fish appear to be extending their range northwards with ocean warming (Stebbings *et al.* 2002).

Black Scorpionfish

# REDFISH

FAMILY  Sebastidae

## NORWAY REDFISH  Pysgodyn coch Norwy  *Sebastes viviparus*

**Other names: Norway Haddock**  35cm

Blue-mouth,
*Helicolenus
dactylopterus*

**KEY IDENTIFICATION FEATURES**  This fish can be identified in the field with a reasonable degree of certainty though telling the different species of *Sebastes* apart in trawls from mixed depths, could be difficult. As the name suggests Norway Redfish are always a reddish colour though often a yellowish red. Many fish have a dark patch on the gill cover but this may not be unique to this species. Although sometimes difficult to see, all members of this family have a bony ridge that runs across each cheek below the eyes. The head, mouth and eyes are all large and spines edge the pre-operculum. There is a single dorsal and anal fin both of which have strong spines in the front half and soft rays in the rear portion.

**SIMILAR SPECIES**  Red-fish *Sebastes marinus* are very similar but live in deeper water from about 100–400m from Scotland northwards. Blue-mouth *Helicolenus dactylopterus* is also similar in colour and shape but again usually live in deepwater, to the west of the British Isles and further south – this fish has been recorded from shallower water in north-west Scotland recently. The inside of the mouth and gill cavity is dark greyish blue and the lower rays in the pectoral fins are free at the ends. Although in different families, Wreckfish and seaperches have a similar general shape with the dorsal fin part spiny and part soft.

**BEHAVIOUR**  Divers have reported that this fish shows little fear of them and can be closely approached.

**HABITAT**  Inshore waters from about 40–100m mainly near the seabed in rocky areas. Range from 10m to 300m.

**DISTRIBUTION**  Like other members of this genus *Sebastes*, the Norway Redfish is a northern species but it extends south into the Irish Sea and just into Welsh waters where it has been recorded. It also extends into the southern North Sea whilst its northern limits are northern Norway and Iceland.

**NATURAL HISTORY**  Unusually for bony fish, Norway Redfish produce live young, up to 30,000 at a time. The eggs are retained until they have developed into young larvae about 4–5mm long. This is a long-lived, slow growing fish that can reach 30 years old. It feeds on a wide variety of small crustaceans and fish.

**SIGHTINGS**  Divers might see this fish on dives to deep reefs and rocky areas and it is popular as a sportsfish amongst anglers in some areas. Norway Redfish have been photographed by divers in Norwegian fjords. Unlike its larger, better known deep water relatives the Red-fish *Sebastes marinus*, and *S. mentella* it is not targeted by trawlers but is sometimes caught in shrimp trawls, suggesting it is not confined to rocky areas.

# GURNARDS

## FAMILY Triglidae

Gurnard are easily recognised as such but the different species can be hard to tell apart in the field. These fish have a characteristic, bony, armour-plated head with a steep, sloping profile and strong spines on the gill covers. But perhaps the easiest way to recognise gurnards is to look for three finger-like feelers either side below the head, which they use like delicate feet. These are actually the three lowest rays of the large pectoral fins. They are separate and can move independently. There are two dorsal fins, the first relatively short and spiny and the second long with soft rays.

Of the six species of gurnards found in northern European waters, only Red, Tub and Grey Gurnard are commonly found in Welsh waters. Streaked Gurnard and Long-finned Gurnard are southern species and are occasional summer visitors to British waters. Piper live in deep water near the edge of the Continental Shelf and are not described here.

Right. East Atlantic Red Gurnard.
Below. Juvenile Grey Gurnard; a black mark was present on the first dorsal fin but does not show up in the photograph.

# EAST ATLANTIC RED GURNARD   Chwyrnwr coch   *Aspitrigla cuculus*

**Other names: Red Gurnard**                                          **40–50cm**

**KEY IDENTIFICATION FEATURES**  It may not always be possible to identify this fish with certainty in the field. A really red gurnard with a pale belly and no blue markings on the fins is likely to be this species. Look also at the lateral line which is covered by a row of large scales which are expanded vertically i.e. from a dorsal to ventral direction on the fish. With a fish in the hand, check whether the pectoral fins reach back to the beginning of the anal fin. They should, just.

**SIMILAR SPECIES**  Gurnard cannot easily be confused with other types of fish but the species themselves are not always easy to tell apart. An all red gurnard is usually this species but Tub Gurnard can also be red and Red Gurnard are not always as bright as the one shown here. To tell these two species apart, look out for the pectoral fins which are mostly red to yellowish in Red Gurnard but, at least in males, have peacock blue markings in Tub Gurnard. It is not always possible to tell these two species apart in photographs if the pectoral fins are not visible.

**BEHAVIOUR**  Gurnard of all species are fascinating fish to watch. They use their pectoral feelers to walk over the seabed and taste for buried food. When they find a buried crab, shrimp or fish they stop and root it out with their strong armoured snout. Often found in small groups, they communicate by sharp grunting noises made by vibrating the walls of their swimbladder. Most gurnard species make similar noises which may serve to keep the fish together.

**HABITAT**  This pretty gurnard seems to be happy on almost any type of sediment, shell and gravel bottom and is also sometimes found in rocky areas. It lives mainly in shallow water from about 5m down but extends as deep as 250m, possibly 400m.

**DISTRIBUTION**  Red Gurnard are found all round the Welsh coastline though rarely in large numbers. With the exception of the east coast where it appears to be largely absent, this species extends all round the British Isles and through the English Channel to Denmark. Further south it reaches Mauritania and the Mediterranean.

**NATURAL HISTORY**  There is little detailed information available. Red Gurnard spawn in summer. Like other gurnards they grow fast and mature at a young age, but can live for at least 20 years. This is one of the smallest European gurnards.

**SIGHTINGS**  As this fish lives mostly within scuba diving depths, it can easily be seen by divers and even snorkelers. It is sometimes caught on rod and line by anglers and is often taken as by-catch in trawls but is not an important commercial species. This gurnard is though, the species most commonly eaten.

# TUB GURNARD    Ysgyfarnog fôr    *Chelidonichthys lucernus*

**Other names:** *Trigla lucerna* (synonym); Sapphirine Gurnard    75cm

**KEY IDENTIFICATION FEATURES** If the fish is an adult and the pectoral fins are displayed then it should be possible to identify this gurnard with reasonable certainty in the field. It is very variable in colour from red to brownish but has large pectoral fins that can be blue all over but are more commonly yellowish, clearly edged with blue and marked with beautiful blue spots, blotches or darker lines. These markings are the reason for its alternative name of Sapphirine Gurnard. The lateral line appears as a raised line but does not have expanded or spiny scales. This is the largest European gurnard. Anything over 50cm is likely to be this species.

**SIMILAR SPECIES** Young fish can closely resemble Red gurnard but adults are also often red. However, Red Gurnard do not have blue pectoral fins. With a dead fish, fold the pectoral fins back and see if they reach beyond the start of the anal fin. This is not the case in Red and Grey Gurnard.

**BEHAVIOUR** Small schools of Tub Gurnard search the seabed for hidden invertebrates and fish. However, this fish is also a good swimmer and can be found up in the water column feeding on sand eels and other fish. Their impressive pectoral fins may be used for courtship and aggressive displays. More observations of breeding behaviour are needed.

**HABITAT** Tub Gurnard prefer combinations of mud and sand rich in invertebrates in inshore locations. Young fish are common in shallow water to around 20m whilst larger fish extend down to at least 200m.

**DISTRIBUTION** Tub Gurnard is relatively common all round the Welsh coastline and the British Isles and extends north to Norway and south to Cape Blanc (Africa) and the Mediterranean. It is much less common north of the Irish Sea.

**NATURAL HISTORY** Tub Gurnard spawn in summer from May to July. They can grow quite large and the Welsh rod-caught record is around 5kg. They can live for 15 years though most seem to have a much shorter life span.

**SIGHTINGS** Only divers willing to stray away from rocky areas onto sediment are likely to see this photogenic fish. Its large size makes it of interest to anglers and it is also a reasonably important commercial fish, especially in continental Europe. It is mostly caught in mixed demersal trawl fisheries and is vulnerable to over-fishing.

# GREY GURNARD          Chwyrnwr llwyd          *Eutrigla gurnardus*

**45cm**

**KEY IDENTIFICATION FEATURES** As it is rather non-descript, making a positive identification of this slightly drab gurnard in the field may be difficult. A good photograph that can be studied later will help. Most fish are a greyish to reddish brown with darker saddles or blotches and usually white to cream speckles. Look out for a dark blotch on the rear of the first dorsal fin. This is only clearly visible when the fish is holding the fin fully erect as shown here. The lateral line shows up as a raised line looking a bit like tiny beads. These are actually spines on the lateral line scales. The pectoral fins are short and with a dead fish can be pressed back against the body, to show that they do not quite reach the beginning of the anal fin.

**SIMILAR SPECIES** Reddish brown ones could easily be confused with dull coloured Red Gurnard or young Tub Gurnard without the blue pectoral fin markings. A combination of a dark blotch on the dorsal fin, short pectoral fins and a spiny lateral line should be diagnostic.

**BEHAVIOUR** Grey Gurnard feed on a wide variety of bottom-living fish and invertebrates and also on fish caught up in the water column, especially at night. Observations of captive Grey Gurnard have demonstrated that some of the sounds they produce are connected with competition for food resources.

**HABITAT** Whilst this gurnard can be found on a variety of sediments and in rocky areas, it prefers sand. In general it is found further offshore than Red and Tub Gurnard and lives mostly between 20m to 150m depth. In summer young fish can be found a few metres below the shore. In the Mediterranean it extends down to over 300m.

**DISTRIBUTION** Grey Gurnard is the commonest of the five gurnards described here and is found all round the Welsh coastline and the British Isles. It extends north to Norway and Iceland and south to Madeira and the Mediterranean.

**NATURAL HISTORY** Grey Gurnard spawn in deep water between April and August and the eggs and larvae float in the plankton. Adults mature at three or four years old and this species appears to have a relatively short life span of around six years. As is common with bony fish, males mature earlier than females and breed at a younger age and smaller size.

**SIGHTINGS** Divers will probably see Grey Gurnard less often than Red or Tub Gurnard because it lives rather deeper. Like other gurnards Grey Gurnard are taken as by-catch in trawl fisheries, especially offshore but are not directly targeted.

# STREAKED GURNARD    Chwyrnwr rhesog    *Trigloporus lastoviza*

**Other names:** *Chelidonichthys lastoviza (synonym)*                    **40cm**

**KEY IDENTIFICATION FEATURES** It is likely to be difficult to identify this gurnard in the field with any degree of certainty as it looks very much like a dull Red Gurnard and has pectoral fins coloured similarly to Tub Gurnard. However, a good close-up photograph should allow later identification. The reason for its name is a series of skin ridges running down the body from the lateral line to the belly. This is easy to see in dead fish but not easy underwater. The head profile is very steep, much more so than in the other species and this should be obvious underwater. Most references describe the pectoral fins as having a series of large blue spots but not all fish have these. Like Tub Gurnard, it has long pectoral fins.

**SIMILAR SPECIES** Annoyingly Streaked Gurnard often have a blue edge to their pectoral fins like that in Tub Gurnard and there is probably considerable confusion over these two species in the field. Only a really close look or photograph will show the skin ridges characteristic of this species.

**BEHAVIOUR** This is mainly a summer migrant to the British Isles.

**HABITAT** Streaked gurnard can be found in depths from 10–150m but seems to prefer water deeper than about 40m. Not a lot is known of its habitat requirements but it has been found on sediment and in areas of mixed sediment and rock.

**DISTRIBUTION** This is an uncommon gurnard that is on the edge of its northern distribution in the British Isles. It has been recorded occasionally in Welsh waters and more often in the English Channel. It extends north up the Atlantic coast of the British Isles to Scotland and may reach southern Norway but is rare anywhere north of the English Channel. In the south it extends into the Mediterranean and a subspecies is found in South Africa.

**NATURAL HISTORY** Streaked Gurnard are thought to feed only on crustaceans

**SIGHTINGS** As this gurnard is rare north of the Channel, all records would be of great interest. This species could become more common in Welsh waters if water temperatures continue to rise and photographs of any gurnard that doesn't quite fit the descriptions for other species should be carefully reviewed. Good photographs or a specimen would be needed to be sure of the record.

# LONGFIN GURNARD    Chwyrnwr asgell hir  *Chelidonichthys obscurus*

**Other names:** *Aspitrigla obsucura* (synonym)                                    **36cm**

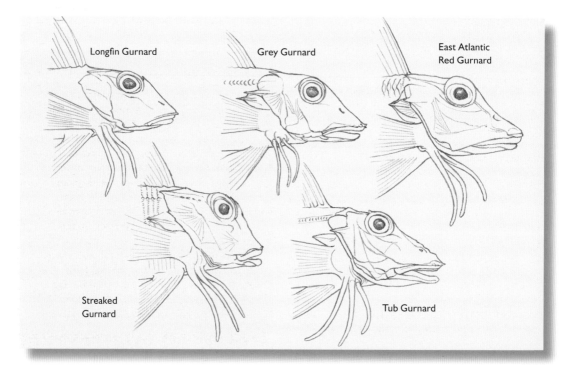

There are no records of this gurnard from Welsh waters and it is a rare visitor even as far north as the western English Channel. It is however, worth looking out for as water temperatures continue to increase. It can be identified relatively easily because the second ray of the first dorsal fin is twice as long as all the others. This can be clearly seen when the fins are partially or fully erect – not the case in the photograph shown here – but look closely and you can still see it as a filament lying along the body.

Longfin Gurnard

Grey Gurnard

East Atlantic
Red Gurnard

Streaked
Gurnard

Tub Gurnard

# FLYING GURNARD          Chwynwr hedegog          *Dactylopterus volitans*

**50cm**

**KEY IDENTIFICATION FEATURES** If you see one of these fish you will not mistake it for anything else! Its huge fan-like pectoral fins are obvious even when folded back and have a regular pattern of bright blue spots. It has a blunt head with a steep profile similar to true gurnards and a flat-topped back. Of the two dorsal fins, the first is shorter and has two free rays at the front.

**SIMILAR SPECIES** This is the only species found in Europe, although other similar species are found in the Indo-Pacific. Flying fish are fast open water fish and do not rest on the seabed like Flying Gurnard.

**BEHAVIOUR** Contrary to the popular belief that results from their name, Flying Gurnard do not glide through the air as Flying fish do. But they do 'fly' through the water. When the fish is moving slowly around or resting on the bottom, the pectoral fins are kept folded back. If a diver disturbs the fish then it will often unfold its fins and take off through the water, as shown here. Such a display may intimidate and confuse potential predators.

**HABITAT** Like the true gurnards, Flying Gurnard live on the seabed in sandy and muddy areas and areas of mixed sediment and rock. They are a coastal, inshore species that can be found as deep as 100m but more usually between about 10–30m, at least in the Mediterranean.

**DISTRIBUTION** This is a southern species that has not yet been recorded in Wales but extends as far north as the English Channel and has been recorded from Cornwall. It extends south to Angola, the Mediterranean and the Azores and is also found in the western Atlantic.

**NATURAL HISTORY** Flying Gurnard feed mainly on crabs and other bottom-living crustaceans and will also eat bivalves and small fish. Like gurnards these fish search out their prey by 'walking' over the seabed, but use their pelvic fins, moving each one alternately. They spawn in the summer.

**SIGHTINGS** If this beautiful fish starts to expand its range with global warming, and moves as far north as Wales, then it is likely to appear first in sheltered warm water areas. Sighting from anywhere in the British Isles are of great interest.

## Fin freedom

The Flying Gurnard is just one amongst many bony fish that have developed their fins in extravagant ways for uses other than just swimming. This is possible either because they have a swim bladder to help keep them up in the water column (see page 78), or because they live down on the seabed and have given up very active swimming. So Flying Gurnard, male dragonets, Butterfly Blennies and many others use their fins to impress potential mates and signal to rivals. Lumpsucker and clingfishes hang on tightly with pelvic fin suckers. Weeverfish and scorpionfish present an array of venomous dorsal fin spines to their enemies. Gurnards both walk and taste with their pectoral fins. These multifarious fin designs help bony fish to live in a huge range of different habitats and at the same time provide us with useful clues as to their identity!

# AGONIDS

FAMILY Agonidae

## HOOKNOSE                    Penbwl môr                    *Agonus cataphractus*

**Other names: Armed Bullhead, Pogge**                                    **21cm**

**KEY IDENTIFICATION FEATURES** This fish can be identified in the field with a high degree of certainty. It has a very distinctive, large head with numerous catfish-like barbels on the underside and around the mouth. Its body tapers to a long thin, angular tail that looks rather like the rear end of a pipefish. Even if this is the only bit showing, its angular shape and alternate light and dark bands should give the game away. The body and head are both armoured with hard bony plates, and spines on the gill covers and snout give further protection. There are two short dorsal fins.

**SIMILAR SPECIES** In general body shape, Hooknose could initially be mistaken for one of the two species of sea scorpions but a closer look at the head with its numerous chin barbels will soon dispel that idea.

**BEHAVIOUR** Although a good-sized snack for predatory fish, Hooknose avoid predation by keeping still and relying on their camouflage colours. This means they will often stay still when being observed and photographed by divers. Their bony armour also helps protect them from predators. They search out food using their head barbels.

**HABITAT** Although usually described as preferring sandy and muddy bottoms, divers have photographed these fish on shell gravel, stones, mussel beds and algae-covered maerl beds. They are an inshore fish that will enter sheltered bays, harbours and estuaries but are most common below 20m. Young ones can be found as shallow as 2m especially on offshore sediment banks. They have been recorded down to 270m.

**DISTRIBUTION** This is a relatively common species in Wales and Hooknose are found all round the Welsh coastline and all round the British Isles but no further south than the English Channel. In the north they extend to northern Norway and the White Sea and to Iceland.

**NATURAL HISTORY** Hooknose spawn in spring between about February to April. Females lay batches of yellow eggs amongst seaweeds within the kelp forest and below. Presumably deeper water individuals either migrate inshore or lay their eggs in other types of undergrowth. The eggs are slow to develop and may take 10–12 months to hatch into well-developed larvae. These drift in the plankton and settle on the bottom at around 2cm long.

**SIGHTINGS** This fish is frequently spotted by divers, less often by snorkelers. It also comes up in bottom dredges and shrimp trawls over sediment areas but has no commercial use. It can, however make itself a nuisance on commercial shellfish beds where it eats young individuals.

# LUMPSUCKERS

**FAMILY** Cyclopteridae

## LUMPSUCKER          lâr fôr          *Cyclopterus lumpus*

**60cm**

**KEY IDENTIFICATION FEATURES** With the exception of really young fish, it would be hard to confuse the Lumpsucker with any other fish. Shaped like a rugby ball with fins, it is covered in lumps and bumps that are the ends of rows of bony plates beneath the skin. The pelvic fins are modified to form a strong sucker, which is not usually visible but with which the fish can cling tightly onto rocks. All the fins are large and have thick rays. In adults the first of two dorsal fins is low and almost buried in flesh but in juveniles it is clearly visible as a tall flesh-covered crest. The colour is variable but females are mostly blue-green with males taking on a red to orange colour, especially on the belly, when breeding.

**SIMILAR SPECIES** None similar to adults. Juveniles could be mistaken for small or juvenile Sea snails or even clingfish but are usually green or blue, but can be orange.

**BEHAVIOUR** Male Lumpsuckers are tenacious protectors of their egg clumps, laid between rocks by one or several females. They will stay on duty even when approached by a large diver or when battered by waves and attacked by seabirds in shallow water. Out of the breeding season they stay close to the seabed foraging for crustaceans, worms and fish and are not the most exciting of fish to watch. There is some evidence that some fish may return to the same area each year to spawn.

**HABITAT** These fish live on the bottom in rocky areas from about 5–150m but also down to at least 400m and with one record from more than 800m. They can be found in kelp forests

and amongst seaweeds and animal undergrowth in deeper water.

**DISTRIBUTION** Lumpsucker are found all round the Welsh coast and the British Isles and can be locally common. They have a wide distribution in the North Atlantic from Iceland and the Barents Sea to Spain in the east; and from Greenland and Canada to New Jersey, USA in the west.

**NATURAL HISTORY** Lumpsucker move inshore from deeper water between about February to May often into very shallow water or even onto the shore to lay their eggs. Spawning on the shore seems to be more common in Scotland and the north of their range. The male guards and fans the egg masses until they hatch between four to eight weeks later. The larvae may float off but attach themselves to seaweeds after only a few days. The fish return to deeper water for the winter.

**SIGHTINGS** Young Lumpsuckers the size of marbles, appear in rock pools as early as March and can be seen clinging to seaweeds near low water mark and below. They can be found attached to seaweed until about two years old. Immature adults are sometimes caught in pelagic trawls out in the open sea where they hunt planktonic crustaceans and other drifting animals. Mature adults are most often seen by divers during the breeding season in shallow rocky areas and even by swimmers wading at the water's edge. Sometimes large numbers are washed ashore after late winter storms when they are in shallow water ready to breed.

# SEA SNAILS

FAMILY Liparidae

## STRIPED and MONTAGU'S SEA SNAIL
### Môr-falwen & Môr-falwen Montagu
### *Liparis l. liparis* and *L. montagui*

15cm (Striped); 10cm (Montagu's)

Liparis spp.

**KEY IDENTIFICATION FEATURES** Adult sea snails can be recognised in the field with a reasonable degree of certainty but telling the two species apart underwater is more of a challenge. These are soft, slimy fish with a large head and a smoothly tapering body, like an elongated tadpole. Like their close relative, the Lumpsucker, they have a strong sucker on the underside derived from the pelvic fins. There is a single long dorsal and anal fin. Colour is no help in telling the two species apart as both are variable. A close up digital photograph may help, as in Montagu's Sea Snail the dorsal and anal fins stop short of the tail fin. In Striped Sea Snails they are joined to the tail fin. This is not very clear in the young fish shown here. Montagu's rarely grow larger than 6cm.

**SIMILAR SPECIES** Juvenile sea snails could easily be confused with juvenile Lumpsuckers except that the latter have a high first dorsal fin. Small clingfish look similar but have pointed snouts and a single dorsal fin. Tadpole Fish are a similar shape but much larger, with no sucker and different habits.

**BEHAVIOUR** Sea snails spend most of their time clinging to seaweeds and rocks, releasing their hold only to pick off small crustaceans and in the case of the larger Striped Sea Snail, other items such as small fish and worms. A favourite resting place is draped along a kelp stipe.

**HABITAT** Montagu's Sea Snail is primarily a shore fish but is said to occur down to 30m or so. As the two species are easily confused the depth limits may not be accurate. Striped Sea Snail can also be found in shallow rocky areas but not on the shore, and extend down to 150m.

**DISTRIBUTION** Both sea snails are found all round the Welsh coastline and the British Isles and although they can be locally common, neither is recorded very often. These are essentially northern fish not found south of the English Channel. The Striped Sea Snail has a number of subspecies and a wide distribution in the North Atlantic. Montagu's is more restricted but the two species have been widely confused.

**NATURAL HISTORY** Sea snails attach their eggs to seaweeds or other attached growths such as hydroids and bryozoans. When they hatch after a few weeks, the larvae drift in the plankton until they settle on the seabed at around 1cm long. Striped Sea Snail spawn mainly in mid winter whilst Montagu's extend their breeding into spring.

**SIGHTINGS** Only Montagu's Sea snail can be found in rock pools, on the lower shore, where turning over stones and searching seaweeds may be productive. Divers might see either species but usually only by careful searching. Hardy winter divers may have the best chance of spotting Striped Sea Snails which appear to move down into deeper (cooler) water in the summer.

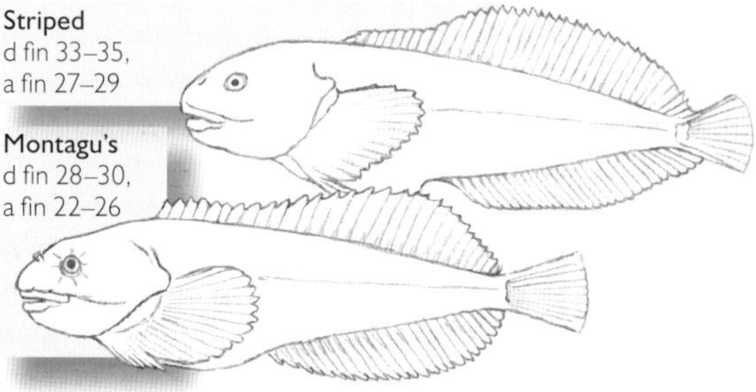

Striped
d fin 33–35,
a fin 27–29

Montagu's
d fin 28–30,
a fin 22–26

# Flatfishes

## RIGHT-EYED FLATFISH

Most right-eyed fish belong to one family called the Pleuronectidae of which there are seven species found in Welsh waters. Soles have a different and distinctive shape and are placed in a different family (Soleidae). Halibut, Witch and Long Rough Dab are deepwater species that are unlikely to be seen by divers but are important commercial species. Plaice, Flounder, Lemon Sole and Dab all have rather deep (appearing wide) bodies, whilst Witch, Long Rough Dab and Halibut are narrow-bodied (though very large in the case of Halibut).

European Plaice

European Plaice

Common Sole

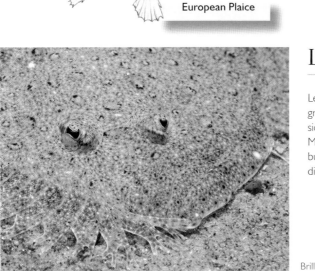

Brill

## LEFT-EYED FLATFISH

Left-eyed flatfish (Scophthalmidae) are a small group of flatfish in which both eyes are on the left side of the head. This family includes Brill, Turbot, Megrim and topknots. Scaldfish are also left-eyed but are covered separately because they in a different but related family (Bothidae).

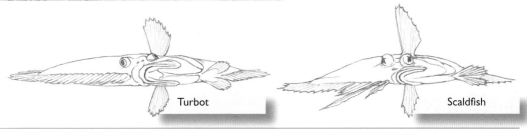

Turbot

Scaldfish

# SCALDFISHES

Scaldfishes (Bothidae) are sometimes referred to as lefteye flounders but this is confusing as they are not flounders. They have their eyes on the left side and are allied to the other left-eyed family of flatfish Scophthalmidae which includes Brill, Megrim and Topknot. When scaldfishes are caught in trawl nets they usually look a little battered as their scales come off very easily – a useful clue as to their identity.

Three species of scaldfishes are found in northern Europe but only Scaldfish are regularly found around Wales. **Thor's Scaldfish**, Lleden Thor, *Arnoglossus thori* is a southern and Mediterranean species that sometimes extends into the Celtic Sea and up past Cornwall along the west coast of Ireland and there are so far no records from around Wales. **Imperial Scaldfish**, Lleden gribog, *Arnoglossus imperialis* is a moderately deepwater fish found between about 60–350m with a southern distribution that extends all round Ireland, through the Irish Sea to west Scotland. There are no confirmed records from around Wales but it is likely to be in deepwater nearby.

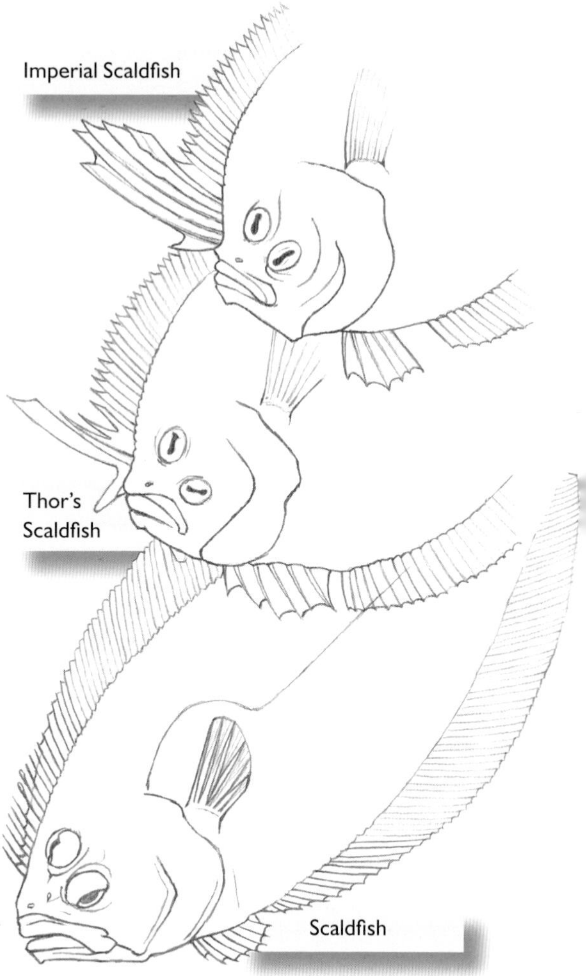

Imperial Scaldfish

Thor's Scaldfish

Scaldfish

Comparison of the head and anterior fins of scaldfish.

All three images on these pages are of Thor's Scaldfish simply because this is the one that we have been able to photograph alive and in the wild, though not in Wales.

# SCALDFISH

## Lleden chwith fach

## *Arnoglossus laterna*

**25cm**

Thor's Scaldfish

**KEY IDENTIFICATION FEATURES** This small flatfish would be quite difficult to identify underwater unless a very close look was possible or a close up photograph taken to look at later. With a fish in the hand it should be relatively straightforward to distinguish from other left-eyed flatfish but a close look is needed. This is a small, slender flatfish that only grows to 25cm long making it the smallest of the left-eyed flatfish except for the rock-living topknots. The dorsal fin begins well in front of the upper eye and the front part looks like a fringe because here the rays are partly free from the fin membrane (this might be difficult to see). The scales are fragile and come off very easily and many will be missing in trawled fish. It is an unremarkable brown colour with darker blotches.

**SIMILAR SPECIES** Imperial Scaldfish are very similar to Scaldfish but have elongated rays at the start of the dorsal fin and are generally found deeper than Scaldfish (below 60m depth). Female Imperial Scaldfish have only slightly elongated rays and so telling the species apart may be difficult. Thor's Scaldfish has a single very elongated ray (the second ray) but this flatfish has not been recorded from Welsh waters.

**BEHAVIOUR** Little specific information.

**HABITAT** Scaldfish are found mainly on sandy seabed in depths of around 10–60m but also down to at least 200m. However this flatfish does not seem to be common within diving depths as it is rarely if ever reported or photographed, but this may be due to it being small and inconspicuous.

**DISTRIBUTION** Welsh waters are well within the global range of this flatfish but it is does not seem to be common here as there are relatively few confirmed records mostly from the north. However this is probably because it is not a commercial species and is under-recorded. It is caught in the south when small mesh beam trawls are used. It occurs all round the British Isles and is especially common in the southern North Sea. Further afield it extends north to southern Norway and south to the Mediterranean and Angola.

**NATURAL HISTORY** Like many other flatfish with a predominantly southern distribution, this one spawns in spring and summer around the British Isles. The larvae drift in the plankton until they are around 16–30mm long, when they settle on the seabed. Few other life history details are available. It feeds on small invertebrates and may itself be an important food for larger commercial fish in areas where it is abundant.

**SIGHTINGS** Rarely reported or photographed by divers. Most records are of trawled fish but this is not a commercial species as it is too small. Many are likely to slip through normal commercial nets. A true reflection of its distribution in Welsh waters is only likely to be obtained from targeted scientific trawls. All new records from Wales of any scaldfishes would be of interest. Scientific surveys sampling the Celtic Sea should look out for Thor's Scaldfish.

Thor's Scaldfish Although it is easy to mistake scaldfishes for topknots, a close scrutiny will reveal that they are not.

# EUROPEAN PLAICE          Lleden goch          *Pleuronectes platessa*

**Other names: Hen-fish**                                    **50cm but 100cm in the past**

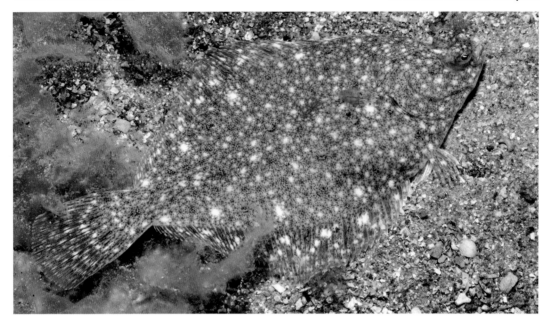

**KEY IDENTIFICATION FEATURES** This common, right-eyed flatfish can be identified in the field with a high degree of certainty. However, reversed left-eyed fish and strangely pigmented individuals can cause confusion. This is a broad flatfish with tall dorsal and anal fins. Most plaice can be recognised instantly from their colour pattern – numerous conspicuous orange or reddish spots on a brown background. There is a row of bony tubercles running between the eyes and the gill covers which can be felt in dead fish. The rest of the body feels smooth.

**SIMILAR SPECIES** Plaice sometimes hybridize with Flounder which can cause confusion!

**BEHAVIOUR:** Plaice are happy to lie around for most of the day, partly covered by sand and will often allow divers to take really close photographs. At night they search actively for food. Like Dab and Lemon Sole, young Plaice are expert in nipping off mollusc siphons that stick above the sediment surface.

**HABITAT** Most plaice are found in sandy areas but they can also be found on muddy and gravelly bottoms. This is an inshore flatfish most common between 10–50m but also found on the shore and down to about 200m depth. Juveniles up to about 4cm long are fairly common in sandy shore pools near low water. Adults will swim over intertidal sand and mud flats at high tide in search of food.

**DISTRIBUTION** Plaice are common throughout Welsh waters. They used to be abundant all round the British Isles but over-fishing has affected many stocks. Their distribution extends north to Greenland, Iceland, Norway and the White Sea and south to Morocco and the western Mediterranean.

**NATURAL HISTORY** Plaice spawn in well defined spawning grounds, and the adults migrate to these areas from their feeding grounds between February and March. The most important spawning areas are in the North Sea but there are smaller spawning areas within Cardigan Bay and in Liverpool Bay. The eggs are laid in fairly shallow water between about 20–40m deep and the young settle in shallow sheltered nursery areas including estuaries. Plaice are long-lived and mature when they are two to seven years old. They can live for 30 years and there are records of 50 year old fish. Most are caught long before this.

**SIGHTINGS** Juveniles can be caught with a push net in the surf zone at low tide on sandy beaches and in sandy pools. This is probably the flatfish seen most often by divers who encounter them in sandy patches between rocks and out on sediment plains or perhaps on the sediment surrounding a shipwreck. This is one of the most important European commercial flatfish. The Irish Sea stock is fished using demersal otter trawls and is currently healthy and harvested sustainably. They are also taken as by-catch by vessels targeting sole. Other stocks are over-fished and there is an EU minimum landing size for Plaice.

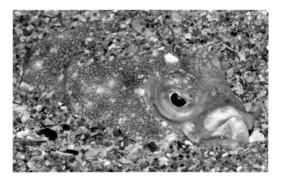

# FLOUNDER

## Lleden fwd

## *Platichthys flesus*

**Other names: Butt** 50cm

**KEY IDENTIFICATION FEATURES** This right-eyed flatfish can be identified in the field with a high degree of certainty especially with dead fish. However, up to 30% of fish may be reversed specimens with the eyes on the left. They also occasionally hybridise with Plaice. Flounder are similar in shape to Plaice but the dorsal and anal fins are very tall in the middle making the fish outline rhomboidal. With dead fish, run your fingers along the base of the long fins which will feel rough due to rows of short prickles. This is especially useful in small fish. Flounder also have a patch of prickles above the pectoral fin on the upper side. Most flounder are an olive-green brown and may have dull red spots. These are not as bright as in Plaice. Flounder can grow to 50cm but 30cm is more usual.

**SIMILAR SPECIES** The most likely confusion is with Plaice especially with not very spotty Plaice. Compare the tail fins – Flounder have square-cut tails whilst Plaice have rounded, convex tails. With dead fish feel the fin bases as described above; Flounder feel rough, whilst Plaice feel smooth. Dab have a distinctive curve in the lateral line, whilst Flounder and Plaice have nearly straight lateral lines.

**BEHAVIOUR** Flounder spend most of the day lying partially buried on the seabed. They are much more active at night and will move close inshore to feed. They will follow the tide in as it rises especially if it is dark at high tide. In winter they move offshore to avoid extremes of temperature.

**HABITAT** Flounder live mostly on rather soft sediment especially on mud and sand. They are tolerant of very brackish water and will swim some distance up rivers. Juveniles live in very shallow water and can be found in sandy and muddy tide pools. Adults range down to about 100m especially in winter. In summer they are found mostly in shallow coastal water and estuaries.

**DISTRIBUTION** Flounder are common in inshore and estuarine waters all round the Welsh coastline. They are also found all round the British Isles, up the coast of Norway to the White Sea and throughout the low-salinity Baltic, the Mediterranean and the Black Sea.

**NATURAL HISTORY** Flounder spawn in spring in the deeper water where they have spent the winter, between about 20–50m. The larvae and young juveniles move inshore and use tides to move upstream in estuaries. Adult flounder first breed between two to four years old and can live for at least 15 years if they are not caught. They eat a range of small invertebrates such as shrimp, worms and small shellfish.

**SIGHTINGS** Juveniles can be caught in push nets in very shallow water on sandy and muddy shores. Adults readily take a bait such as lugworm and are caught by anglers in estuaries and harbours. Divers and snorkelers may come across flounder in shallow bays and sheltered sites. They are not a very important commercial fish and most are taken as by-catch from trawls for other species. A minimum landing size applies to Flounder in some areas covered by this book.

# DAB                    Lleden dywod                    *Limanda limanda*

**Other names: Common Dab**                                                    **40cm**

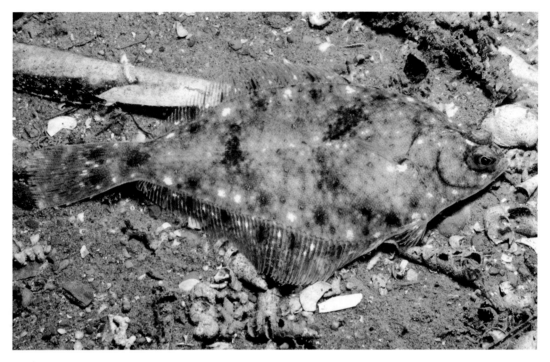

**KEY IDENTIFICATION FEATURES** This right-eyed flatfish can be identified in the field with a high degree of certainty. Dab are relatively small, wide-bodied flatfish similar in shape to Plaice. They are usually under 25cm long but can grow to over 40cm given the chance. The most characteristic feature is the semi-circular curve in the lateral line above the pectoral fin. With dead fish, feel the upper surface which is rough unlike Plaice, Flounder and Lemon Sole which feel smooth. It is usually sand coloured, sometimes with scattered yellowish marks.

**SIMILAR SPECIES** Dab are most likely to be confused with Plaice, especially those Dab individuals which have scattered small yellow spots. However, the semi-circular hump in the lateral line is obvious even in small fish, as long as a close look can be had. Halibut also have a strong curve in the lateral line but confusion with them is unlikely.

**BEHAVIOUR** Dab share with lemon sole the habit of 'pouncing' on invertebrates, especially worms, as they emerge from their burrows. This may be one reason they take anglers' bait so readily.

**HABITAT** Dab live in shallow inshore waters mostly on sand but also on other sediments. Juveniles up to 4cm or so long live in very shallow water and sometimes in sandy shore pools near low water mark. Adults are most common below 20m and extend down to 150m depth. They are tolerant of brackish water and are found in estuaries.

**DISTRIBUTION** This is a common flatfish found all round the Welsh coastline. It is also found all round the British Isles and has a very similar wider distribution to the Lemon Sole.

**NATURAL HISTORY** Dab feed on a very wide variety of bottom-living invertebrates. They also specialize in biting off bivalve siphons when they are extended above the sediment surface. This behaviour has rarely been seen or photographed in the wild but can be inferred from stomach contents. Dab spawn from as early as January through to August, depending on the water temperature and spawning is earliest off southern England.

**SIGHTINGS** Young fish might be caught in push nets at low water on sandy shores and in pools. Divers often see them in sandy patches or out on sediment plains. They are fairly often caught by anglers because they readily take a bait. Dab are a commercial flatfish and are caught by inshore trawlers, but usually as a by-catch, also in seine nets and young ones may come up in shrimp trawls. A minimum landing size applies to Dab in some areas covered by this book.

# LEMON SOLE      Lleden lefn      *Microstomus kitt*

**Other names: Lemon Dab**                                    **70cm**

**KEY IDENTIFICATION FEATURES**   Although incredibly variable in colour, this right-eyed, rock-loving flatfish can be identified in the field with a high degree of certainty. It is a wide-bodied flatfish with a small head in relation to the size of its body and thick, protuberant lips. The dorsal and anal fins reach almost to the tail fin and the lateral line is slightly curved over the pectoral fin. On sediment the colour is often rather drab but on rocks it may be marbled with red, orange, yellow, green, brown or black. There are often a few to many dark rings or part rings, sometimes with bright yellow in the centre. It can grow to 70cm and a weight of 2kg.

**SIMILAR SPECIES**   This is the only right-eyed flatfish regularly found on rock. When on sediment, it is most likely to be confused with the similarly shaped Dab but the latter has a sharp curve in the lateral line and dorsal and anal fins that stop well short of the tail fin (note: tail fin not tail stalk).

**BEHAVIOUR**   In winter, there is a general movement of fish from shallow water into deep water where temperatures are more stable. Lemon Sole have an interesting way of feeding on worms, their favourite food. After locating a likely hole, the fish rears its head up and waits until something emerges before striking down at it.

**HABITAT**   Unlike other right-eyed flatfish, Lemon Sole is at home both in rocky areas and on sand and occasionally mud. It is also happy on shell and shell gravel. This is a coastal flatfish found between about 10–250m depth, sometimes deeper. They are especially common on offshore sediment banks. It is mostly the young fish that live in shallow water and are seen by divers.

**DISTRIBUTION**   Lemon Sole are locally common in inshore waters all round the Welsh coastline. This flatfish is also found all round the British Isles, throughout the North Sea and north to Iceland and the White Sea. It extends south only to the Bay of Biscay.

**NATURAL HISTORY**   The fish spawn in the warmer months between April and September, northern populations spawning later than southern ones. Most spawning is in fairly deep water, around 100m. Once settled on the seabed at around 3cm long, the young fish grow fairly slowly and do not mature until they are three to six years old and around 25cm long. Fish as old as 23 years have been caught.

**SIGHTINGS**   Divers will often sight this flatfish when diving on rocky reefs, though its expert colour camouflage may make it difficult to spot. Anglers are not likely to catch it but it is fished commercially from sediment areas, mainly in trawls and is often caught as by-catch in directed white fish fisheries. A minimum landing size applies to Lemon Sole in some areas covered by this book. Lemon Sole appears on many restaurant menus. It is sometimes seen in public aquaria.

# WITCH                Lleden wrach            *Glyptocephalus cynoglossus*

**Other names: Witch Flounder**                                    **60cm**

**KEY IDENTIFICATION FEATURES** It should be possible to identify caught fish in the field with a high degree of certainty. Divers will see this fish so rarely it will be unfamiliar to most. This is a long, slender right-eyed flatfish that can reach over 60cm long and a weight of 2.5kg, though most are around half this size. It has very large eyes, set close together and a small mouth. The lateral line runs more or less straight with just a small curve above the pectoral fin. Dead fish should be turned over to look for cavities in the skin under the head. These are large pores that produce mucus. It is a fairly uniform pale brown or grey brown with small, scattered black spots. The upper pectoral fin has a black end whilst the one on the underside is wholly black.

**SIMILAR SPECIES** Shape, eyes, mouth and colour should all help to distinguish Witch from other deepwater flatfish.

**BEHAVIOUR** Little information available.

**HABITAT** Witch live in moderately deep, cool water most commonly from around 100–400m on soft mud. Their full depth range extends from as shallow as 20m to over 1500m but they are rarely found in diving depths. They are common in Norwegian fjords and have been photographed there in only 15m depth, probably because of the cool water temperatures this far north.

**DISTRIBUTION** Witch have been recorded from the Bristol Channel and around north Wales and also from the Celtic Sea and NW Irish Sea basin. Records from the shallow Severn Estuary may be strays on power station screens. They probably occur in deep water all round Wales but more records are needed to confirm their distribution and abundance. They are also found round most of the British Isles and from Bay of Biscay to northern Norway, Iceland, Greenland and northern Canada and USA.

**NATURAL HISTORY** Witch spawn in summer between May

and September and the larvae settle onto the seabed in deep water. They feed mainly on small invertebrates including worms, crustaceans and brittlestars.

**SIGHTINGS** This would be a very rare sighting for a diver anywhere and there are no records from divers around Wales. They appear to be rarely caught by anglers but are fished commercially by trawling, often as by-catch with other more valuable species. A minimum landing size applies to Witch in some areas covered by this book. More confirmed records (specimens or photographs) are needed.

# ATLANTIC HALIBUT  Lleden Ffrengig  *Hippoglossus hippoglossus*

**Other names: Halibut**  300cm

Greenland Halibut. If this were a Halibut the eyes would be closer together towards the middle of the head.

**KEY IDENTIFICATION FEATURES** Adults can be identified in the field with a high degree of certainty. Atlantic Halibut are right-eyed flatfish with a long, thickset body, and a very large mouth. The dorsal fin starts beneath the front edge of the nearest eye. Unlike most other flatfish, it has an almost square-cut tail fin. The lateral line makes a strong upward curve above the pectoral fin. Most adults are a dark greenish brown or even almost black. Young fish are often peppered with small light and dark spots.

**SIMILAR SPECIES** Large adults cannot be mistaken for any other flatfish due to their size. Greenland Halibut *Reinhardtius hippoglossoides* have a northern distribution and have not been recorded from Welsh waters. Young fish could be confused with Long Rough Dab *Hippoglossoides platessoides* which is the only other Atlantic right-eyed flatfish to have a very large mouth. However, Long Rough Dab have a convex tail fin and only a very slight curve in the lateral line.

**BEHAVIOUR** Unlike most flatfish, halibut do not spend all their time on the seabed but swim up into mid-water to hunt a very wide variety of fish, squid and prawns.

**HABITAT** Halibut live in moderately deep cool water and are most common from around 100–2000m depth. However, young halibut live closer inshore and can be found as shallow as 10m. Mature males live the deepest, on the edge of the Continental Shelf, whilst females and adolescent young are common on offshore sand banks. They are found on a wide range of sediment seabed from sand to gravel and also on rocky grounds.

**DISTRIBUTION** Halibut have been over exploited and are now very rare around Wales, Britain and Ireland which is the southern end of its range. It extends north from the Bay of Biscay up the Atlantic coast of the British Isles to Iceland, and the Barents Sea. It is also found around the south of Greenland and north-east Canada and USA.

**NATURAL HISTORY** Atlantic Halibut spawn in late winter or early spring in deep water near the edge of the Continental Shelf. The eggs float to the surface and larval fish drift inshore and settle on the seabed when they are 4–7cm long. The young stay near the coast for up to four years, gradually moving offshore into deep water. They do not breed until they are 12–13 years old, but fish up to 50 years old have been caught in the past.

**SIGHTINGS** The rarity of this fish in Welsh waters due to widespread over-fishing means sightings are few and far between. Only young fish are likely to be seen by divers but as the fish feeds in mid-water it will take an angler's bait. It is a highly-prized commercial fish caught mainly on lines but as numbers are so low it is now of minor importance for fisheries. It is listed as 'Endangered' in the IUCN Red Data List. Attempts are being made to rear these fish in captivity (but not in Wales) and they are sometimes kept in public aquaria. All new records from the wild are of great interest.

## LONG ROUGH DAB  Lleden gennog
*Hippoglossoides platessoides*

With its large mouth and relatively narrow body, Long Rough Dab, also known as American Plaice, looks similar to small Halibut. Adults only grow to about 35cm in Welsh waters, the length of a two or three year old Halibut. A close look will show the tail fin has a convex, rounded outline rather then a straight-cut one and the lateral line has only a slight curve. It also has rough skin on the eyed side, hence the common name. Long Rough Dab have been recorded from North Wales but very little reliable information is available and more photographs or specimens are needed. It has a similar northern geographical range to Halibut. The usual depth range is between 40–250m and in the north they often come up in by-catch from shrimp trawls.

# MEGRIM             Lleden Fair    *Lepidorhombus wiffiagonis*

**Other names: Sail-Fluke**                                              **60cm**

**KEY IDENTIFICATION FEATURES** This left-eyed flatfish can be identified in the field with a high degree of certainty. It is a long, but slender flatfish that grows up to about 60cm. It has a large and prominent mouth and large, close-set eyes with a narrow bony ridge between them. The dorsal and anal fins are taller along the rear half of the body and the ends just curl round the base of the tail stalk. The lateral line curves almost vertically down behind the pectoral fin and then runs very straight along the body. The colour is a pale brown with lighter and darker blotches and sometimes darker rings. The underside is usually very white.

**SIMILAR SPECIES** Four-spot Megrim *Lepidorhombus boscii* are very similar but have two round black blotches on both the dorsal and anal fins near the rear, the second one being less clear. There are no records of this fish in Welsh waters; it might occur as a rare vagrant in deeper parts of the Celtic Sea.

**BEHAVIOUR** Little information available.

**HABITAT** Megrim seem to prefer muddy seabed but are also found in sandy areas. They live in fairly deep water usually below 50m and down as far as 700m. Very occasionally they are found in shallow water and near coasts, for example in deep sea lochs.

**DISTRIBUTION** There are confirmed records of Megrim from around most of the Welsh coast. It also occurs around most of the British Isles except the southern North Sea and as far north as Iceland and northern Norway. It extends south to the western Mediterranean and Western Sahara.

**NATURAL HISTORY** Megrim spawn in deep water in spring and the larvae float and develop in the plankton, settling on the seabed when they are about 19mm long. With their large mouths they are able to feed on a wide variety of small bottom-living fish such as gobies, dragonets and scaldfishes. They also eat crustaceans and other invertebrates including, when they can catch them, squid.

**SIGHTINGS** Megrim are sometimes spotted and photographed by divers but live mostly below normal diving limits. They are a relatively important commercial flatfish, caught by offshore trawling. A minimum size limit applies to landings within the area covered by this book. More records are needed to clarify its distribution in Welsh waters.

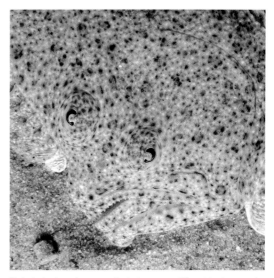

Turbot also have large mouths but are very different in shape and colour.

# TURBOT                    Lleden chwith                    *Psetta maxima*

**Other names: Breet, *Scophthalmus maxima* (synonym)**                    100cm

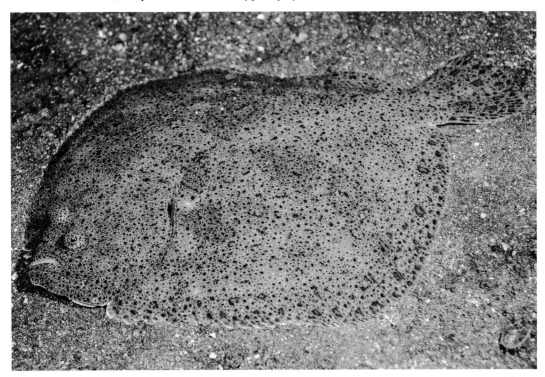

**KEY IDENTIFICATION FEATURES**  Turbot are left-eyed and can be identified in the field with a high degree of certainty. Underwater buried fish may need the sand wafting gently off them to confirm identification. These large flatfish are almost circular in outline and normally grow to around 50–80cm long but can reach 1m, larger than any other Welsh flatfish though Brill reach a similar size. Large bony tubercles are scattered over the body and can easily be felt in dead fish. These help protect the fishes' skin which has no scales. Colour is variable according to background but is generally sandy with many darker spots and blotches and often tiny white spots. There is a distinct hump in the lateral line just above the operculum and this may help when identifying juveniles and small fish (Brill have a similar hump).

**SIMILAR SPECIES**  Brill are similar in shape, size and colour – see Brill see page 154.

**BEHAVIOUR**  Turbot, like Brill, are camouflage experts and spend much of their time lying still on the seabed and so can be quite hard to spot. They will often partially bury themselves in sand and divers need to look carefully for sand hummocks with eyes!

**HABITAT**  Turbot live in shallow inshore areas from the shoreline down to about 80m on sand, gravel and shell grounds. Large adults tend to be found away from the shoreline and in some places occur in quite rocky areas. Juveniles up to about 5cm long can be found living in sandy shore pools in southern parts of their range including south and south-west England and Ireland. Turbot are tolerant of brackish water and so can be caught in estuaries.

**DISTRIBUTION**  Turbot are found throughout Welsh waters both inshore and for some distance offshore. They are found all round the British Isles but are commonest in the south (when not over-fished), in the Irish Sea and English Channel. They have a similar wider distribution to Brill but extend further north into the Arctic Circle. However this is also essentially a southern species and extends south to Morocco and throughout the Mediterranean and most of the Baltic Sea.

**NATURAL HISTORY**  Large females move up into shallow water of about 10–20m to spawn between April and August. The larval fish drift in the plankton for anything up to six months, finally settling on the seabed when around 2.5cm long. During this time they may disperse widely from where they were spawned. Each female can lay 10-15 million eggs which helps compensate for the huge losses during the long larval phase. Turbot have a voracious appetite for other bottom-living fish including sand eels, gobies, dragonets and even other flatfish and also eat crustaceans and shellfish.

**SIGHTINGS**  Juveniles can be caught, along with Brill, in push nets along the surf line on sandy shores and in pools, especially near low water. This does not seem to be the case in the north of their range and it would be useful to know how common they are in Welsh intertidal areas. Divers might find turbot in areas of mixed sand and rock as well as on sediment. Turbot are a very important commercial flatfish caught on lines, in trawls and seine nets. A minimum size limit applies to landings within some areas covered by this book.

# BRILL

## Lleden fannog

### *Scophthalmus rhombus*

**75cm**

**KEY IDENTIFICATION FEATURES** Brill are left-eyed and can be identified in the field with a high degree of certainty. They are one of the largest flatfish (the other being Turbot) found in Welsh waters and can grow to 75cm long though a 50cm fish is a more normal maximum. Brill have a much more rounded outline than most other flatfish, almost the shape of a dinner plate. A close look will show that the first few rays of the dorsal fin are branched and partly free from the fin membrane. The basic colour is brown or olive brown freckled with darker and lighter spots and larger yellowish patches.

**SIMILAR SPECIES** The Turbot is very similar in shape and colour, but remember that 'Brill has a frill'; branching, partially free rays at the front end of the dorsal fin. In dead fish it might be necessary to spread the dorsal fin out to see this. Also with dead fish, feel for bony tubercles on the back; if they are present then it is a Turbot not a Brill.

**BEHAVIOUR** Divers often find they can take close up photographs of a Brills' head without it moving at all. Brill have a superb ability to change the colour pattern of their upper side to match that of the sediment they are lying on. They rely on this camouflage to avoid detection, and so keep very still and the problem for a diver is spotting them at all!

**HABITAT** Divers should look for Brill in sandy areas between about 10–50m deep, though these flatfish are also found on gravel and mud. Juveniles and young adults live in shallow water and tiny ones up to about 4cm long, are common in sandy pools on the shore near low water mark. Adults will also enter estuaries as they can tolerate brackish water.

**DISTRIBUTION** Brill are found throughout Welsh waters both inshore and offshore. They are also common all round the British Isles and as far north as Denmark and mid-Norway. This flatfish is much rarer in the north of its range because it is essentially a southern species, distributed south to Morocco and throughout the Mediterranean.

**NATURAL HISTORY** The fish spawn mostly between May and June in relatively shallow water between about 10-20m. The females are quite large before they first spawn, at a length of around 25-30cm long and this is reflected in minimum landing size limits. Each female can lay around 1 million eggs which float and hatch in the plankton. These large flatfish eat a wide variety of other fish including Sprat, sand eels, Whiting and Haddock, as well as numerous invertebrates.

**SIGHTINGS** Juvenile fish can be caught in push nets in the surf line on sandy shores at low tide and in sandy pools especially in late summer. Sharp-eyed divers are often able to spot Brill and take close-up photographs because the fish rely on their superb camouflage and often stay perfectly still. Brill are a popular sport fish and are also sometimes caught incidentally by anglers. They are fished commercially by trawlers and are sometimes caught as by-catch in seine nets. A minimum size limit applies to landings within some areas covered by this book.

# TOPKNOT
## Lleden benclwm    *Zeugopterus punctatus*

**Other names: Bastard Brill**                                    25cm

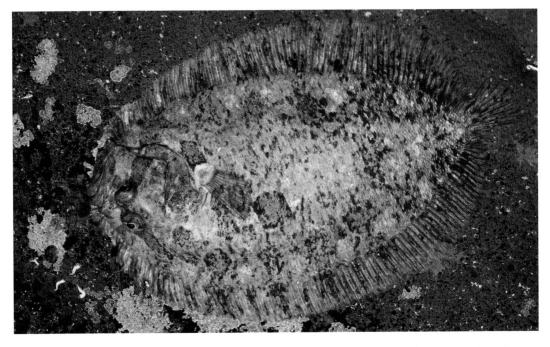

**KEY IDENTIFICATION FEATURES** This left-eyed flatfish can be identified in the field with a high degree of certainty. Although colour is not usually a good guide to flatfish identity, Topknot have two distinctive curved dark lines that run from the side of the head one to each eye, plus a dark blotch behind the pectoral fin near the centre line. It has a broad body, large head and steeply angled, almost vertical mouth. The dorsal fin runs right up to the upper lip and both the dorsal and anal fins run right up to and slightly under the tail where they form a distinct lobe (as they do in the other two topknot species). If a fish has been caught then feel the skin on the upper side which has slightly rough, spiny scales.

**SIMILAR SPECIES** Topknot can be distinguished from other topknots and other flatfish by the colour pattern.

**BEHAVIOUR** Topknots cling to the underside of boulders and onto vertical surfaces in crevices and upside down under overhangs and so can be difficult to spot. They will also cling to encrusting sponges and kelp holdfasts.

**HABITAT** These are one of the few flatfish to live in rocky areas rather than on sediment. They are mainly found within the seaweed zone but extend down to around 40m. Young fish and sometimes adults can be found in rock pools low on the shore especially in sublittoral fringe kelp areas. The only other Welsh flatfish habitually found on rock are the two other species of topknots, though Lemon Sole and Turbot are sometimes found in rocky or rough grounds.

**DISTRIBUTION** Topknots are rather uncommon but are found in shallow inshore areas all round the Welsh coastline. They are also found all round Britain and Ireland but are scarce or absent in south-east England due to lack of suitable habitat. They extend north to northern Norway and south to the Bay of Biscay.

**NATURAL HISTORY** The biology of this flatfish is not well known as it has no commercial value. It feeds on small invertebrates and fish. Spawning in the western Channel, and probably also in Welsh waters, is in spring from February to May.

**SIGHTINGS** In the south of their range (English Channel and Atlantic coasts) small Topknot can be found in rock pools but only by a really careful search under and between rocks. It would be useful to know if Topknot occur regularly in Welsh rock pools. Divers see these fish when they are out in the open hunting for food and they are occasionally caught by anglers and are quite tasty. They are sometimes kept in public aquaria.

# ECKSTOM'S TOPKNOT    Lleden benglwm Eckström    *Zeugopterus regius*

**Other names: Bloch's Topknot, *Phrynorhombus regius* (synonym)**      **20cm**

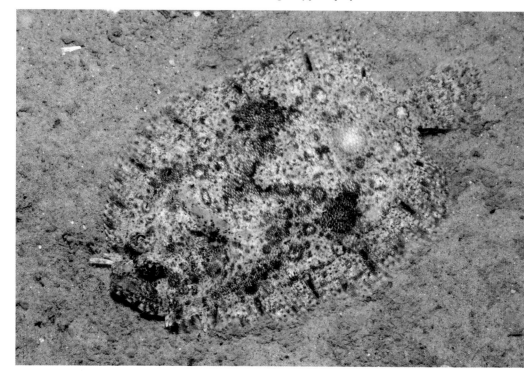

**KEY IDENTIFICATION FEATURES** Whilst this topknot has often been wrongly identified and so is little known and under-recorded, it can be identified in the field if a close look is taken. It is similar in shape to the Topknot but with a different colour pattern. The authors' observations suggest that it has an inverted 'V' marking (looking towards the head from the tail) flanked by three spots, one large one often with a yellow centre below and two above the 'V' as in the photos. The colour of the body and the spots is very variable though and it is probable that the markings fade rapidly on the death of the fish. This would explain why the distinctive V-mark is not mentioned in books and papers where dead fish have been used for descriptive purposes.

**SIMILAR SPECIES** With dead fish Eckstom's can still be distinguished from other topknots by looking closely at the head. It has a distinct notch in the snout just in front of its eyes. Some fish have an elongated first dorsal fin ray but this may be restricted to males in the breeding season and more photographs and records are needed to establish this.

**BEHAVIOUR** Little information is available and more observations are needed from divers.

**HABITAT** Eckstrom's Topknot certainly occurs and has been photographed on rocks, but in the authors' experience, in Wales at least it is more usually seen on softer muddy/sandy sea-beds, as shown here. It lives mainly below 10m and at least in the Mediterranean, down to 300m.

**DISTRIBUTION** This topknot does occur around the Welsh coastline but there are few confirmed records. It extends from west coast British Isles south to Morocco and the Mediterranean.

**NATURAL HISTORY** Little is known of the biology of this elusive topknot. It spawns in spring and summer and the eggs and larvae drift with the plankton.

**SIGHTING** Eckstrom's Topknot can be spotted by sharp-eyed divers on both rock and sediment. In sediment areas it may be trawled up with other flatfish. All Welsh records and especially photos of the colour patterns and head are of interest.

# NORWEGIAN TOPKNOT

## Lleden benclwm Norwy
### *Phynorhombus norvegicus*

**12cm**

**KEY IDENTIFICATION FEATURES** With practise this left-eyed flatfish should be recognised in the field with a high degree of certainty but a close look is needed. It is slim and oval in outline and is the smallest Welsh flatfish only growing to around 12cm long. It is also the most colourful as it matches the red and pink calcareous algae and encrusting animal growths covering the rocks it lives on. It has noticeably large scales and in dead fish these feel rough on both sides.

**SIMILAR SPECIES** The most likely confusion is with Topknot and Eckstom's Topknot which live in similar habitat. It might be tempting to dismiss Norwegian Topknot as a small Topknot but colour and shape should distinguish them. If a really close look is possible (such as in good, close photos) then look at the front of the dorsal fin. In Topknot it extends right up to the lips whereas in Norwegian and Eckstom's Topknots, it begins further back near the eyes. Lemon Sole are also colourful and can be found amongst rocks but are right-eyed.

**BEHAVIOUR** Like Topknots, this flatfish can cling to rocks using the suction of its flat body. It relies on its camouflage colours for protection and will often keep still while being photographed.

**HABITAT** This small flatfish lives on rocks and rough ground between about 10–180m and is most common between 20–50m.

**DISTRIBUTION:** Norwegian Topknot are recorded less frequently than Topknot in Welsh waters. Most confirmed records are from around North Wales but it probably occurs all round the Welsh coastline in small numbers. This is a northern flatfish that extends all round Ireland, up the west coast of Britain to Iceland and northern Norway. They appear to be absent or scarce on east coast Britain due to lack of suitable habitat. They extend south only to northern Bay of Biscay.

**NATURAL HISTORY** Not a lot is known about these elusive small flatfish, mainly because they are not easy to find or catch. They spawn in April to August depending on locality (water temperature) and feed on small invertebrates, and fish larvae and eggs.

**SIGHTINGS** Divers do not often record seeing these flatfish but that may be because they are mistaken for Topknot or Lemon Sole and because of their small size and hideaway tendencies. More records are needed from around Wales to clarify the distribution and abundance of this delightful flatfish. They are not found on the shore and are rarely caught by anglers or in nets.

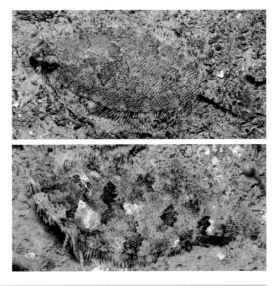

# GET ON TOP OF TOPKNOTS

As the table and head photographs below show, it is perfectly possible to tell these three fish apart underwater. However, time is often short when diving and it is much easier to make notes and photograph the fish for later analysis. The table summarises the features you need to record to make a definitive identification. All of these except the general body shape and size can be encapsulated in a single good shot of the head, although it is always a good idea to get a shot of the whole fish first in case it takes fright and swims away.

Even very small juvenile topknots can be very colourful – this one is only about 1cm long.

|  | TOPKNOT | NORWEGIAN | ECKSTOM'S |
|---|---|---|---|
| Broad-bodied | Yes | No | Yes |
| Slim oval | No | Yes | No |
| Dorsal fin starts on upper lip | Yes | No | No |
| Dorsal and anal fins extend under tail | Yes | Yes | Yes |
| Large very obvious scales | No | Yes | No |
| Notch in snout in front of upper eye | No | No | Yes |
| First ray of dorsal fin elongate | No | No | Sometimes |
| Distinct dark blotch on side | Yes | No | Yes |
| Dark lines running to the eyes | Yes | No | No |

TOPKNOT

NORWEGIAN

ECKSTOM'S

# SOLES

Soles are a family (Soleidae) of right-eyed flatfish that are fairly easily identified as such from their slender oval shape and small crescent-moon shaped mouth that is not quite at the end of their snout. In soles the preoperculum is hidden by skin and is not visible. In other flatfish this structure, which is part of the gill flap or operculum, is visible in front of the operculum as a bony ridge, similar in shape but smaller than the main opercular bone. This is a useful feature when deciding if a flatfish is a sole but can only really be used when looking at dead or captive flatfish. In Welsh waters (and in northern European waters in general) there are only four species likely to be seen and all these are described here. Sole can be identified as such in the field with a high degree of certainty but telling the different species apart requires careful examination and may be difficult underwater.

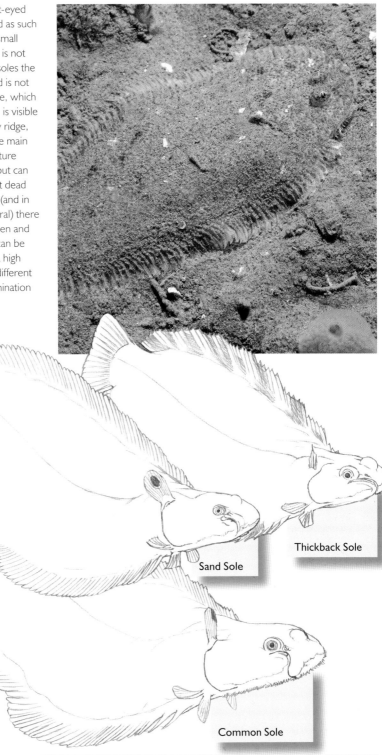

Sand Sole

Thickback Sole

Solenette

Common Sole

Common Sole, note it's 'designer stubble' fringing it's head.

# HOW TO SORT YOUR (CAUGHT) SOLES

This table summarises differences between the four soles found in Welsh waters that should help in telling them apart. Whilst some of the features might be visible underwater, this is mainly designed to help with caught specimens. Even then, patience and a hand lens will be needed and close up photographs of both sides should be taken for later examination.

| | SOLE<br>*Solea solea* | SOLENETTE<br>*Buglossidium luteum* | THICKBACK SOLE<br>*Microchirus variegatus* | SAND SOLE<br>*Pegusa lascaris* |
|---|---|---|---|---|
| Dorsal and anal fins | Plain | Striped: every 4th to 6th ray is dark | Dark patches | Plain |
| Pectoral fin on eyed side | Black spot at extremity extending to edge | No mark | No mark | Round dark spot with a pale border in the middle of fin |
| Pectoral fin on blind side | Normal | Vestiginal | Vestiginal | Normal |
| Nostril on blind side | Small and tubular | Small and tubular | Small and tubular | Rosette-shaped, diameter as large as the eye |
| Eyes | Eye length equal or slightly greater than eye-snout distance | Eyes small, < eye-snout | Eyes large, length > snout-eye distance | Eyes small, < eye-snout distance, upper eye slightly in advance |
| Tail base | Dorsal and anal fins overlap the tail fin rays | Dorsal and anal fins overlap the tail fin rays | Dorsal and anal fins clearly separate from tail fin | Dorsal and anal fins overlap the tail fin rays |
| Colour | Very variable as sole are masters of camouflage | | | |

# COMMON SOLE                    Lleden chwithig                    *Solea solea*

**Other names: Dover Sole, Sole**                                    **70cm, usually 30–40cm**

**KEY IDENTIFICATION FEATURES** Common Sole can be identified in the field with a reasonable degree of certainty. They reach a much larger size than the other soles described here and may grow to around 70cm long, although 30–40cm is a more usual size. Look out for small filaments fringing the fishes' head, looking like designer stubble but remember Solenette have this as well. The upper side pectoral fin has a distinct black mark at the tip but the extent of this is variable. The lower side pectoral fin is about the same size as the upper one but is not coloured. Both the dorsal and the anal fins are joined to the tail fin.

**SIMILAR SPECIES** In shallow water: Solenette are similar but much smaller also with filaments around the mouth. Divers should look out for striped dorsal and anal fins. Dead fish can be turned over to see the vestigial pectoral fin on the blind side. In deep water: Sand Sole also have a dark mark on the upper pectoral fin but this is usually in the middle and does not extend to the fin end. Dead fish can be turned over to see the expanded rosette-like anterior nostril which the Common Sole does not have.

**BEHAVIOUR** Sole are mostly inactive during the day and feed under cover of darkness especially at dawn and dusk. At night they may swim up off the seabed and have even been caught at the surface. However on overcast days and in murky water they may also feed during the daytime. Adult sole swim offshore in winter into deeper water and although normally solitary, may concentrate in areas where the water is slightly warmer.

**HABITAT** This is a fish of sandy and muddy bottoms down to around 150m (remains shallower in summer). It prefers areas of muddy sand and fine sand as this is where ragworms – its favourite food – are abundant. Young fish can be found in very shallow water and on sandy shores in the surf zone as well as in sandy pools near low water mark.

**DISTRIBUTION** This and Solenette are the commonest of the four soles found in Welsh waters. It occurs throughout Welsh waters both inshore and offshore and is also found all round the British Isles, throughout the North Sea and as far north as southern Norway. It extends south to Senegal and throughout most of the Mediterranean.

**NATURAL HISTORY** Sole spawn near the seabed in early summer between about April to June in Welsh waters. There have been local spawning grounds in the outer southern part of Cardigan Bay, in the outer parts of the Bristol Channel and in the Irish Sea between Anglesey and the Isle of Man and the mainland. Young sole up to around two years old remain in shallow inshore nursery areas including estuaries. The coasts along the inner Bristol Channel and along north Wales are important nursery coasts.

**SIGHTINGS** Young sole can easily be caught in push nets along the edge of the sea on sandy shores at low tide. Divers may spot adults partially buried in sandy patches in areas of mixed sand and rock or even lying on stones and shells. This is a very important commercial flatfish and is heavily exploited. Traditionally main fishing areas in Welsh waters have been along the Pembrokeshire coast and throughout the Bristol Channel. It is caught by bottom trawls such as otter trawls and specially designed twin trawls. They are also caught using gill nets in the English Channel. A minimum landing size applies to Sole in some areas covered by this book. Stocks in the Celtic Sea are considered healthy but fishing pressure is high. The Marine Stewardship Council has certified Dover Sole from the Hastings Fleet trammel net fishery in the Eastern Channel as an environmentally responsible fishery.

# SOLENETTE

**Lleden felen fach**    *Buglossidium luteum*

**Other names: Yellow Sole, Lambs Tongue Sole (by commercial fishermen)**    15cm

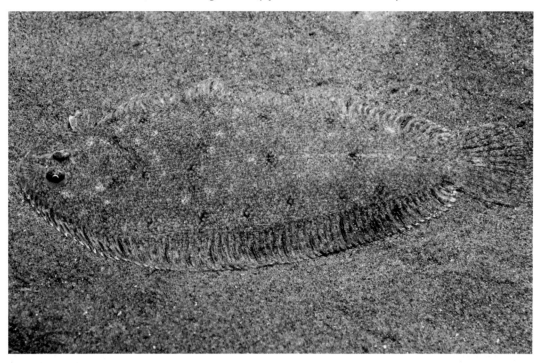

**KEY IDENTIFICATION FEATURES** Solenette can be identified with a reasonable degree of certainty in the field. This is the smallest Welsh sole and adults only reach around 15cm long. For divers the main feature to look at is the fins. Every fifth or sixth ray of the dorsal and anal fin is black and this gives the fins a striped appearance. Dead fish should be turned over to examine the pectoral fin on the underside. This is tiny and vestigial with only one long ray and two smaller ones.

**SIMILAR SPECIES** Young Common Sole might be mistaken for Solenette but the majority of young sole live in very shallow water and they do not have striped dorsal and anal fins.

**BEHAVIOUR** Like Common Sole, Solenette spend much of the day lying quietly on the sand and can be very difficult to spot. When they do move, they seem almost to glide over the seabed. At night they are more active as they search for small invertebrates to eat.

**HABITAT** Mostly found on sandy seabed offshore, between about 5m and 40m deep but can extend down to around 450m.

**DISTRIBUTION** Solenette are common and can sometimes be abundant throughout Welsh waters. They have a similar wider distribution to Common Sole.

**NATURAL HISTORY** Spawning is in early summer but as this is not a commercial fish, not much is known about where any spawning hot spots might be. The larval fish drift in the plankton and settle onto the seabed when they are around 12mm long.

**SIGHTINGS** Divers often see small soles in shallow sandy areas and these are usually Solenette. However snorkelers rarely see Solenette as they are mostly found in water deeper than 5m

or so and they are not usually caught in push nets for the same reason. This tiny sole has no commercial value and although it may be caught in trawl nets, it is small enough for most to slip through the nets. However they are sometimes found caught up in trash weed if the boats have been trawling over sediment with a lot of seaweed.

## Mimic fish

Partially buried sole lying on the seabed often hold up the upper pectoral fin vertically in the water. The fin has a dark mark at the free end and it is thought that this is an attempt to mimic the venomous dorsal fin of a Weever fish, and so deter predators. Plaice, and perhaps some other flatfish also show this behaviour.

# THICKBACK SOLE        Lleden wadn braff        *Microchirus variegatus*

**Other names: Bastard Sole**                                    **35cm**

**KEY IDENTIFICATION FEATURES**   Caught fish can be identified in the field with a reasonable degree of certainty provided they are examined carefully, looking both at the top and underside. As its name suggests, this sole has a thicker body than a Common Sole. A close look at the tail will show that Thickback Sole have a distinct gap between the end of their dorsal and anal fin and the beginning of the tail fin. The other three species described here have these fins almost touching or joined to the tail fin. The pectoral fin on the blind side is very small and vestigial and the fin on the eyed side is dark all over. Colour is variable but most Thickbacks have five dark brown irregular bands running across their body and onto the dorsal and anal fin which may therefore appear striped.

**SIMILAR SPECIES**   Adults are most likely to be confused with Common Sole when trawled up, but a close look will soon distinguish the two (see 'How to sort your soles page' 160). Young could be mistaken for Solenette especially as both species have striped dorsal and anal fins but again a close look will sort them out. Thickbacks in mixed catches can often be spotted by their broad vertical fin stripes.

**BEHAVIOUR**  Little known.

**HABITAT**   This sole lives on sand and in mixed sand and gravel areas. It is an offshore species and is found mainly in water about 40–90m deep. It is occasionally found as shallow as 20m and as deep as 400m.

**DISTRIBUTION**   Thickback Sole have a more southerly distribution than Common Sole and Solenette. There are confirmed records from the Bristol Channel and Severn Estuary and from around North Wales but it is not a common fish. It extends as far north as Scotland but becomes increasingly rare. It is found throughout the Mediterranean and south to at least Senegal.

**NATURAL HISTORY**   Not much detail is known of the breeding biology of Thickback Sole. In the English Channel they spawn in spring and early summer in deep water around 55–75m. They are fairly long-lived and can reach at least 14 years old.

**SIGHTINGS**   The depth at which this sole lives and its comparative scarcity in Welsh waters mean that it is rarely if ever seen by divers. It is caught in commercial trawls and is good to eat but is only landed in low numbers.

# SAND SOLE        Lleden y tywod        *Pegusa lascaris*

**Other names: *Solea lascaris*, French Sole**                    **40cm**

**KEY IDENTIFICATION FEATURES**   Caught fish can be identified in the field with a reasonable degree of certainty provided they are examined carefully, looking both at the top and underside. On the underside the fish has a large anterior nostril which is shaped like a rosette and has about the same diameter as its eye. Like the Common Sole it has a dark mark on the upper side pectoral fin and this is ringed with white, though this may not always be clear. Sand Sole tend to be more spotty than Common Sole.

**SIMILAR SPECIES**   Most likely to be confused with Common Sole but with dead or captive fish, the rosette-like anterior nostril on the underside should distinguish this sole from the others. Identification would be more difficult underwater but this sole is rarely seen by divers.

**BEHAVIOUR**  Little known.

**HABITAT**   Like the Thickback Sole, this fish lives mainly offshore on muddy and sandy seabed and there have only been a few

records from water as shallow as 10m. The usual depth range is between 30–350m with the fish remaining at the deep end of the range in winter.

**DISTRIBUTION**  Sand Sole are rare in Welsh waters. There are records round the whole Welsh coast but most sightings are from the southern part. They are rarely found further north than the northern Irish Sea but extend south into the Mediterranean and down the coast of Africa possibly as far as the Gulf of Guinea.

**NATURAL HISTORY**   Not a lot is known about how and where this fish feeds and breeds. It spawns in July in the western English Channel and like other sole, the larvae float and disperse in the plankton before settling on the seabed. It eats a wide variety of invertebrates especially crustaceans and molluscs.

**SIGHTINGS**  Diver reports of this fish are few and far between and most records are from trawlers or research ships. It is too scarce to be important commercially but is good to eat.

# TRIGGERFISHES

Family  Balistidae

## GREY TRIGGERFISH          Pysgodyn clicied          *Balistes capriscus*

**Other names: Triggerfish, *Balistes carolinensis* (synonym)**                    **60cm**

**KEY IDENTIFICATION FEATURES** Only one species of triggerfish is found in Welsh waters and it is easy to identify in the field. Grey Triggerfish have a deep, but relatively thin, oval body, a small mouth with rodent-like teeth and rather beady eyes. Look first for the 'trigger'. This is the first dorsal fin which consists of one long, strong spine followed by two short ones. The long spine can be locked upright by a knob on the second spine, like the safety catch on a gun trigger. The second dorsal fin and the anal fin are both tall and floppy and the tail fin has elongated tips. The fish has no functional pelvic fins. Although they can reach 60cm, 40cm is more normal.

**SIMILAR SPECIES** Spotted Oceanic Triggerfish *Canthidermis maculata* is a rare oceanic stray into British waters. It is distinctively spotted.

**BEHAVIOUR** All triggerfish swim in a very characteristic fashion using undulating movements of their second dorsal and the anal fin. When threatened they wedge themselves head first into a crevice and erect and lock their first dorsal fin spine, making it impossible to drag them out (not that you would want to but a predator might).

**HABITAT** In Welsh waters Grey Triggerfish are usually encountered in rocky and stony areas and divers sometimes report congregations of them around rocky reefs or wrecks. They are probably found over a wide variety of seabed types. This fish is happy in the open ocean and can be found drifting in mid ocean often associated with wreckage or mats of seaweed. This is especially the case with young fish.

**DISTRIBUTION** This fish is thought to have become an increasingly numerous and regular visitor to Wales and the south of Britain and Ireland and has been recorded all round the Welsh coastline. In some places such as Mumbles Pier near Swansea, small schools turn up each year. This fish has a wide distribution right across the Atlantic, mostly south of the British Isles but in some cases as far north as Scotland and even Norway. Angling records suggest they move or drift north hitting Cornwall first and then moving along the English Channel and further north.

**NATURAL HISTORY** Female Grey Triggerfish lay their eggs in pits excavated in the seabed and these are guarded aggressively by the male. It is still not certain whether these fish are breeding in British waters. They are only seen in numbers in summer but there are now some records of fish in the English Channel in spring and autumn and also of young fish around 10cm long.

**SIGHTINGS** Divers usually encounter this fish near the seabed where it roots out molluscs and crustaceans. It sometimes turns up in lobster and crab pots having gone in after the bait. They are also regularly caught in small numbers in fishing nets and trawls. Anglers catch them from rocks and piers and they can often be clearly seen and are fed by visitors. They do well in public aquaria. Any records of breeding behaviour and young fish in Welsh waters would be of particular interest.

# PUFFERFISHES

Family Tetradontidae

## OCEANIC PUFFER    Chwyddbysgodyn    *Lagocephalus l. lagocephalus*

**61cm**

**KEY IDENTIFICATION FEATURES**  Even in a deflated condition pufferfish are easy to recognise as such. They are however, extremely rare vagrants and so will be unfamiliar to most people. The Oceanic Pufferfish has a stout body but a rather long tail. The giveaway features are prickly spines all over the belly and plate-like teeth. There is a single tall dorsal and anal fin with soft rays, no pelvic fins and a concave tail fin.

**SIMILAR SPECIES**  In colour they resemble other open water fish with a dark bluish back and white belly and with a fleeting glance on the surface could be mistaken for a mackerel or similar fish. When washed up the identification is obvious. Blunthead Puffer *Sphoeroides pachygaster* has also been recorded from southern Britain. One was caught in a trawl in Cornwall in 2003. This species has no prickles on its belly.

**BEHAVIOUR**  Like other pufferfish, this one can suck in water and inflate itself like a prickly balloon, an effective defence against would-be predators. Again like others in this family, parts of it are highly poisonous to humans. Pufferfish are eaten in Japan as 'fugu' after careful preparation to get rid of the dangerous parts but eating it is a risky business!

**HABITAT**  As its name suggests Oceanic Puffer is a fish of the open ocean that drifts along with ocean currents and has been recorded from near the surface to nearly 500m down.

**DISTRIBUTION**  This fish has an extremely wide distribution in the Atlantic, Pacific and Indian oceans and has been recorded as far north as Orkney, though it is really a tropical and subtropical fish.

**NATURAL HISTORY**  There is not a lot of information available. It is known to eat squid and crustaceans and presumably feeds on anything it can find as it drifts and swims along.

**SIGHTINGS**  Oceanic Pufferfish are occasionally captured in fishing nets or stranded on the shore usually in late summer.

## EATING DANGEROUSLY

Pufferfish, of which there are many tropical species, contain a lethal poison called tetradotoxin which is contained in the skin and internal organs. The flesh, however, is not poisonous and is eaten in Japan as a delicacy called 'fugu'. As tetradotoxin is as deadly as cyanide, eating this dish has been likened to playing Russian roulette! In Japan only specially licensed chefs can prepare the dish but even so a few people die every year from eating it.

# SUNFISHES

Family Molidae

## OCEAN SUNFISH  Pysgodyn haul  *Mola mola*

**Other names: Sunfish**    400cm

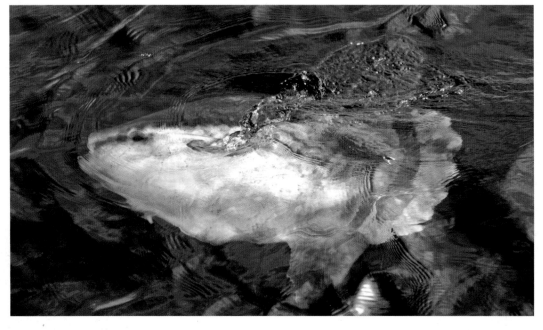

**KEY IDENTIFICATION FEATURES**  This, the world's heaviest bony fish, is unmistakable. Shaped like a huge disc, its body ends, not in a true tail, but in a frill-like structure called the clavus, that is actually derived from extensions of fin rays from the very tall dorsal and anal fin. It has no pelvic fins and a tiny gill opening. Its mouth is small for its huge size, and has fused teeth that look a bit like a bird's beak.

**SIMILAR SPECIES**  The Slender Sunfish *Ranzania laevis* has also been recorded from British waters and the Celtic Sea but sightings are much rarer. It is longer and thinner than the Ocean Sunfish and is marked with sinuous black-edged stripes down the head and across the belly.

**BEHAVIOUR**  Sunfish are sometimes found lying on their side at the water's surface, apparently basking whilst drifting along. Whether this is natural behaviour perhaps related to getting rid of skin parasites or whether these are just sick fish is not known. They swim in a normal upright manner thrusting their dorsal and anal fins from side to side in unison.

**HABITAT**  Sunfish live out in the open ocean and have been found from the surface down to about 500m.

**DISTRIBUTION**  The Ocean Sunfish is a widespread but uncommon fish in all temperate, sub-tropical and tropical oceans. It has been recorded all round Wales but mainly from the southern end where it is closer to the open Atlantic.

**NATURAL HISTORY**  Relatively little is known of this ocean giant but it produces up to 100 million eggs, the most known for any fish. Out at sea it eats jellyfish and salps but probably has a wider diet including crustaceans and algae when in inshore waters.

**SIGHTINGS**  Most sightings are made from boats and are of fish drifting at the surface or just of the dorsal fin sticking above the surface. In some tropical locations, divers see them possibly because they come near to reefs to be cleared of skin parasites by cleaner fish.

# PERCIFORMES

Two-banded Bream *Diplodus vulgaris*; this has now
been recorded from Guernsey (2009).

A vast array of different fishes belong to this, the
largest and most diverse Order of bony fish containing
many Families and nearly 10,000 species (including
freshwater fishes). With an Order such as Flatfishes
(Pleuronectiformes), it is easy to see the similarities
between the different families for example Soles and
Scaldfish – all of them have the same sort of shape and
lifestyle. In contrast most of the features uniting fish
families in the Perciformes are complex and depend
on internal skeletal and other features and in fact some
of the families may not actually be very closely related.
Classification within this group is constantly being revised
as experts work on the various groups within it. This often
results in fish families being moved from this Order into
another, sometimes new Order. All that can be said here is
that most fish in this Order have both spines and soft rays
in their dorsal and anal fins and their pelvic fins are situated
close to their pectoral fins.

Fish from twenty three families within the Perciformes
are described here ranging from gobies to swordfish.

# TEMPERATE BASSES, WRECKFISHES & SEA PERCHES

## Families Moronidae, Polyprionidae and Serranidae

Temperate basses (Moronidae) and wreckfishes (Polyprionidae) are both small families of fish that used to be united in one family (Percichthyidae). They and the sea perches and groupers (Serranidae) all look superficially quite similar and are related. Only one species of temperate bass, the European Seabass and one wreckfish are found in Welsh waters. Sea perches are a large family of mainly tropical and warm temperate fish but only two species the Comber and the Dusky Grouper are found in northern Europe.

These are all solid-looking fish with large heads and mouths and plenty of spines in their dorsal and anal fins. All those described here have a single, long dorsal fin with a spiny front section and a soft rear section, except the European Seabass which has two separate dorsal fins.

European Seabass

# EUROPEAN SEABASS       Draenogyn môr       *Dicentrarchus labrax*

**Other names: Bass**                                                    103cm

**KEY IDENTIFICATION FEATURES** European Seabass can be identified in the field with a high degree of certainty. This is a powerful, streamlined, predatory fish that can disappear almost instantly with a flash of silver. It has a large mouth and two dorsal fins, the first spiny and the second with soft rays. The tail fin is large and concave. The scales too are large and obvious and the curved lateral line is clearly visible. Young fish may have scattered dark spots on the back and sides and some fish have a dark patch on the rear of the gill covers.

**SIMILAR SPECIES** The most likely confusion, at least for a diver, is with grey mullets. These too are silvery, greyish fish with two dorsal fins. But mullet have small mouths and distinct longitudinal stripes.

**BEHAVIOUR** Warm water attracts these fish and there are many records of young fish from Hinkley Power station in the Severn Estuary. They also move offshore in winter to avoid extremes of temperature. Young fish often form schools but large ones are more often solitary. These fish are powerful swimmers and Welsh and UK populations are swelled in summer with fish migrating up from further south.

**HABITAT** Whilst these fish can be caught some distance offshore and down to 100m, they are usually found in the vicinity of inshore rocky reefs. However, young fish especially, will also enter estuaries, and saltmarsh creeks. Young fish up to 40cm or so live close inshore and can be found near the surf zone of sandy beaches.

**DISTRIBUTION** European Seabass are found throughout Welsh waters where they are locally common. They also occur all round the British Isles and extend north to Norway and south to Senegal and throughout the Mediterranean.

**NATURAL HISTORY** The fish spawn in inshore waters and the eggs and larvae drift freely in the plankton. The young fry move close inshore into sheltered bays and estuaries, where they stay for several years. They grow slowly and do not mature until between three to eight years (31–45cm length) the males maturing first. They can live for at least 15 years, sometimes up to 25 years.

**SIGHTINGS** European Seabass is a valuable recreational fish and anglers will perhaps be best acquainted with it. They are seen less often by divers as they are very shy. European Seabass are increasingly caught commercially and are an important part of the local economy in parts of Wales and southern Britain. Line and fixed net fisheries avoid the problems of cetacean by-catch associated with trawled fish, especially pair-trawling – pelagic pair-trawling has recently been banned in UK coastal waters. There is a minimum landing size in EU waters. These fish are also successfully farmed and do well in public aquaria. To protect stocks, Bass nursery areas in certain estuaries are closed to fishing.

# WRECKFISH          Pysgodyn broc môr    *Polyprion americanus*

**Other names: Atlantic Wreckfish**                                    **210cm**

**KEY IDENTIFICATION FEATURES**    If you were lucky enough to encounter an Atlantic wreckfish, you would be able to identify it in the field with a high degree of certainty. This is a heavily-build, solid-looking fish with a very large head and mouth and a protruding lower jaw. It has a single long dorsal fin with a dip in the middle between a spiny front part and a soft rear part. A bony ridge runs across the gill cover and can be clearly seen. Although the fish shown here is very silvery, adults are often much browner and young fish can be blotchy and marbled with white patches and blotches.

**SIMILAR SPECIES**  Atlantic Wreckfish look very similar in shape and size to groupers but these do not have a bony ridge on the gill cover.

**BEHAVIOUR**  Young Atlantic Wreckfish do not seem to be afraid of divers and snorkelers and may treat them as floating debris! Adults are generally solitary fish but drifting young frequently form small schools.

**HABITAT**    Adults live near the seabed and often lurk inside shipwrecks and under overhangs. Juveniles on the other hand often float near the surface and it is their habit of associating with drifting debris and wreckage that has given this fish its name.

**DISTRIBUTION**  This is a rare fish in UK and even rarer in Welsh waters. It has been seen in south Wales. In Ireland it is seen fairly frequently in the summer months. It has a wide global distribution in the Atlantic, Pacific, and Indian oceans and in the Mediterranean.

**NATURAL HISTORY**  Not a lot is known about the lifestyle of this fish. They are known to feed on other fish, crustaceans and molluscs. Young fish presumably eat crustaceans and other animals they can find associated with their floating homes. In the Mediterranean, these fish spawn in the spring and summer.

**SIGHTINGS**  Most encounters are of juvenile fish at the surface, following drifting debris that gets blown into our waters. In warmer waters, snorkelers encounter these fish amongst floating seaweed and debris. Further south, the bottom-living adults are caught by anglers and sometimes in nets and are marketed and eaten.

# DUSKY GROUPER

## *Epinephelus marginatus*

**Other names: Dusky Sea Perch, *E. gauza* (synonym)**

150cm

**KEY IDENTIFICATION FEATURES** Grouper species are quite difficult to tell apart but easy to recognise as such. In our waters, it would be difficult to mistake this fish for anything else. This is a large, solid fish with a smoothly sloping head and thick lips. The front part of the dorsal fin has strong, sharp spines (groupers actually have two dorsal fins joined together to look like one). It is a beautiful brown to orange brown colour with irregular white to cream blotches. On the head these tend to radiate out from the eye whilst on the body they are clumped into rough vertical bands. The fins have pale edges.

**DISTRIBUTION AND HABITAT** This fish is rare north of Biscay and has only very rarely been recorded in British waters, from Cornwall and southern parts. So far it has not been recorded from Welsh waters. It extends throughout the Mediterranean and south to South Africa and Madagascar. This solitary, territorial fish lives in rocky areas where it hides out under overhangs, or in holes and caves. It can be found from 10m to at least 300m depth.

**SIGHTINGS** In the Mediterranean, divers frequently see this fish but it would have to be a very lucky diver indeed to see it in British waters. It might also turn up in trawls or it could be caught by anglers. Catches of this fish in Europe have declined drastically in the last 15 years and it is now listed as 'Endangered' in the IUCN Red List.

# COMBER

## Pysgodych garw bach *Serranus cabrilla*

**Other names: Gaper**

40cm

**KEY IDENTIFICATION FEATURES** Comber is rather like a slimline version of a grouper and they too have a very spiny dorsal fin. This is a colourful fish but one that has variations to its basic pattern according to age and sex. The back and sides are brown with dark vertical bars, though these are often broken, whilst the head has dark stripes that often extend along the sides. The fins are often spotted. At first sight a Comber could be mistaken for a colourful wrasse, though not for any of our five common species. However, it has a concave tail fin, whilst wrasses have a convex one and does not swim using its pectoral fins as a wrasse does.

**DISTRIBUTION AND HABITAT** Comber is a southern species that extends north to the English Channel but is uncommon. It has been recorded on rare occasions from Welsh waters. It is common in the Mediterranean and south to South Africa. It does breed in the English Channel but most fish are visitors from further south. In our waters it is mostly found from 20–50m or so.

**SIGHTINGS** Most sightings are from anglers who sometimes catch this fish over rocky reefs.

# CARANGIDS

## Family Carangidae

Carangid fish form a large family, most of which are found in the tropics or in warm temperate seas such as the Mediterranean. It includes Jacks and Pompanos. Only one species, the Atlantic Horse Mackerel or Scad is a common resident in Welsh waters. At least seven other species are rare visitors to British waters from further south, including Greater Amberjack, and Pilotfish (both with Welsh records), Vadigo and Derbio all briefly described here and Blue Runner *Caranx crysos* for which there is one Welsh record. Most species are fast swimming predators and have a strong forked tail. There are two dorsal fins although the first is often reduced to a few spines, such that the fish appears only to have a single fin. There are two spines in front of and separate from the anal fin.

Greater Amberjacks

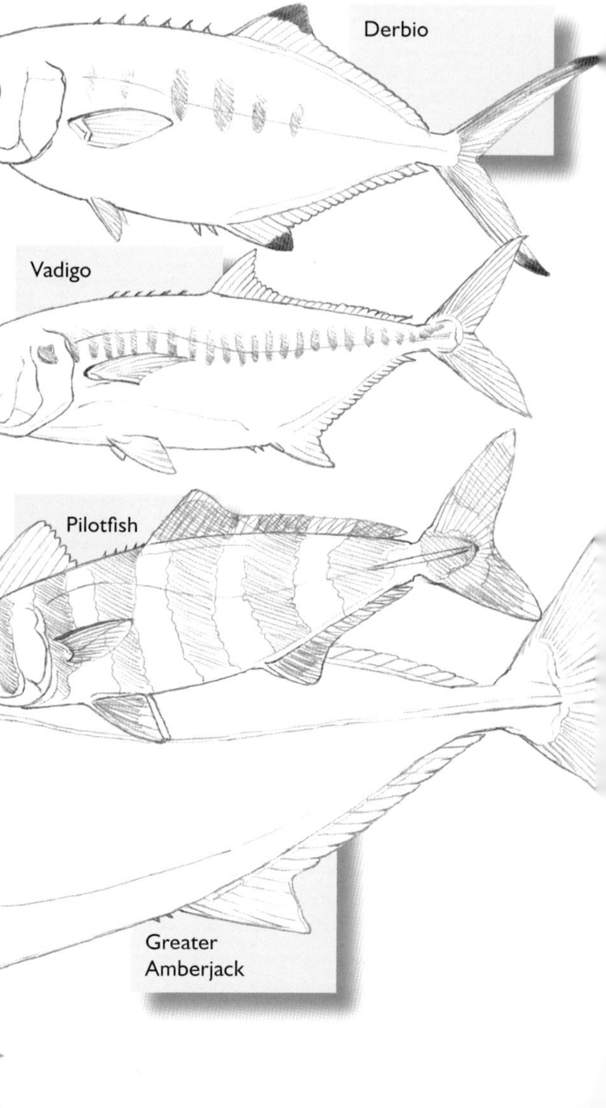

Derbio

Vadigo

Pilotfish

Greater Amberjack

# ATLANTIC HORSE MACKEREL     Marchfacrell     *Trachurus trachurus*

**Other names: Horse Mackerel, Scad**                                    **70cm**

**KEY IDENTIFICATION FEATURES** It is always difficult to identify schools of silvery fish at a distance underwater but with a close look this fish can easily be identified with a high degree of certainty. The most obvious feature is the lateral line which curves sharply down half way along the body and shows up because it is covered by a row of large bony scales or scutes. The first dorsal fin is short and spiny whilst the second is long and is high at the front and lower near the tail. This is mirrored by the anal fin. There is a large black spot on each gill cover. Although a few reach 50–70cm long, most are under 25cm.

**SIMILAR SPECIES** Mackerel or other silvery schooling fish but the lateral line gives the game away.

**BEHAVIOUR** Like many other open water fish, Atlantic Horse Mackerel swim in schools for protection. During the summer the schools move further inshore and feed on rich plankton and can be seen swimming along with their mouths wide open. Large fish will also take smaller schooling fish and squid. In winter they move further offshore into deeper water and feed to some extent on bottom-living invertebrates.

**HABITAT** Schools of Horse Mackerel live in open water, mostly in coastal waters and usually in the top 100m but it can go much deeper.

**DISTRIBUTION** Horse Mackerel are found throughout Welsh waters and all round the British Isles and are relatively common. It has a wide distribution in coastal waters of the East Atlantic from Iceland and Norway, south to South Africa.

**NATURAL HISTORY** Spawning is in spring and summer in open water and the eggs and larvae float freely in the plankton.

**SIGHTINGS** Divers do not often see these fish due to their open water habitat, but sometimes see juveniles sheltering amongst the tentacles of large jellyfish such as the stinging Lionsmane Jellyfish. They are caught in pelagic (mid water) trawl nets mostly as by-catch in Welsh and British waters. The main fishery is in the North Sea by Dutch ships. There is a minimum landing size in EU waters. This is an important food fish for larger commercial fish and for seabirds.

## PILOTFISH                    Llywbysgodyn                *Naucrates ductor*

**70cm**

With its distinctively striped, torpedo-shaped body, white-tipped tail fin lobes and the same fin arrangement as other Carangid fish, Pilotfish are be easy to recognise should anyone be lucky enough to see or catch one. This is a rare vagrant visitor to southern British waters and the only record in Welsh waters is from south Wales. It is however, not surprising that it occasionally turns up as it is an open sea fish with a propensity to follow larger animals and objects such as sharks, turtles, sailing boats and drifting objects. It has a distribution right round the world in a wide swathe in tropical and warm seas and is probably carried north by currents such as the Gulf Stream.

## GREATER AMBERJACK    Seriola mawr           *Seriola dumerili*

**190cm**

This is a large carangid fish with a sloping head and a large mouth. The first dorsal fin is very small with 5-7 spines, the anal fin is shorter than the second dorsal fin and it has a deeply forked, powerful tail. Amberjack occasionally turn up as a rare vagrant in southern parts of the British Isles, usually washed up on the shore. There are a few records from Cornwall, Devon and Ireland and one from Milford Haven in 2006. It has a similar wide distribution to the Pilotfish but although found in open water tends to associate with reefs and islands. Two other similar species *Seriola carpenteri* and *Seriola rivoliana* have also been recorded from southern British waters but not so far from Welsh waters.

## VADIGO
### *Campogramma glaycos*

**60cm**

The Vadigo is a powerful predatory fish similar in shape to Derbio but with a larger mouth that extends beyond the eye. It is a silvery fish with a characteristic pattern of zigzag vertical lines running down from the back to the lateral line. Six small separate spines precede the dorsal fin. This is a very rare vagrant north of Spain that has been recorded from Cornwall but could turn up elsewhere. Its main distribution is the Mediterranean, and south to Senegal including Madeira and the Canary Islands. It lives in shallow, open water down to about 30m.

## DERBIO
### *Trachinotus ovatus*

Other names: Pompano                          **70cm**

Another name for this fish is Pompano. It has a very thin oval body with a small head and mouth and a long, forked tail. Instead of a first dorsal fin it has a row of 5-6 short, separate spines followed by a normal dorsal fin. This is a silvery fish with a row of about five dusky blotches along both sides. The tips of the tail, dorsal and anal fins are black. Derbio are common in the Mediterranean and their distribution extends from West Africa to the English Channel and very occasionally as far north as southern Scandinavia. This is a rare fish in British waters with only about 20 records of dead fish or from anglers in the last 60 years or so. It is an open water fish that lives near the surface down to about 200m both offshore and in coastal waters.

# SEABREAMS

## Family Sparidae

Most seabreams are warm water fish found in the tropics and the Mediterranean but a number are found regularly in Welsh waters and around the British Isles, mainly in the summer when they move further north. Black Seabream are relatively common in Welsh waters in summer. Gilthead bream breed in the English Channel, but probably no further north, though this could change. Twelve other species have been recorded from British waters. These are regular, rare or very rare visitors. Records of all seabreams in Welsh waters are of interest especially when accompanied with photographs or specimens in the case of dead fish.

Seabreams are deep-bodied fish with a single long dorsal fin, spiny at the front and soft at the rear but more or less the same height along its length. The anal fin is similar with three spines at the front and the tail is forked. Although not an easy field identification feature, the teeth differ widely between species according to their diet. With dead or captured fish, try taking a head-on photograph with the lips pulled back to show the teeth, then refer to more detailed texts.

## Juvenile Seabream & the fishing pot

Whilst filming for the television series 'Natur Cymru' we discovered that although primarily designed to capture crustaceans, a fishing pot has other uses. Young Seabream quickly discovered the fresh bait inside this pot, and soon realised that the mesh provided them with a handy refuge into which they could swim and be safe from larger predators. These fish showed territorial behaviour as they constantly chased each other apparently in an effort to exert their authority and attempt to become dominant.

Many species of seabream are common in warmer waters far to the south of Britain where many are shallow water shoaling fish. Records of some of the warmer water species appear to be rising off southern Britain and these may start being seen off the south Welsh coast too.

# BLACK SEABREAM     Merfog du     *Spondyliosoma cantharus*

**Other names: Old Wife**                                                  **60cm**

**KEY IDENTIFICATION FEATURES** This fish can be identified in the field with a high degree of certainty, especially young fish. Its name is slightly misleading as this is really a silvery fish, sometimes with dusky vertical bars. It is the breeding males that are almost black. Young fish can appear rather different with numerous, thin, discontinuous yellow lines along the sides, spots on the fins and a dark edge to the tail fin. It has a small mouth that doesn't quite, or only just reaches the front edge of the eye and a steep, smooth, convex head profile (except in mature males which become 'dented'). The scales are large and easily visible.

**SIMILAR SPECIES** Other species of seabream, but this is by far the most likely to be seen in Wales.

**BEHAVIOUR** The nest building activity of this fish can result in a 'lunar landscape' of excavated sand pits. Males dig the nests with their tails and entice the females to lay their sticky eggs there. They are gregarious and may form large schools.

**HABITAT** Most fish are found in inshore waters but they have been recorded from 5m down to 300m. In British waters they can be found near rocky reefs, cliffs and wrecks but certainly in Dorset have been found in seagrass beds and over sand, the typical habitat in the Mediterranean.

**DISTRIBUTION** Black Seabream have been recorded all round the Welsh coastline albeit infrequently. Records currently seem to be increasing. Around the British Isles it is commonest in the English Channel. Although essentially a southern species it extends north to Norway. It is found in the Mediterranean and south to Namibia.

**NATURAL HISTORY** Young fish stay in and near the nest after hatching, until they are around 7-8cm long. They then tend to move into slightly deeper water.

**SIGHTINGS** Divers see these fish in rocky areas and around wrecks and they are caught locally from similar habitats by anglers. They are trawled up commercially though never in large numbers but further south and in the Mediterranean they are an important food fish.

Juvenile

# GILTHEAD SEABREAM     Merfog eurben          *Sparus aurata*

**Other names: Gilthead**                                          **70cm**

**KEY IDENTIFICATION FEATURES**  The most obvious feature of this large bream is a yellow stripe across the head between the eyes, which at least in large males overlies a bony ridge. It has a dark blotch behind the gill cover at the start of the lateral line and most individuals are grey to yellowish and faintly striped. Colours fade on death. This is a deep-bodied, heavy lipped fish with a steep profile.

**SIMILAR SPECIES**  Common or Couch's Seabream *Pagrus pagrus*, synonym *Sparus pagrusi*, is an extremely rare vagrant in British waters that has not yet been recorded from Welsh waters. However, it has now been found breeding in Devon and Cornwall and could move further north into Wales. It lacks the yellow bar of the Gilthead but instead has a dark band through the eye from top to bottom.

**DISTRIBUTION AND HABITAT**  Gilthead are now relatively common from South Wales to Hastings but are still rare further north. They do, however, appear to be becoming more common and may be breeding off south and south west Ireland where juveniles have been found. In the south they extend into the Mediterranean and south to Senegal. They live in shallow water mostly over sediment, commonly from the surf zone to about 30m but down to 150m.

**SIGHTINGS**  This is the bream that is most often kept in public aquaria, usually as part of North Atlantic fish display tanks and it is also farmed, though not in the UK.

# OTHER VISITING SEABREAMS

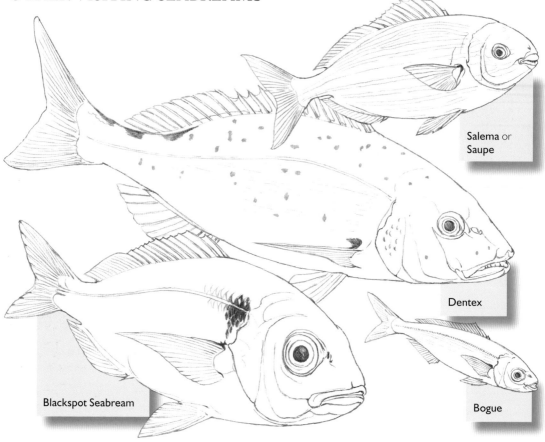

Salema or Saupe

Dentex

Blackspot Seabream

Bogue

# BLACKSPOT SEABREAM     Merfog coch     *Pagellus bogaraveo*

**Other names: Red Seabream**     **70cm**

**KEY IDENTIFICATION FEATURES**    Although rarely seen adults of this seabream can be identified in the field with a reasonable degree of certainty. The two common names indicate its usual red to orange colour, with a large black spot just above the pectoral fin base. It has a large eye, and long pectoral fins. Juveniles often lack the black spot which makes them difficult to distinguish from other *Pagellus* species.

**SIMILAR SPECIES**    Two other similar species of *Pagellus*, Axillary or Spanish Seabream *P. acarne* and Common Pandora or Becker *P. erythrinus* have been recorded from southern Britain and could turn up in Wales. They are however, both rare visitors from further south. Axillary Seabream has a black spot right at the base of the pectoral fins. Common Pandora has a red edge to the gill cover and sometimes blue spots and a small eye.

**BEHAVIOUR**    Young fish live in large shoals and these are the fish seen in inshore waters. Older fish form much smaller shoals.

**HABITAT**    It is shoals of young fish that are encountered inshore close to the bottom over a variety of seabed types, but most often

near rocks and wrecks. Older fish live further offshore on the continental slope in water down to 700m.

**DISTRIBUTION**    This species is frequent, at least in summer, in the English Channel and southwest British Isles but is only rarely recorded from Welsh waters and further north. Its distribution extends north to Norway and south to the western Mediterranean and Mauritania.

**NATURAL HISTORY**    Like many members of this family, a sex change is involved in the life history. The fish start off as males and change into females when they get to four to six years old and 20–30cm long. They grow slowly and can live for 15 years. This makes them vulnerable to over-fishing. They probably do not breed in British waters.

**SIGHTINGS**    Blackspot Seabream have increasingly been caught by anglers since 2000 and might also be seen by divers, though they tend to live below diving depths. They turn up in commercial catches in Cornwall and are fished by deepwater trawlers in Biscay but stocks there are severely depleted.

## BOGUE                    Pysgodyn llygad llo                    *Boops boops*

**36cm**

Bouge is an uncommon but regular visitor to British waters that has been recorded occasionally from Welsh waters and extends as far north as Norway. It is common south of Biscay and in the Mediterranean as far south as Angola.

This bream can be recognised from its long, slimline shape and slightly curved, dark lateral line that stands out clearly from the background blue-green to greyish colour. Two to three thin, dark to yellowish lines run parallel below the lateral line and there is a small black spot at the base of each pectoral fin, but these markings fade in dead fish.

## DENTEX                    Merfog ysgithrog                    *Dentex dentex*

**100cm**

Occasionally large Dentex migrate north as far as the British Isles where it is a rare visitor. There is at least one confirmed record from Welsh waters. It is common in the Mediterranean and extends south to Senegal.

This is a large, deep-bodied bream with a big head, strong jaws with large teeth and a steep profile. The eyes are small and set high on the head. It has no obvious markings to distinguish it, but in life is often peppered with small blue spots. It has an overall silvery look underwater, bluish on the back and really large ones take on a dark reddish hue. The fins often have a rosy tint to them. The spines in the front part of the dorsal fin have their tips free from the fin membrane.

## SALEMA or SAUPE           Salpa                    *Sarpa salpa*

**50cm**

This is a very rare visitor to the British Isles and has only been recorded a few times from northern European waters. There is a recent (2008) record from Swansea (Herdson pers. comm.) and at least one from Cornwall. It does however have a wide distribution from Bay of Biscay to South Africa including the Mediterranean.

This is a pretty greyish blue, silvery bream marked with 10–12 yellow, longitudinal stripes and a yellow ring around the eye. There is a small dark spot at the base of each pectoral fin. It has a moderately deep body and a small eye.

# DRUMS

Family Sciaenidae

## MEAGRE                    Drymiwr                    *Argyrosomus regius*

**Other names: Croaker**                                          **230cm**

**KEY IDENTIFICATION FEATURES** This large, rare visitor to our waters can be recognised fairly easily and can be identified in the field with a high degree of certainty. This is a long fish, shaped rather like a salmon but with two, close-set dorsal fins. The first is spiny and the second is soft and about twice the length of the first. It has a large, gently rounded tail. It is a silvery grey to brown colour, the back darker than the sides. The fins are darker grey or brown or in some large fish, distinctly reddish. The lateral line and the scales are clearly visible.

**SIMILAR SPECIES** At first sight, this could be mistaken for a large Seabass but it has a much longer second dorsal fin and a different tail shape. Another member of this family, the Shi drum or Corb *Umbrina cirrosa* very occasionally reaches British waters and has been recorded from Cornwall but not Welsh waters. It has a beautiful pattern of dark-ringed pale spots and squiggles or diagonal stripes.

**BEHAVIOUR** Along with other members of this family, Meagre produce loud noises, by vibrating the walls of their large swimbladder. This sound can be heard several metres away and is useful in keeping the fish together in murky coastal or estuary waters. They respond to changing water temperature by moving in and out from the coast.

**HABITAT** In the Mediterranean this fish is found in shallow water amongst rocks and over sand, near the seabed as well as in mid-water. Juveniles and immature adults will swim into estuaries and lagoons. It ranges from 15–300m.

**DISTRIBUTION** Meagre is a rare visitor to British and Welsh waters although it reaches the English Channel fairly frequently. It has been recorded from Norway in the north to Congo in the south including the Mediterranean and the Canary Islands. Large fish are now rare throughout European waters.

**NATURAL HISTORY** In the spring and summer the fish move close inshore to spawn. It feeds mainly on small schooling fish such as sardines.

**SIGHTINGS** In British and Welsh waters, sightings are rare and are usually from anglers or trawls. It makes an excellent sports fish. Some countries such as Greece grow them in aquaculture units.

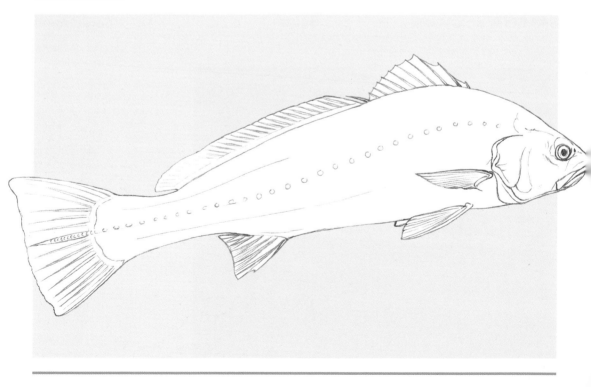

# POMFRETS

## Family Bramidae

## ATLANTIC POMFRET          Merfog môr          *Brama brama*

**Other names: Ray's Bream**                                    100cm

**KEY IDENTIFICATION FEATURES**  This is a relatively easy fish to recognise and adults can be identified in the field with a high degree of certainty. In shape it is rather like a thin rugby ball with a steep, smooth head profile and an upturned mouth. The dorsal fin has a tall lobe at the front whilst the rest of the fin is long and low. This is mirrored in the anal fin and it has a thin, forked tail. When dead the fish looks dull brown but in life it is a silvery greenish brown.

**SIMILAR SPECIES**  Three other pomfrets, Rough Pomfret *Taractes asper*, Bigscale Pomfret or Long-finned Bream *Taractichthys longipinnis* and Atlantic Fanfish or Silver Pomfret *Pterycombus brama* are very rare visitors to west coast British waters, but have not yet been recorded from Welsh waters.

**BEHAVIOUR**  Atlantic Pomfret is a highly migratory species whose movements are dependent on water temperature. It migrates north in summer from the Iberian Peninsula and returns south for the winter, moving in small schools.

**HABITAT**  This is an open sea, mid-water fish with a depth range from the surface to 1000m. It is found mainly on the edge of the Continental Shelf but it occasionally comes close inshore.

**DISTRIBUTION**  Atlantic Pomfret is an occasional visitor to British and Welsh waters although Welsh records are sparse. However, in some years large numbers sweep north in summer, moving up to Scotland and Norway and down into the North Sea. In 2008, eight tons were caught off the west of Ireland in late summer and some off Wales too. Stranded fish are regularly recorded in North Norfolk in autumn and winter and this was certainly the case in 2008. These fish are probably trapped by cold water during their return south.

**NATURAL HISTORY**  Small fish, crustaceans, squid and other pelagic animals are all eaten by this opportunist fish. There is little information on its life history. Young have been caught in mid Atlantic but not near European coasts.

**SIGHTINGS**  The distribution of this fish is heavily influenced by water temperature and if numbers and sightings in Wales and elsewhere increase on a year to year basis then this may be a good indication of increasing ocean temperatures. Sightings are usually of stranded fish and in warm years, when larger numbers move north, from mid-water trawls. It is fished commercially off the Atlantic coast of Spain and Portugal.

# GOATFISHES

Family Mullidae

## RED MULLET                    Mingrwn coch          *Mullus surmeletus*

**Other names: Striped Mullet**                                    40cm

**KEY IDENTIFICATION FEATURES** Red Mullet can be identified in the field with a high degree of certainty. Their most characteristic feature is a pair of long, sensitive chin barbels which are kept constantly in motion. This is a slim fish with a blunt, steep head, two dorsal fins and a forked tail fin. Colour is variable and changes at night. During the day the fish are usually striped lengthwise with yellow on a red or pink to pale brown background. The central stripe from head to tail tends to be darker. The first dorsal fin has characteristic horizontal black and white stripes of varying intensity. At night the pattern of stripes breaks up and the fish becomes marbled with red. Fish from deeper darker water are often an overall red colour.

**SIMILAR SPECIES** A second very similar species, *Mullus barbatus barbatus*, also called Red Mullet or Striped Mullet has been recorded from the British Isles but is an offshore species that usually occurs in deeper water down to 300m or so. It has a much steeper, almost vertical head profile and is not striped.

**BEHAVIOUR** Red Mullet are fascinating fish to watch as they move slowly over the seabed using their sensitive chin barbels to probe for hidden food. When they find something they dig it out and often produce a cloud of silt, which may attract other fish such as gobies and wrasses on the look out for a free meal. Red Mullet are usually found in small groups but can also be solitary.

**HABITAT** Like tropical and warm water goatfishes, Red Mullet live on sandy and muddy seabed from just a few metres deep down to about 100m (much deeper in parts of the Mediterranean). They can also be found in areas of mixed sediment and rock or stones.

**DISTRIBUTION** Red Mullet are found all round the Welsh coastline but are commoner in southern parts and are mainly a summer visitor. They occur all round the British Isles and extend north to southern Norway, but are basically a Mediterranean species and also extend south to Senegal and the Canary Islands. Numbers increase in summer in the English Channel as fish move up from further south.

**NATURAL HISTORY** Red Mullet spawn in May to July in the English Channel area and occasionally they spawn further north or in Wales. Eggs and larvae float and the young planktonic fish are a camouflaged silvery blue. They become sexually mature at about two years old and 22cm long and are reported to live for 10 years.

**SIGHTINGS** Divers are the most likely to see these fish in southern parts of Wales although in some years they are quite common in the north too. They are sometimes trawled up as by-catch in mixed trawl fisheries but are too scarce to be targeted, although they taste good. Further south and in the Mediterranean they are heavily exploited.

# BANDFISHES

## Family Cepolidae

## RED BANDFISH        Pysgodyn rhesen goch        *Cepola macrophthalma*

**Other names: *Cepola rubescens* (synonym)**                    **80cm**

**KEY IDENTIFICATION FEATURES**    It would be very difficult to confuse this elegant fish with any other. Shaped like a long ribbon, its eel-like body is flattened from side to side and ends in a pointed tail. It is a beautiful orange red in colour. The long dorsal and anal fins are edged with blue or violet in males, which is especially bright in the breeding season. Look also at the front of the dorsal fin which is usually marked with red.

**SIMILAR SPECIES**  None

**BEHAVIOUR**  Divers will generally only see the heads of these fish sticking out of their mud burrows and they will quickly withdraw down out of sight unless approached very quietly. They feed on plankton picking pieces from the water, often with the tip of the tail still in contact with the burrow. However, they will also leave their burrows and feed within a few metres radius of it, especially in deep, dark water or at night.

**HABITAT**  This fish has specialised habitat requirements. It lives in vertical burrows excavated in mud and fine muddy sand, usually in deep water down to at least 400m. It is usually gregarious sometimes with many hundreds of burrows in an area but individual burrows have also been found. Some populations occur as shallow as 15–30m, well within diving depths, in sheltered harbours and estuaries such as Plymouth Sound, Brixham harbour and off the east coast of Lundy Island in the Bristol Channel. In Wales they occur in the vicinity of Milford Haven.

**DISTRIBUTION**  Red Bandfish have been recorded from a few sheltered areas around Wales. They have been found at various locations up the Atlantic coast of Britain to Scotland, and round Ireland but are much commoner around the south west and in the English Channel. They also extend south to Senegal and into the Mediterranean.

**NATURAL HISTORY**  In the south west of the British Isles the fish spawn in summer. Studies of Adriatic populations have shown an extended spawning period from late spring to autumn, maturity at two to two and a half years old and a maximum age of four years.

**SIGHTINGS**  Divers will only see these fish if they choose to dive in sheltered muddy areas. More shallow water populations may well turn up around Wales if divers search in more such places. With known populations, diving at night is often rewarding as the fish will generally emerge further out of their burrows. Anglers also catch these fish from deeper water and they may come up in trawls such as those designed for catching Norway Lobster *Nephrops norvegicus*.

# WRASSES

## Family Labridae

Of all the fish you will see in Welsh waters, wrasses are perhaps the most colourful and fascinating – at least in our opinion! Five species, Ballan, Cuckoo, Goldsinny, Rock Cook and Corkwing are common resident species and all are described in detail here. Baillon's Wrasse now appears regularly in the Channel Islands and the west of Ireland and there are indications that they may be resident there. This and two other wrasses found occasionally in British waters are briefly described on page 190.

Wrasses are relatively easy to recognise as such. They have a single long dorsal fin along the back with a spiny front portion and a soft rear portion and a convex tail fin. Their eyes are relatively large and mobile and their lips are thick and obvious in most species. Their scales generally show up well as they are large and often outlined in a contrasting colour. Wrasses can also be recognised by the way they swim leisurely through the water 'rowing' with their pectoral fins – a trait shared with their warm water relatives, parrotfish.

Most wrasses have interesting sex lives. Many, including Ballan and Cuckoo Wrasse, change colour and sex part way through their lives. Some build intricate nests and may court their females with a graceful dance. They are certainly fascinating and entertaining fish to watch and are often kept in public aquaria.

## Ballan cross

Wrasse can cope with a diet of hard shelled invertebrates because they have special flattened teeth on pharyngeal bones in the throat. In Ballan wrasse this structure is shaped like a cross and has been worn through the ages as a good luck talisman.

# BALLAN WRASSE                Cleiriach y gwymon        *Labrus bergylta*

**60cm**

**KEY IDENTIFICATION FEATURES** Ballan Wrasse can be identified in the field with a high degree of certainty. This is the largest of our wrasses and any wrasse over about 20cm long with the exception of unmistakable Cuckoo Wrasse, is likely to be a Ballan. Ballan are very variable in colour but mostly a mottled mixture of greens and browns. Their scales frequently have a dark edge and pale centre giving a spotty appearance. Some fish have a distinct white line running along the body. The brightest colour is seen in the largest fish, which have pale scales outlined with orange as seen here. Caught fish with this colour have invariably turned out to be males. However, killing these large fish which may be 20–30 years old should be discouraged.

**SIMILAR SPECIES** Small Ballan are most likely to be confused with Corkwings or Rock Cooks but a careful look or a good photograph will show the distinctive colour marks of these species.

**BEHAVIOUR** Ballan Wrasse have very strong teeth and can be seen pulling mussels off rocks and wrecks or crunching up crabs. At night they have been observed sleeping tucked away between rocks or amongst seaweed, a trait shared by many tropical wrasse.

**HABITAT** These fish are usually encountered in kelp forests and around rocky reefs and cliffs. Young fish are common in rock pools whilst adults are common down to around 50m. They probably also live much deeper than this in suitable rocky areas but deeper records are scarce.

**DISTRIBUTION** Common all round the Welsh coastline and round most of the British Isles though commonest on western and southern coasts. Further afield it extends north to Norway and south to Morocco, the Canary Islands and the Azores.

**NATURAL HISTORY** In early summer Ballan Wrasse can be seen building nests made from bits of seaweed stuffed between rocks or into a rock crevice. Here the female lays her eggs attended

by the male. Males may protect the nest to some extent but more detailed observations of their breeding are needed. The most interesting part of their life history is the fact that all the young larval fish develop into females. Most remain female all their lives but a proportion change sex and become fully functional males. Although this can happen as young as seven, most change at a much older age. Unlike Cuckoo Wrasse they do not change colour when they change sex although the oldest males do have a distinctive colour pattern (see above). These are long-lived, slow-growing fish that can reach at least 29 years old.

**SIGHTINGS** Young fish up to 10cm long can be caught in deep rock pools near low water. Look out for bright emerald green fish just a few centimetres long. These are the current year's young fish. Divers will see this fish patrolling through the kelp forest singly or in small groups. These fish are easily caught by angling but should always be returned unharmed if possible. The largest fish are males and killing these can skew the sex ration in a local area. They have greenish flesh and are not especially good to eat though prized in some areas.

# CUCKOO WRASSE          Gwrachen resog          *Labrus mixtus*

**Other names: *L. bimaculatus* (synonym)**                    **35cm**

**KEY IDENTIFICATION FEATURES** It would be difficult to confuse a Cuckoo Wrasse with any other fish found in Welsh waters. It is a slimmer fish than the Ballan wrasse with an elegant pointed head. Males and females have different colour patterns but both are distinctive. Females are a rosy pink to orange red and have alternating white and black patches along the back beneath the rear portion of the dorsal fin. Males have blue heads and brilliant blue markings running along the flanks and onto the tail whilst the belly and fins and rest of the body are bright orange to rosy red. Look out for fish with colour patterns intermediate between the female and male colours. These are fish that are changing sex.

**SIMILAR SPECIES** None. Even small fish are usually distinctive.

**BEHAVIOUR** Cuckoo Wrasse are very inquisitive especially the males and will often approach divers that enter their territory. This is especially the case at popular dive sites where divers are the norm such as around the Tudwals Islands of Abersoch on the Llyn. Some divers report seeing the same fish, recognised by distinctive blemishes, at the same sites from year to year and they are certainly territorial. In the breeding season males can be seen displaying to females using an elaborate swimming dance and blanching pure white over the head for a few seconds at a time. These fish are hardly ever seen in winter and probably seek deeper water with more stable temperatures.

**HABITAT** In summer this is an inshore species found in rocky areas with plenty of hidey holes such as reefs and boulder fields. It frequents kelp forests but mostly below about 10m. It has been recorded down to 200m.

**DISTRIBUTION** Found all round the Welsh coastline and most of the British Isles, though commonest on western and southern coasts. It extends north to Norway and south to Senegal, and throughout the Mediterranean.

**NATURAL HISTORY** The Cuckoo Wrasse has an even more colourful sex life than Ballan Wrasse! Males excavate and build a nest and entice in females to lay their eggs, though there are few documented details. All the young fish have the female colour and the majority of them develop into mature females. Some females then undergo a dramatic colour change from red to blue and become fully functional males. This happens at various ages but mostly when the fish are 7–13 years old and a reasonable size. It is these males that hold territories. A few young fish retain the red female coloration but develop into males. The role of these 'primary' males has not yet been fully ascertained.

**SIGHTINGS** This is the only one of the five common Welsh wrasses, which is not found on the shore. Divers will see it in summer, the large males generally on their own and the smaller immature fish and females sometimes in groups. They are not a good angling fish but sometimes come up in crab and lobster pots where their inquisitive and scavenging tendencies have taken them.

# ROCK COOK    *Gwrachen y graig bol melyn*    *Centrolabrus exoletus*

**Other names: Small-mouthed Wrasse**    15cm

**KEY IDENTIFICATION FEATURES**  Rock Cook can be identified in the field with a high degree of certainty, especially with practice. It has a small head and mouth, hence its alternative common name. Its body colour grades from warm browns on the back through greenish yellow on the sides to cream on the underside. The head is adorned with blue lines and in breeding males, like the one shown here, these are very bright. At this time the males also have bright blue reticulations and spots on the back and fins. Both sexes have a dusky crescent line across the tail fin but this is not always easy to see.

**SIMILAR SPECIES**  The most usual confusion is with Corkwing Wrasse or immature Ballan Wrasse. Corkwing have a spot on the tail base and Ballan do not have blue lines on the head. In good photographs it might be possible to count the anal fin spines. Rock Cook have four to six whilst Corkwing and Ballan have three.

**BEHAVIOUR**  With their small mouths, Rock Cook are adept at picking small crustaceans, worms and so on out from the undergrowth and may even be able to 'pick' planktonic crustaceans from the water. On occasion, these fish have been observed to pick parasites off larger fish, a trait better known in tropical cleaner wrasse. At popular diving sites these fish will sometimes approach divers but are not as curious as Cuckoo Wrasse.

**HABITAT**  This small wrasse is almost always associated either with seaweed covered rocks or seagrass and is found down to about 25m depth. Small ones occur on the shore but only at extreme low water level.

**DISTRIBUTION**  Found all round the Welsh coastline but not seen as commonly as Ballan and Corkwing Wrasse and not as common here as along the south coast of England and west coast of Scotland. It is also found round most of the British Isles but seems to be absent on the east coast of England. Further afield it extends north to southern Norway and south to Portugal.

**NATURAL HISTORY**  This is still the least well known of the five common wrasse species described here. Males take on their brighter breeding colours in late spring and summer and young fish of the year appear in mid to late summer. Males build seaweed nests but there is little published information on this. There is no indication that they change sex.

**SIGHTINGS**  Although young fish can be found on the shore they rarely are and so are not usually seen by rock poolers. Divers will find these fish within and just below kelp forest wherever there is a dense cover of seaweeds.

# GOLDSINNY WRASSE       Gwrachen Fair       *Ctenolabrus rupestris*

**Other names: Goldsinny**                                                    15cm

**KEY IDENTIFICATION FEATURES** Goldsinny Wrasse can be identified in the field with a high degree of certainty. This is a beautiful golden to pinkish brown, small wrasse shading to white underneath. It has a slightly striped appearance along its sides especially below the lateral line. There is a large, characteristic black spot at the top of the tail base from which the fish can be identified even if only a glimpse of a departing tail is seen. There is another black spot on the front of the dorsal fin but this is often difficult to see.

**SIMILAR SPECIES** The Scale-rayed Wrasse has a similar black tail mark and is also a brownish colour. It generally lives in deeper water and as yet there are no confirmed records from Welsh waters (see page 190 below).

**BEHAVIOUR** Like Cuckoo Wrasse Goldsinny are naturally curious and with patience can be enticed near by the glint of a camera or by gently scrabbling fingers amongst the undergrowth. The fish will come over to see what edible titbits might have been uncovered. Goldsinny are known to pick parasites off larger fish and this may partly account for their lack of fear.

**HABITAT** Goldsinny prefer rocky reefs and boulder slopes which provide numerous hidey holes in which they can loiter. They are found both within and well below the kelp forest down to about 50m and also within seagrass beds. Small ones can be found in deep weedy rock pools but are never common there.

**DISTRIBUTION** Goldsinny are relatively common all round the Welsh coastline and around the British Isles, with the exception of the east coast of England where it is rare, due to lack of suitable habitat. Further afield it extends north to Norway and south to Morocco and throughout the Mediterranean.

**NATURAL HISTORY** Unlike the other wrasse described here, Goldsinny Wrasse do not build nests, but males do seem to establish territories before spawning. The eggs then float off and develop in the plankton.

**SIGHTINGS** Rock poolers sometimes find small ones in deep rock pools near low water mark. Divers frequently see these fish hanging around near cliff faces, overhangs and boulder caves, less often out in the open. These fish are used commercially to clean skin parasites off caged fish such as salmon.

# CORKWING WRASSE          Eurben          *Symphodus melops*

**Other names:** *Crenilabrus melops* (synonym)                                    15cm

**KEY IDENTIFICATION FEATURES**  Of the three smaller wrasses Corkwing are the most variable in colour but they can still be identified in the field with a high degree of certainty. Even from an early age they have a characteristic black tail spot in the centre of the tail stalk and a brown or black comma-shaped mark immediately behind each eye. They are adorned with blue and brown lines on their head and operculum rather pale in females but bright in males. Females are mostly mottled greens and browns, though some are reddish. Males are brighter with more blue colour in the centre of the scales especially in the breeding season.  At that time they develop numerous blue spots on their fins. This is a small wrasse but males exceptionally reach 25–30cm.

**SIMILAR SPECIES**  The most common confusion is with small Ballan wrasse which can have a similar coloration, but without the tail spot. Corkwing can also change colour at night, obscuring the tail spot, and this also fades in aquarium-kept fish. Baillon's wrasse is very similar and divers should keep an eye out for this southern species which appears to be moving into Wales (see page 190).

**BEHAVIOUR**  Corkwing Wrasse tend to ignore divers as they hunt through the undergrowth for crustaceans, worms and molluscs and so are not as easy to watch and photograph as some of the other wrasse. The exception is nest building males who get completely absorbed by their occupation and also become a lot braver. This fascinating behaviour is described below.

**HABITAT**  Like the other wrasse described here Corkwing are found mainly in rocky areas where they prefer a dense cover of seaweeds so are much less abundant below the seaweed zone. However, they do also frequent seagrass beds. Unlike the others, they are common in the intertidal, in rock pools. The maximum depth they are likely to be found is about 30m except in winter when they seem to move deeper.

**DISTRIBUTION**  This is the commonest of the small wrasses in Wales and can be found all round the Welsh coastline and the British Isles. It extends north as far as Norway and south to Morocco and the Azores and into the western Mediterranean.

**NATURAL HISTORY**  Males are territorial and build an elaborate mound-like nest of algae rather reminiscent of a stickleback nest only larger. He entices one or more females to lay her eggs inside the nest and then guards and fans the eggs until they hatch.  Rival males are chased off but in a bizarre twist some males have female coloration and sometimes succeed in entering the nest where they try to fertilise the eggs. When the eggs hatch the larvae drift off and develop in the plankton eventually drifting into shallow water where the young settle in late summer and autumn.

**SIGHTINGS**  Corkwing Wrasse are frequently caught by rock poolers and seem quite resilient when released. They are also commonly seen by snorkelers and by divers, especially in shallow water. They are easily enticed into fish traps and large ones sometimes get trapped in crab and lobster pots.

# RARE WRASSES – Scale-eyed, Rainbow & Baillon's

As well as the five common species described above, three other wrasses have been positively identified in British waters. There are confirmed records of Scale-rayed Wrasse *Acantholabus palloni*, Rainbow Wrasse *Coris julis* and Baillon's Wrasse *Symphodus bailloni*. Divers should look out for these wrasse as they could extend their ranges north with increasing water temperatures.

**SCALE-RAYED WRASSE, Gwrachen gennog,** has not been recorded in Welsh waters. It lives in rocky areas in deep water, usually below about 50m. It has been found off south west England and also in Norway where it has been photographed in sheltered fjords at 20m (see Moen & Svensen, 2004). It is possible that this is a rarely seen fish rather than a rare fish. Its preference for hiding out in deep rocky terrain means it is not easily caught or seen by divers.

**RAINBOW WRASSE, Gwrachen seithliw,** is a common species in the Mediterranean and warm eastern Atlantic coasts. It has not been recorded from Welsh waters but there are a few records from Cornwall and the south west of England and Ireland. It is well illustrated in books covering the Mediterranean.

**BAILLON'S WRASSE** or **VIELLE**, Gwrachen Baillon

This small wrasse has not yet been recorded from Welsh waters. It is known to extend as far north as the English Channel but has rarely been recorded there. In 2006 one of the authors (Paul Kay) photographed the nesting fish shown here, which we believe to be Baillon's Wrasse, in Connemara, west Ireland. So potentially, it could be found in Welsh waters too.

Baillon's Wrasse resembles Corkwing Wrasse in size and colour. Perhaps the most distinctive feature of the fish photographed so far, is the pink colour of the lips and fins. This is not mentioned in other texts and may only be present during the breeding season. In Jersey these fish showing the same coloration, have also been photographed building nests (Sue Daly, pers. comm.). Like Corkwing, Baillon's Wrasse has a dark spot in the middle of the tail stalk and another one at the base of the dorsal fin just where the soft rear portion begins. The latter is clearly visible in the photograph(s) shown here but the tail spot does not show up. Possibly, like Corkwing, this spot may fade under certain conditions. There is a dark grey to blue arc at the base of the pectoral fin which can also be seen here. In enlarged digital photographs and in dead fish it is also possible to see that the edge of the pre-operculum (flap just in front of the gill cover edge), is finely serrated.

If and when a specimen is caught, then it will be possible to make fin ray counts and lateral line scale counts to confirm the identity of these fish. Meanwhile any records and especially digital photographs from Welsh waters (and elsewhere) would be very useful. Baillon's Wrasse may in fact be resident in Wales, but has, as yet, not been recognised nor recorded.

Both photographs on this page are of Baillon's Wrasse.

Above. Corkwing Wrasse often appear to 'rest' on the seabed when the water is cold.

Left. Cuckoo Wrasse are both inquisitive and territorial and although small they will sometimes attack divers and even draw blood.

Below. Rock Cook can be seen in loose 'shoals' especially in areas of rocks and kelp.

# WEEVERFISHES

Family Trachinidae

## LESSER WEEVER     Môr-wiber fach     *Echiichthys vipera*

Other names: Weever, *Trachinus vipera* (synonym)     15cm

## GREATER WEEVER     Môr-wiber fawr     *Trachinus draco*

53cm

Greater Weever

**KEY IDENTIFICATION FEATURES** These fish can be identified in the field with a high degree of certainty. Weevers have a long body and a small head with the mouth turned up at an oblique angle. The most obvious feature is a short, spiny, venomous first dorsal fin which the fish instantly erects if disturbed. This is jet black in Lesser Weever and shows up against its mottled, sandy coloured body. In Greater Weever only the tip is black and the fish is decorated with an elegant pattern of dark diagonal lines running from back to belly. It is also patterned with blue lines on the head and body especially in the breeding season. The second dorsal and anal fins are long with soft rays.

**SIMILAR SPECIES** None.

**BEHAVIOUR** Weevers are mostly inactive during the day and lie hidden beneath the sand with only their eyes and first dorsal fin showing, so are quite difficult to spot. At night they come out to hunt shrimp, and small bottom-living fish, mainly gobies, dragonets and sand eels. If a weever itself is threatened, it erects its venomous, spiny first dorsal fin as a deterrent.

**HABITAT** Weevers live on sandy seabeds and spend much of their time partially buried. Lesser Weevers like warm water and often occur on intertidal sand flats, moving in and out with the tide and this is what makes them a danger to bathers. They extend down to around 50m depth, and 150m in winter. Greater Weevers in contrast, rarely stray up into the intertidal preferring water from about 30–100m but are occasionally found as shallow as 3m.

**DISTRIBUTION** Both species are found all round the Welsh coastline and the British Isles but the Lesser Weever is recorded more often. They can also be found throughout the Mediterranean and north to Denmark (Lesser Weever) and Norway (Greater Weever).

**NATURAL HISTORY** These fish spawn in summer and the eggs and larvae float in the plankton.

**SIGHTINGS** In summer bathers wading in the shallows, sometimes tread on Lesser Weevers, a painful and unforgettable encounter. Divers and snorkelers might see either species if they look carefully. Both species, but especially Lesser Weever, come up in inshore shrimp trawls in summer and are a hazard to fishermen and research scientists. Anglers also catch these fish when fishing for flatfish. Greater Weever is widely eaten in southern Europe and can be found for sale in some local fish markets in Wales and southern England but is not very popular here.

## Sea Viper

Weever is a word derived from the Anglo-Saxon for a viper and is very appropriate for fish that can deliver such as painful sting. The venom is injected through the strong spines in the first dorsal fin and is a nerve toxin. Usually the fish acts entirely out of self-defence. However, Lesser Weever can be aggressive and some books on dangerous marine creatures describe this fish darting forward and lashing out with its opercular spines of which there is one on each side. How common this is and how anyone would have the opportunity to watch this behaviour is unclear.

The pain from a weever sting can be relieved by soaking the affected part (usually a foot or hand) in hot water and then treating it to prevent infection. On Abersoch beach, Penllyn, in north Wales, the café provides a bucket of hot water for victims as it is not uncommon for people paddling here to stand on a fish buried in the shallow sand. The pain may reoccur when the affected part is taken out of the hot water and it may take from a few minutes to as long as an hour before this stops. As some people react worse than others, medical advice should always be sought especially for children. Anaphylactic shock is a possible consequence of a weever sting!

# SANDEELS

## Family Ammodytidae

Sandeels are notoriously difficult to identify underwater as they twist and turn in shifting silver shoals or dive into the sand for protection. Five species are found in Welsh and British waters. Two of these, the Lesser Sandeel *Ammodytes tobianus* and the Greater Sandeel *Hyperoplus lanceolatus* are common in Welsh waters and are most likely to be seen, whilst the others are rarely recorded. However, this may to some extent reflect difficulties in identification.

**KEY IDENTIFICATION FEATURES** With a little care, sandeels can be recognised as such in the field with a reasonable degree of certainty but different species cannot. However, it should be possible to distinguish *Hyperoplus* species from the others. Sandeels are all slim, silvery fish, slightly flattened from side to side with a long dorsal and anal fin and a forked tail fin. In all of them the lower jaw is longer than the upper one when the mouth is closed. Features that can with practise be used to distinguish the species with a dead fish or very close photograph are described below.

**GREATER** or **GREAT SANDEEL**, Llymrïen fawr
*Hyperoplus lanceolatus* 35cm
**CORBIN'S** or **GREATER SANDEEL**, Llymrïen fawr
*Hyperoplus immaculatus* 35cm

Sandeels longer than about 25cm are likely to be one of these two species. Unlike the *Ammodytes* sandeels, *Hyperoplus* species cannot extend their upper jaw forward to make a tube-like structure when feeding. They have a pair of large conspicuous teeth in the roof of the mouth. To tell the two species apart, look for a black blotch on each side of the snout in front of the eyes. This is a useful field identification feature for *H. lanceolatus* and is lacking in *H. immaculatus*. Also in this species the pectoral fin reaches back to the start of the dorsal fin whereas in *H. immaculatus* it does not. Also see Habitat.

Whilst it is easy to tell that these are sandeels, it is not possible to tell which species they are.

Even with a fish in the hand, it is necessary to look closely at the mouth, teeth and dorsal fin rays to be sure which species of sandeel you have.

## SMALL or LESSER SANDEEL, Llymrïen
*Ammodytes tobianus* 20cm
## LESSER or RAITT'S SANDEEL or LAUNCE, Llymrïen Raitt
*Ammodytes marinus* 25cm

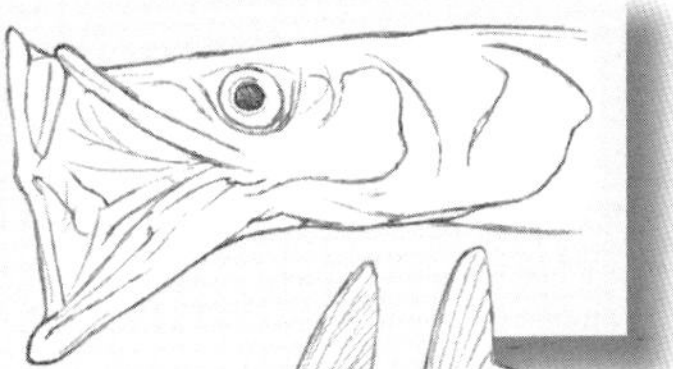

These are smaller sandeels and *A. tobianus* is the commonest species. All *Ammodytes* species can extend the upper jaw forward to form a tube and they do not have large teeth in the roof of the mouth. To tell these two species apart is very difficult. Look carefully at the base of the tail. In *A. tobianus* scales extend out onto the tail fin itself whereas in *A. marinus* there are no scales on the base of the tail fin. There are also differences in the belly scales and dorsal fin counts.

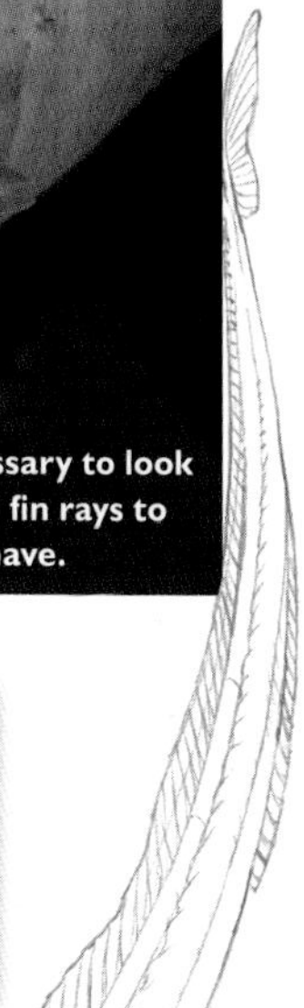

## SMOOTH SANDEEL, Llymrïen lefn
*Gymnammodytes semisquamatus* 24cm
This small sandeel is very similar to the two *Ammodytes* species. As its name suggests it only has scales on the posterior third of its body. There is a short body groove below the pectoral fin. The lateral line has short branches above and below.

**BEHAVIOUR** Divers usually see shoals streaming along a few metres above the seabed. Greater Sandeels *Hyperoplus lanceolatus* often swim with shoals of *Ammodytes*.

**HABITAT** Sandeels swim up in the water column above sandy seabeds mainly inshore from the shore to about 200m. However, Corbin's Sandeel *H. immaculatus* is mainly found offshore below about 50m depth.

**DISTRIBUTION** Smooth Sandeel has the most southerly distribution extending from Norway to Spain. Corbin's Sandeel has the most restricted distribution from the British Isles to northern Biscay. The others extend further north to Iceland.

**NATURAL HISTORY** Sandeels shed their eggs over sandy seabed areas where the sticky eggs remain. The larval fish swim up out of the sand into the water column. They mostly feed on plankton especially small crustaceans but larger ones can eat other small fish as well.

**SIGHTINGS** The larger sandeels *Hyperoplus* spp. are sometimes caught by anglers. *Ammodytes* species and occasionally young *Hyperoplus* are caught in seine nets or even push nets from sandy shores. Divers and snorkelers often see these fish in sheltered sandy bays. They are heavily exploited commercially, usually for processing into fishmeal, which can have far reaching effects. Sandeels are a very important component of the marine food chain and many seabirds such as Puffins rely on them as a food source as well as fish such as Herring and Mackerel.

# GOBIES

### Family Gobiidae

Gobies are a family of small, mostly bottom-living fish that are notoriously difficult to identify, especially underwater. In Welsh waters 14 species have confirmed records and are described here. A further three rare or southern species are also described as these have been found in adjacent waters and have the potential to expand their distribution northwards with ocean warming. All the gobies described here can be divided into three groups according to the ease and accuracy with which they may be identified. Although gobies are a difficult group, do not be put off as, with a little practice, study of photos, and visits to aquaria, you can learn to recognise many, using specific characteristics outlined here and details of habitat.

Black Goby head with lines of sensory papillae visible

## ROCKY SHORES

Rock Goby
Two-spotted Goby
Giant Goby            No Welsh record; rare
Couch's Goby          No Welsh record; rare

## INSHORE ROCKY AREAS

Rock Goby
Two-spotted Goby
Leopard-spotted Goby
Red-mouthed Goby      No Welsh record; rare

## INSHORE SEDIMENT

Black Goby
Painted Goby
Sand Goby
Common Goby
Fries's Goby ??
Lozano's Goby

## OFFSHORE SEDIMENT (below 15m)

Fries's Goby
Jeffreys's Goby
Lozano's Goby

## OFFSHORE SEDIMENT (below 30m)

Diminutive Goby
Lozano's Goby
Norwegian Goby

## PELAGIC

Transparent Goby
Crystalline or Crystal Goby

The first group includes a number of Welsh gobies found in various habitats, which have very specific characteristics and can be relatively easily identified with a high degree of certainty. These are the Rock, Black, Leopard-spotted, Two-spotted, Transparent and Crystal Gobies.

The second group of gobies live only in sediment habitats, often on sand, and are basically similar in overall appearance. Three small gobies, the Sand, Common and Painted, commonly found in shallow water and seen by divers, are particularly difficult to tell apart. However, Painted Gobies can be picked out with practise. The others species are rarely recorded or under-recorded because they live in deeper water and require specialist knowledge and guides to identify them. However, divers' recent photographic records indicate that Fries's Goby is relatively easy to recognise.

The third group includes rare species with very limited distribution around the British Isles. These are the Giant, Couch's and Red-mouthed Gobies.

## GOBY FEATURES

Gobies are mostly small, elongate fish with thick lips, swollen cheeks and bulbous eyes set close together near the top of the head. Unlike blennies almost all (all northern European) gobies have two separate dorsal fins and a large, rounded tail fin. The pectoral fins are fused together to form a weak suction disc which helps them to cling on to the seabed. Females lay their pear-shaped eggs in nest sites chosen by the male, usually attaching them to the roof of an empty shell, crevice or underside of a stone. Males guard the eggs until they hatch and the larvae drift away.

## EYE LINER

Gobies do not have a lateral line system along the sides of their body but they do have rows of sensory papillae around their eyes and on other parts of the head and front of the body. These show up clearly in some species as black lines, especially in close up photographs. The exact arrangement of these rows can be a useful identification aid but usually only under the microscope. However, the fact that they are visible at all may help distinguish some species – these lines are clearly visible in Black Gobies, especially the paler-coloured ones, helping to distinguish them from Rock Gobies, especially in habitats such as sediment overlain by stones and rocks, where the two may overlap.

This Black Goby clearly shows the distinctive black mark on its 1st dorsal fin – a second black mark on the front of the 2nd dorsal is also visible.

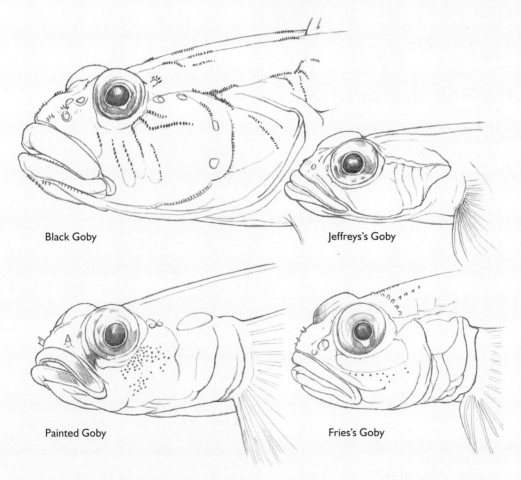

Black Goby

Jeffreys's Goby

Painted Goby

Fries's Goby

# PELAGIC GOBIES

## TWO-SPOTTED GOBY    Gobi brych    *Gobiusculus flavescens*

**6cm**

**KEY IDENTIFICATION FEATURES**    This goby can be identified in the field with a high degree of certainty. Both habitat and markings make it easy to recognise. The first of its 'two spots' is a large black one with a pale edge at the base of the tail fin. Only males have the second spot, on the sides below the first dorsal fin. In the breeding season, males develop iridescent blue lines along both dorsal fins and blue spots along the sides. Females and non-breeding males are reddish brown with darker reticulations and pale saddles over the back.

**SIMILAR SPECIES**    When swimming up in the water column there should be no confusion with any other goby.

**BEHAVIOUR**  Most gobies live on the seabed but this entertaining little fish swims and hovers in small schools, slipping between and around seaweed clumps. Individuals will often allow photographers to approach within a few inches. In summer, the fish sometimes gather in large schools.

**HABITAT**    A familiar inshore goby that is most often found swimming in small groups amongst kelp and other brown seaweeds and in seagrass beds, in shallow water down to about 15–20m depth. It is also perfectly at home in deep rock pools from about mid tide level downwards.

**DISTRIBUTION**    A common and widespread goby found all round the Welsh coastline and the rest of the British Isles. It also extends north to the Faroes, northern Norway, and the Baltic and south to Spain and the western Mediterranean.

**NATURAL HISTORY**    During the breeding season, males give up their semi-pelagic lifestyle and take to the seabed to guard their eggs. Females deposit the sticky eggs in seabed hollows, or attach them within kelp holdfasts or beneath and on other seaweeds.

**SIGHTINGS** Divers are most likely to see these little fish, though shore visitors will find peering through a 'goggle box' in a deep rock pool rewarding.

# TRANSPARENT GOBY    Gobi tryloyw    *Aphia minuta*

8cm

**KEY IDENTIFICATION FEATURES**  This goby can be identified in the field with a high degree of certainty but requires practice and a close look. It resembles many larval fish in that it is almost transparent and its internal swim bladder and gut show up as dark blobs. Dark pigment dots are scattered over the back and head and the body may have a reddish tinge. A sideways view will show that the mouth slants up at an oblique angle unlike most other gobies. Grows to about 6cm, occasionally to 8cm.

**SIMILAR SPECIES**  Once established that this is a goby, then the most likely confusion would be with the Crystal Goby, which has a similar pelagic lifestyle. However, Transparent Gobies have relatively large scales whilst Crystal Gobies have none at all. A really close look or photograph is needed to see this and caught specimens lose their scales easily. Also see captions for small photos for both these fish.

**BEHAVIOUR**  Schools of fish, which may occasionally number several thousand, pick zooplankton from the water.

**HABITAT**  Except in the breeding season, Transparent Gobies spend their lives swimming and drifting in coastal inshore waters, usually above mud, sand and other sediment or over eelgrass beds and in estuaries. They can be found from the surface down to around 90m depth.

**DISTRIBUTION**  A moderately common goby in Welsh coastal waters, also found all round the rest of the British Isles, north to southern Norway and south to Morocco, the Mediterranean and the Black Sea.

Even in poor conditions a photograph which captures detail showing more than two spines in the first dorsal fin will be of a Transparent Goby – the Crystal Goby has two or less spines in this fin.

**NATURAL HISTORY**  When the fish are ready to spawn in the summer months, they move down to the seabed in search of suitable nest sites. Females lay several thousand eggs in empty shells or similar places. They spawn only once and die shortly afterwards when they are about a year old.

**SIGHTINGS**  These small fish have mostly been spotted by divers who are specifically searching for small creatures to photograph and have found them on the seabed in the breeding season. Large schools up in the water column would be more obvious. From boats, their small size means they are only caught in fine mesh shrimp or research nets.

# CRYSTAL GOBY

**Gobi gwydraidd** *Crystallogobius linearis*

**5cm**

**KEY IDENTIFICATION FEATURES** This goby can be identified in the field with a high degree of certainty but requires practice and a close look. No other Welsh fish is as transparent as this one. Non-breeding fish can be almost completely see-through, so much so that you can see objects on the seabed on its far side. The swim bladder shows up as a silvery blob in the middle of the fish. During the breeding season, females appear a milky white due to their load of eggs. A series of distinct black pigment dots are often visible along the fin bases and on the chin. Like the Transparent Goby, it has an oblique, upward slanting mouth. Grows to only about 5cm long.

**SIMILAR SPECIES** See comments under Transparent Goby.

**BEHAVIOUR** This little goby usually swims in loose schools when up in the water column, relying on its transparency for camouflage.

**HABITAT** The Crystal Goby, like the Transparent Goby, is nektonic, that is it swims around up in the water column. It extends further offshore and although usually found near the surface, can be caught in water as deep as 400m over gravel and sediment.

**DISTRIBUTION** The crystal goby appears to have a slightly more restricted distribution than the Transparent goby but is locally common around Wales, especially in the Bristol Channel and Severn Estuary. It extends north to the Faroe Isles and Norway, down the west coast of the British Isles, to Gibraltar and into the Mediterranean.

**NATURAL HISTORY** As this little fish is not easy to observe underwater, not a great deal is known of its detailed life history. During the summer, the fish drop down to the seabed to lay their eggs. These have been found stuck to the inside of the tubes of worms such as *Chaetopterus* and *Protula* but whether they are also

laid elsewhere is unclear. The fish themselves sometimes hide in the tubes; it would be interesting to know if only in empty tubes or along with the live worms. The fish die at the end of their first season, after they have spawned. There are reports of territorial behaviour and the males apparently guard their brood.

**SIGHTINGS** During the summer this goby can be very abundant and thousands can be caught in fine mesh shrimp nets. Divers have photographed them hovering over muddy sediments in sheltered areas. Any photographs and observations of breeding behaviour from around Wales would be useful.

The Crystal Goby has short second dorsal fin spines – all of more or less equal length (about 18 spines in all) whilst the Transparent has fewer (11~13) and they vary in length (longer at the front, shorter at the back).

# LEOPARD-SPOTTED GOBY  Gobi mannog  *Thorogobius ephippiatus*

**13cm**

**KEY IDENTIFICATION FEATURES** This is one of the few Welsh gobies that can easily be recognised from its elegant coloration alone. As its common name suggests, it is marked all over with conspicuous, dark blotches. These vary between individuals from dark brown to brick-red, whilst the background colour is generally pale brown to bluish grey. Some fish have white or pale blue edges to the dorsal and anal fins, especially in the breeding season.

**SIMILAR SPECIES** No other goby in Wales or the British Isles has the same markings (although Fries' Goby does have spots too, it is visually very different to the Leopard-spotted Goby).

**BEHAVIOUR** Anyone who has tried to photograph these fish will know that they are amongst the shyest of all gobies. At the slightest disturbance they rapidly disappear into nearby crevices and boulder spaces. Observing these fish and recording their natural behaviour takes time and patience.

**HABITAT** The Leopard-spotted Goby is mostly found in steep, rocky terrain close inshore where there are plenty of crevices or under-boulder holes for it to hide in and preferably sediment covered ledges or patches where it can search for food near to its retreat. Most records are from between 6–40m depth but the lower limit may be that of the divers not the fish. Very occasionally this goby has been found in large, deep rock pools.

**DISTRIBUTION** This goby is found all round the Welsh coast and most of the British Isles. On the east coast, there are few records south of St. Abbs, probably due to lack of suitable habitat. Adults and juveniles were photographed in 2007 from a bay in North Tyneside (www.glaucus.org.uk.) In the last 15–20 years it has extended from Scotland north to Norway and Sweden. It also extends south to the Mediterranean, Madeira, Canaries and the Azores.

**NATURAL HISTORY** Diver observations suggest this goby is strongly territorial and that, as in most gobies, the males guard egg masses laid by the females during the summer months. Reports of their longevity vary – it would be interesting to know if individuals can be recognised on repeat visits and is so, whether they occupy the same home range during their life time.

**SIGHTINGS** Leopard-spotted Gobies are almost only ever seen by divers due to the inaccessible, rocky places they prefer to live and their great shyness. So diver records of distribution and behaviour are always of interest as the finer details of their natural history are still not fully known.

Although sensory papillae on the head are visible in photos, colouring easily distinguishes this goby from the Black Goby.

# BLACK GOBY                    Gobi du                    *Gobius niger*

**17cm**

**KEY IDENTIFICATION FEATURES** This thick-set goby is similar in size and shape to the Rock Goby. In spite of its name only some individuals are nearly black; the rest vary in colour from light brown or grey through to much darker shades; often they have darker spots and blotches. A series of rounded, dark blotches along mid-flank seems to be characteristic but does not show up in many individuals.

The first dorsal appears to be quite tall and almost triangular, because the middle rays are longer than the front and back ones but this is not the case in young fish. Both dorsal fins have a blackish mark at the top front edge but again this seems to be not entirely universal.

The most useful identification characteristics to differentiate this goby from the Rock Goby are the sensory papillae on both the top and sides of the head. These are dark brown or more usually black and are sometimes visible to the naked eye, relatively easy to see with a magnifying glass and often clear in close up underwater photographs. The Rock Goby has sensory papillae but these are not visible in the way that those of the black goby are.

**SIMILAR SPECIES** Other differences between this and the Rock Goby are described under the latter and commented in above and in the goby introduction. See also Couch's Goby (pages 210–211).

**BEHAVIOUR** There have been some suggestions from divers that this goby may on occasion, hide in the burrows of other animals (as Fries's Goby does) but this has not yet been substantiated.

**HABITAT** In contrast to the similar Rock Goby, the Black Goby prefers sandy and muddy habitats, especially in estuaries and other low salinity areas, but also around sheltered coasts especially in bays and eel-grass beds. It is also found in gravel, maerl and stony areas, and in mixed sediment and rock areas down to around 75m depth.

**DISTRIBUTION** The Black Goby is found all round the Welsh coast where it is considered to be frequent to common. It also occurs

all round the rest of the British Isles, and north to Norway, south to Mauritania and throughout the Mediterranean and Black Sea.

**NATURAL HISTORY** Females lay their eggs in the summer months, attaching them inside or under old mollusc shells and under pebbles and stones or in whatever other cover they can find and arranging them in a dense patch. The male is left on guard until the eggs hatch and the fry drift away.

**SIGHTINGS** This goby can often be caught in push nets at low tide level and in fine beach seine nets from suitable sediment shores. Divers who don't mind visiting the sort of sheltered sediment or stony grounds that it prefers will also see it. It is also caught in beam trawls and is sometimes used as live bait.

# ROCK GOBY     Bili bigog     *Gobius paganellus*

**12cm**

**KEY IDENTIFICATION FEATURES** This fish can be identified in the field with a high degree of certainty. It is a large (up to 12cm long) chunky, solid-looking goby, in varying shades of brown, with darker mottling and blotches. Older fish and breeding males are often very dark to almost black. The first dorsal fin has a pale band of cream or yellow colour along the top edge and is diagnostic, especially in breeding males when it may be a conspicuous orange. A very close look or photograph will show a fringe of tiny filaments around the nostrils and scales on top of its head – useful if only the head can be seen.

**SIMILAR SPECIES** The general colour can be similar to the black goby especially in dark older and breeding fish. However, provided the first dorsal fin can be seen, the two gobies should not be confused. If only the head is visible check for scales as the Rock Goby has them right up to the eyes (see photo on page 33) whilst the Black Goby has some but they are not extensive. In addition these two gobies live in different habitats with little overlap. See also Introduction to gobies.

**BEHAVIOUR** Young fish may be gregarious but larger fish tend to be solitary especially during the breeding season. They can sometimes be seen lying quietly on rock tops, especially when guarding eggs, or out and about searching for crustaceans, worms and small fish.

**HABITAT** The best place to search for this goby is in rock pools and under stones and boulders on sheltered shores with plenty of seaweed cover. They are not usually found higher up the shore than around mid shore level. They also live in inshore rocky shallows down to about 15m depth.

**DISTRIBUTION** This is a widespread goby that is locally common all round the Welsh coast where there is suitable habitat. Its wider distribution extends all round Ireland, along west coast British Isles, English Channel, south to Senegal and in the Mediterranean and Black Sea.

**NATURAL HISTORY** Eggs are laid in protective holes and crevices or under rocks between about April to June in Welsh waters.

**SIGHTINGS** A large goby living on a rocky shore is most likely to be this species. Divers may also see it peering out from rock crevices or out in the open in shallow, rocky areas.

# INSHORE SEDIMENT GOBIES *POMATOSCHISTUS* SPP.

**PAINTED GOBY** Gobi lliwgar, *P. pictus*, **COMMON GOBY** Gobi, *P. microps* and
**SAND GOBY** Gobi y tywod, *P. minutus*

Pomatoschistus pictus

Pomatoschistus microps

Identification of the bottom two gobies remains difficult and features are not always as clear as would be preferred!

Pomatoschistus minutus

## KEY IDENTIFICATION FEATURES

The best way to tell these little gobies apart is to take close up underwater photographs from various angles including, if possible, one with the dorsal fins erect. A leisurely study can then be made later of the body and fin markings. Record of habitat and depth will also help. Gobies caught in nets or trawls can be kept alive and examined in a small tank or jam-jar and likewise photographed. All three are small, sand-coloured gobies with darker markings. All three usually grow to around 6cm long but can reach 9cm.

**PAINTED GOBY**  Look for one (sometimes two) rows of black spots along both dorsal fins. With the fins erect these are often quite clear and definitive. In breeding males the dorsal fins develop a bright, ice-blue colour and the spots may be large and so appear as black bands interspersed by blue bands. A really close look will also often show four pale saddles extending from the back half way down the sides, each with an irregular double black spot beneath it. These are not unique to the painted goby but are helpful in combination with the fin marks and with habitat.

**COMMON GOBY**  Look for a small, triangular black mark at the base of each pectoral fin. Neither of the other two species has this, and it is definitive when it is clear. Males have a dark spot on the rear of the first dorsal fin but in females this is either very unclear or absent, meaning they have hardly any distinguishing markings.

**SAND GOBY**  Males can often be identified if the dorsal fin is held erect. There is a conspicuous dark spot on its rear outlined in white or pale blue. It is not yet clear whether this is present only in the breeding season in males or in both sexes. Other books and references contradict each other over this. Check that there is no black mark at the base of the pectoral fin. Whilst both Common and Sand Goby males have the black mark on the first dorsal fin, it seems that the pale outline is restricted to the Sand Goby (but see also Norway Goby below).

**SIMILAR SPECIES**  The Norway Goby is almost identical to the Sand goby but lives in deeper water (see page 206).

**BEHAVIOUR**  Painted Gobies at least will often treat divers as large fish and will  come in to look for food if a hole is dug in the sediment.

**HABITAT**  Common Gobies are abundant on sandy and muddy shores in pools extending right up to high level, low salinity pools and even into coastal ditches and pools high up in estuaries. Sand Gobies are also found on the shore, but only near low tide level. Painted Gobies can be found in lower shore pools but only in stony areas or near rocks on sandy shores.

Below the shore in coastal areas, the Painted Goby prefers coarser ground to the other two species. It is usually found on gravel, shell gravel or sediment mixed with shells and stones. The Sand Goby is usually found on sand. Common Gobies prefer low salinity estuaries and river mouths.

### HABITAT SUMMARY

Brackish water and high shore pools – probably Common Gobies.

Clean inshore sand – probably Sand Gobies.

Gravel and pebble sediment – probably Painted Gobies.

**DISTRIBUTION**  Painted, Sand and Common Gobies are found all round the Welsh coast. They also extend all round the British Isles, north to Scandinavia. Sand and Common Gobies extend south into the Mediterranean. Painted Gobies may extend into the Mediterranean but there are few records. However the distribution of these gobies needs further work due to widespread misidentifications.

**NATURAL HISTORY**  There are few stones or crevices available in the sediment habitats preferred by these little fish and so the eggs are often laid in or under empty bivalve shells and then guarded by the males. These are more readily available in the shell grounds preferred by Painted Gobies. Sand Gobies can sometimes be seen peering out from a chamber excavated beneath an upturned half shell. The nest is made secure by piling sand on top of the shell.

These small gobies are an essential and abundant food item for many bottom-living fish including commercial species such as cod and flatfish.

**SIGHTINGS**  A search of pools on sandy shores above mid-tide level will mostly come up with Common Gobies. A push net used at low tide on a sandy shore will mostly catch Sand Gobies. Sand Gobies are often caught in large numbers in shrimp trawls working in bays and along coasts, but in low salinity areas such as estuaries, it is largely Common Gobies that are caught. Summer divers mostly see Sand and Painted Gobies. Common Gobies tend to live in shallow areas not generally thought to be good dive spots. However, in winter many migrate into deeper water.

**RECORDS**  School parties and inexperienced adults should record as 'Sand' gobies (*Pomatoschistus* sp.) or send clear photographs for expert identification. See also 'Sand Goby look-alikes' on page 206.

The Painted Goby has a blunt face which, with experience and familiarity, often allows it to be distinguished from the other gobies.

# SAND GOBY *POMATOSCHISTUS MINUTUS* LOOK-ALIKES

**LOZANO'S GOBY**  Gobi Lozano, *P. lozano* and **NORWAY GOBY**  Gobi Norwy, *P. norvegicus*

A goby head peeping out from under a shell probably indicates that the fish is guarding eggs laid on the shell.

**GUIDE (ONLY) TO FIELD RECORDING OF SAND GOBIES**

A sand goby shorter than 8cm, found in shallow/estuarine water (above 10m) is either a **Sand Goby** or Lozano's Goby

A sand goby longer than 8cm found in shallow/estuarine water (above 10m) is a **Sand Goby** (depth range about 0–20m).

A sand goby found offshore below 30m is a **Norway Goby** (depth range about 20–325m, most abundant 50–120m).

There are two other 'sand' gobies almost identical in appearance to the true Sand Goby. Lozano's Goby, *Pomatoschistus lozanoi* occurs in the same inshore and estuarine habitats as the Sand Goby. The Norway Goby *Pomatoschistus norvegicus*, is generally found in deeper water below about 20m. These three gobies can only be reliably told apart by microscopic examination of features such as scale counts and patterns of sensory papillae on the head. However, there are subtle differences (see table below) that, with experience, will sometimes allow these species to be told apart in the field and from close up photographs.

As a consequence of these identification difficulties, whilst there are a few confirmed records of the Norway Goby and Lozano's Goby around Wales, these fish may well be more widespread but unrecognised.

Matching *in situ* photographs and specimens from deeper water might show up clear visual differences but it would be very difficult for divers to catch these fish! Trawled fish might be kept alive and photographed in tanks before preserving them. Further taxonomic work and revision is still needed on all these and other sand-dwelling gobies.

| Detailed features | COMMON GOBY | SAND GOBY | LOZANO'S GOBY | NORWAY GOBY |
| --- | --- | --- | --- | --- |
| Spot on posterior edge of first dorsal fin | Black; males and sometimes females | Blue-edged black; males and possibly females; does not reach edge of membrane | Males (in spring only); reaches edge of membrane | Males and females; reaches edge of membrane |
| Scales on head, nape and breast | No | Yes | | No |
| Front membrane of pelvic fin disc well developed and edged with small villi (finger-like processes) | No | Yes | ?? | ?? |
| Scales along sides (pectoral fin base to tail fin base) | 39-52 | 50-70 | ?? | 55-60 |
| Maximum size | 7cm | 11cm | 8cm | 6.5cm |

# OFFSHORE SEDIMENT GOBIES

## JEFFREYS'S GOBY      Gobi Jeffreys      *Buenia jeffreysii*

**6cm**

**KEY IDENTIFICATION FEATURES** Male Jeffreys's Gobies can be recognised underwater by the long second ray in the first dorsal fin – if the fins are raised. The front part of this fin is a beautiful blue colour (possibly only in the breeding season). Females and males with their fins folded down may be hard to tell from other small sand-dwelling gobies but, with experience the colour and patterning, combined with the habitat, may be sufficient to distinguish this species. Those photographed underwater exhibit rusty-red spots and reticulations on a pale greyish background. Four pale saddles reach across the back and down to four large, dark, diffuse spots on the mid-line on each side. This is often, but not always, clear and needs a good look.

**SIMILAR SPECIES** The Black Goby also has elongated rays in the first dorsal fin but is much bigger, with different coloration. The patterning on the body is similar to the Painted Goby but redder.

**BEHAVIOUR** In photographs from Scottish sea lochs, this goby is seen propping itself up on its pectoral fins.

**HABITAT** This little-known goby has mostly been recorded from dredges and trawl nets in offshore sand, mud and gravel from 5m to about 330m depth. It has also been reported from stony *Lithothamnion*-covered (calcareous algae) grounds. In sheltered Scottish sea lochs such as Loch Fyne, divers have recently photographed this fish as shallow as 10m depth on muddy sand and shell bottoms.

**DISTRIBUTION** In Welsh waters, specimens of Jeffreys's Goby have been found in the Severn estuary, but it is such an easily overlooked or misidentified fish that its distribution may well be more widespread around Wales. Elsewhere it is found from Iceland and Norway down the west coast of the British Isles to Brittany and Portugal and possibly into the western Mediterranean. There appear to be no records from the southern North Sea.

**NATURAL HISTORY** Little is know about the lifestyle of this little fish. Like other sand-living gobies, females appear to lay their eggs in summer in mollusc shells and the males guard them.

**SIGHTINGS** In Welsh waters this goby has so far only been identified from caught specimens. If offshore commercial boats, using small-mesh nets were to keep any small goby-like fish for expert identification, more records might well turn up. Divers should look out for this goby in sheltered inshore bays, inlets and estuaries, with similar sediment habitats to the Scottish sea lochs where it has already been photographed.

# FRIES'S GOBY

## Gobi Freis

### *Lesuerigobius friesii*

10cm

**KEY IDENTIFICATION FEATURES** Divers can easily recognise this goby from its colour pattern. The body and head are covered in large golden to brown blotches, often overlain with yellow, whilst the yellow-edged dorsal, anal and tail fins have scattered bright yellow spots. The first dorsal fin is pointed, with elongated rays, and unlike in most gobies, the tail is also pointed.

**SIMILAR SPECIES** Although identification of dead goby specimens can be difficult, as their the colour fades and fins are often damaged, the spots of Fries's Goby may remain even after freezing and thawing as shown in the dredged specimen below.

**BEHAVIOUR** This beautiful goby has the added attraction of sharing burrows with Norway Lobsters *Nephrops norvegicus*, discovered by resin casting of burrows and diver observations. This association appears to be widespread but not all Fries's Gobies are found with Norway Lobsters. The goby may act as a lookout for its companion in a similar way to the association between tropical gobies and burrowing shrimps. It is certainly shy and will dart back into its burrow at the first sign of danger.

**HABITAT** Burrows in muddy sand and mud, mostly offshore from about 20–130m but sometimes as deep as 350m, and also inshore in sheltered sealochs as shallow as 10m depth.

**DISTRIBUTION** There are a very few confirmed records of this goby from Welsh waters and it does not appear to be common anywhere in northern Europe. It extends from southern Norway, down the west coast of the British Isles, all around Ireland and the Isle of Man, south to Spain and Portugal and into the Mediterranean.

**NATURAL HISTORY** Little information is available. Females lay their eggs in mud burrows in the summer months (May to August in Scotland).

**SIGHTINGS** Most records of this goby are from trawls and nets on offshore muddy sediments, especially boats fishing for Norway Lobster *Nephrops norvegicus*. In recent years, divers have photographed this fish regularly in Scottish sea lochs such as Lochs Carron, Linnhe and Lochaline. Any observations of this apparently rare fish in Welsh waters, especially from divers, would be of great interest.

# DIMINUTIVE GOBY　　　Gobi bach　　　*Lebetus scorpioides*

**4cm**

**KEY IDENTIFICATION FEATURES** This tiny goby only reaches about 4cm long but in spite of its small size, the males at least can be recognised underwater. The most obvious identification feature is the first dorsal fin. This is tall and sail-like in relation to the gobies size and is yellow, edged with white to pale blue. The second dorsal fin is edged in black and decorated with diagonal yellow and white bands. Although often described as yellowish to dusky grey, most fish in underwater photographs are a marbled reddish colour with a paler tail stalk. Females are reported to have clear cross bars on the body and some differences in the colour of the dorsal fin markings including a dark spot at the rear of the first dorsal.

**SIMILAR SPECIES** Guillet's Goby *Lebetus guilleti* is a similar but little known species that seems to occur in shallower water than its relative. It is likely that these two species, especially the females, have and are being confused and more photographs and specimens are needed.

**BEHAVIOUR** No information.

**HABITAT** Most records are from coarse offshore sediments mainly sand and shell gravel and especially amongst stones and shells covered in calcareous algae. It is sometimes found on muddy sand which is the habitat it has been found on in Scottish sea lochs. In southwest Norway this goby has been photographed as shallow as 15m and even shallower in Scotland at around 5m, but it mostly lives between 30–100m and down to a maximum of 375m.

**DISTRIBUTION** There are confirmed records of this goby from the Severn Estuary but so far no underwater sightings in Welsh waters. Elsewhere it has been found from Iceland, the Faroes and Norway south to the northern Bay of Biscay. Its small size and habitat means that records are patchy and incomplete.

**NATURAL HISTORY** Very little is known about this goby. It spawns from February to September, the time probably depending on water temperature.

**SIGHTINGS** This tiny goby can be found by sharp-eyed divers and has recently been photographed underwater in Scottish sea lochs. It is too small for most commercial trawls and most records are from scientific surveys.

This is a female Diminutive Goby which can be confused with Jeffreys's Goby, but its smaller size, a first dorsal fin which is much bigger than the Jeffreys's relative to the rest of the body and the lack of translucence should distinguish it.

# RARE SOUTHERN GOBIES *GOBIUS* SPP.

**GIANT GOBY** Gobi mawr, *G. cobitis*; **COUCH'S GOBY** Gobi mawr, *G. couchi* and
**RED-MOUTHED GOBY** Gobi Mingoch, *G. cruentatus*

Giant Goby

Couch's Goby

Red-mouth Goby

In addition to those already described above, three other large gobies are resident in the British Isles, but have so far been found at only a few places in the south and south west. They are described here because it is likely they have a wider occurrence in southern British waters and may even extend into Welsh waters but they all need careful searching to find them.

## KEY IDENTIFICATION FEATURES

**GIANT GOBY** 27cm. Fully grown adults are so large (for a goby) that they could not be mistaken for any other goby, but small ones are more difficult to identify with certainty in the field. This is a thickset goby with a large head and a wide tail base. It is a rather drab, grey, light brown to olive brown in colour with darker mottling and has a distinctly speckled appearance ('pepper and salt' look).

**COUCH'S GOBY** 8cm. This is another rather nondescript goby that is difficult to identify in the field. It is a pale brown to grey mottled colour but is copiously speckled with golden to yellow flecks on the sides and this is the key feature to look for. It also has a line of dark brown blotches along each side. A good, close photograph should be sufficient for an expert to confirm identification of this rare fish but without this or a specimen, identification will be uncertain.

**RED-MOUTHED GOBY** 18cm. The size and characteristic colour are enough to identify this goby in the field. As its name suggests it has vivid red lips and is a speckled reddish brown colour all over, with darker blotches. Some fish are much brighter than others and have more or less red on the lips. Lines of black papillae can be seen on the head in close up photographs.

**SIMILAR SPECIES** Couch's Goby can all to easily be confused with small Black Gobies although if the latter has a high first dorsal fin this will distinguish it. Small Giant Gobies can also look similar. It is important to record details of the habitat and location as well as take photographs in order to help identification.

**BEHAVIOUR** Red-mouthed Gobies in Loch Hyne, in County Cork, Ireland show little fear of divers and can readily be photographed. Giant Gobies have been seen basking in sunny spots in their pools.

**HABITAT** Red-mouthed Gobies in Loch Hyne are found in shallow, rocky areas. In the Mediterranean they mostly live between 10–40m depth and frequent seagass beds and sandy areas as well as rocky reefs. Giant Gobies in England have mostly been found in stone filled pools on the shore, often those with fresh water trickling into them and with the green alga *Enteromorpha*. In the Mediterranean it occurs down to about 10m and this is probably also the case in our waters. There is a recent (2008) report and photograph on the British Marine Life Study Society website of a Giant Goby that was caught by an angler near Padstow (Cornwall). Couch's Goby has been recorded from weed-filled rock pools and in shallow water.

**DISTRIBUTION** The Red-mouthed Goby has only been recorded from a few sites in southern Ireland, where it is common in Lough Hyne (Co. Cork) and possibly from Worbarrow Bay, Dorset; the Giant Goby in southwest Britain from Wembury to the Scilly Isles and Channel Islands; and Couch's Goby from Helford and Portland in the Channel and in Ireland, from Lough Hyne and Mulroy Bay (Co. Donegal). Red-mouthed Goby and Giant Goby are both found further south to Morocco and in the Mediterranean. Until very recently, Couch's Goby had not been recorded from anywhere else, possibly because it has not been recognised. It has now (2008) been found in the Fal estuary (Cornwall) and from the Mediterranean.

**NATURAL HISTORY** There is still little information about these three gobies, especially Couch's Goby. Giant Goby mature at two or three years old and spawn in spring. The eggs are attached to the undersides of stones and are guarded by the male. They can live for about ten years.

**SIGHTINGS** All sightings of these gobies are of great interest. Look out for them in rock pools and shallow water. Giant Goby and Couch's Goby are both protected species in UK under Schedule 5 of the Wildlife and Countryside Act.

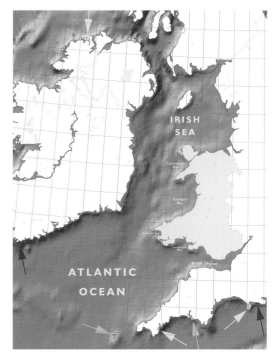

● Red-mouthed Goby
● Giant Goby
● Couch's Goby

# HOW TO PHOTOGRAPH AND RECORD GOBIES

In order to be able to photograph gobies underwater and identify them later from the resulting images, it is important to capture the relevant identifying features in the image. So first of all it is necessary to learn as much as possible about these features from this and any other books on marine fishes.

As gobies are generally small fishes (and some are very small) it is essential to get as close as possible and to use as long (focal length) a macro lens as possible too. Digital single lens reflex cameras fitted with macro lenses with a focal length of about 1.5~2 x their format's diagonal (which equates to around 100mm macro lens on a full frame 35mm camera) are ideal tools for photographing gobies, but still require a good amount of photographic knowledge, excellent diving skills (especially buoyancy control as many gobies live in sediment areas) and patience.

An ideal image should show a full, side-on view of a goby (standing on its pectoral fin if a seabed dweller) with all its dorsal fins fully raised. Unfortunately, whilst this is sometimes (rather rarely in the author's experience) possible with a co-operative fish, most are both nervous and angled in positions where it is impossible to achieve a side-on shot.

**This Jeffreys's Goby is posing nicely but this is not always the case!**

So generally it is best to first try and photograph whatever key identification features are visible, and then try for other shots if the fish hasn't darted away. In order to do this you need to know what these features are beforehand. A little research will show which gobies might turn up at a specific site and so allow you to study their features before going on the dive.

Some features are visible in images, such as the dark coloured sensory papillae on the Black Gobies face, but may not actually be easy or even possible to see underwater. In this case, knowledge that the fish may be, or is likely to be, a Black Goby should be used and this means concentrating on achieving images which focus on the eyes or face around the eyes. Confirmation of the fish's identity can be made by enlarging the images and checking to see if they do in fact show the papillae.

Black Gobies can be identified from the rows of small, black sensory papillae on their faces and heads – these are rarely visible underwater but a high quality, close-up digital image can show them up very clearly indeed.

Fortunately the fish that the Black Goby is most likely to be confused with is the Rock Goby and concentrating on similar images should also reveal whether the head and nape have scales on them – which is a characteristic of the Rock Goby. The Black Goby may have some scales on its head and also sometimes patterning which can look like scales so focus needs to be very accurate! Clearly, head on images may show up the papillae but are unlikely to indicate the presence of these scales on the head or nape.

Some gobies which live in mid-water, such as the Transparent and Crystal Gobies, are extremely difficult to photograph at all, requiring cameras with extremely effective auto-focus capabilities and even so will often need a very strong 'spotting light' mounted on the camera to provide illumination so that the camera can achieve focus. Images of these two species require that the dorsal (and if possible anal) fins and/or mouths be viewable and to capture such images is by no means easy. The secret here is to keep trying and the more images which are taken, the more chance that relevant details will be visible in some of the final images.

Unfortunately, not all images will allow precise identification of gobies that they are of. It is very easy to be tempted to assume that the subject is a particular goby despite all the relevant features not being visible and this is quite acceptable providing that the images are allied to the photographer's natural history 'fieldcraft' and an understanding of what was actually being seen at the time. If doubt still persists then a more generalised description should be logged.

Although taken in very poor conditions, this photo shows scales on the top of this goby's head and no sensory papillae showing it to be a Rock Goby, even at a depth of 20m.

Although Black Gobies also make use of burrows, the orange markings and large scales clearly identify this as Fries's Goby.

With practice and experience, once you have your 'eye-in', it is possible to identify some gobies from their faces. This is a Painted Goby which is more 'snub-faced' than other sandy coloured gobies.

# BLENNIES

## Family Blennidae

Blennies belong to a large family (Blennidae) of small, bottom-living fish found mostly on the shore and in shallow water. They are cryptic fish, hiding away in the undergrowth or in holes, but even if only the head is showing, it should be possible to recognise a blenny as such. These attractive fish have a blunt head with large, bulbous eyes set high up and thick lips. All the species described here, except the Shanny, have a pair of head tentacles or a skin flap just behind the eyes. The pelvic fins are on the underside just behind the head, and consist of only two stout rays, resembling an old-fashioned clothes peg. When resting, a blenny will prop itself up on its pelvic fins whilst it has a good look round. There is a single, long dorsal fin with weak spiny rays at the front and soft rays at the back, with a dip in the fin where the two parts meet. A really close look at a blenny will show that it has no scales and small comb-like teeth; this family is sometimes called Combtooth blennies. With a co-operative Tompot Blenny, the teeth can even be seen underwater.

Perhaps the best time to spot blennies is in spring and summer when they are breeding. The eggs are laid in cracks and crevices and are guarded, usually by the male.

A number of other fish are also commonly called blennies (e.g. Yarrell's Blenny) but although they have some characteristics in common with true blennies, they belong to several other families. These are described below. Four blennies are found in Welsh waters whilst a further two southern species have now been recorded from the English Channel, and may move further north with ocean warming.

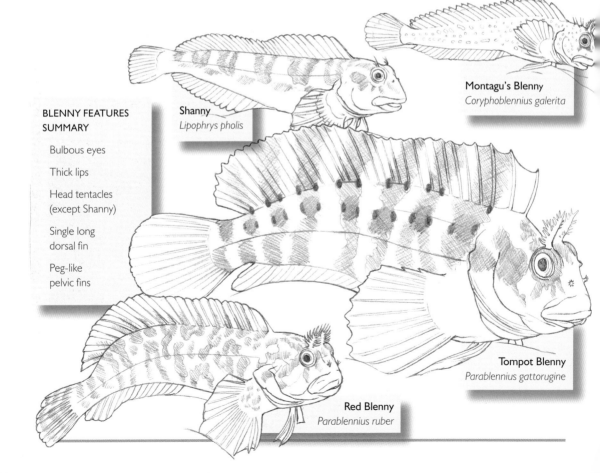

**BLENNY FEATURES SUMMARY**

Bulbous eyes

Thick lips

Head tentacles (except Shanny)

Single long dorsal fin

Peg-like pelvic fins

**Shanny**
*Lipophrys pholis*

**Montagu's Blenny**
*Coryphoblennius galerita*

**Tompot Blenny**
*Parablennius gattorugine*

**Red Blenny**
*Parablennius ruber*

# SHANNY                    Llyfrothen lefn                    *Lipophrys pholis*

**Other names: Irish – An Ceannruán**                                    **30cm**

**KEY IDENTIFICATION FEATURES**  This fish can be identified in the field with a high degree of certainty. Once you are sure that this is a blenny then identification is easy. This is the only European blenny that does not have head tentacles and it has a smoothly rounded forehead. Its mottled brownish or greenish colour is variable with habitat. Usually up to 15cm but can reach 30cm.

**SIMILAR SPECIES**  Like all blennies, the Shanny has one long dorsal fin but this dips down in the middle and could be mistaken for the two separate fins of a goby.

**BEHAVIOUR**  Like the Tompot Blenny, the Shanny will watch you propped up on its pelvic fins, but it is nervous and will disappear quickly into cover.

**HABITAT**  Look for this blenny in rock pools hidden amongst seaweeds, around wrecks and man-made structures and in shallow water to around 10m. In winter most move down to areas below the shore. Maximum recorded depth is about 30m.

**DISTRIBUTION**  Common all round the coast of Wales, and also all round Great Britain and Ireland, north to southern Norway and south to Morocco.

**NATURAL HISTORY**  Almost black Shannies with white lips are breeding and nesting males. This can be seen in aquarium fish as well as in the wild. The male guards eggs laid by the female under rocks and in crevices. He remains on duty for several weeks until the eggs hatch.

**SIGHTINGS**  Usually spotted in rock pools, or in shallow water during shore dives and snorkels. Only records of unusual size or interesting behaviour needed.

**NOTES**  Apparently the name Shanny is the name originally used by Cornish fishermen but its origin is obscure.

## A FISH OUT OF WATER

If stranded by the retreating tide, Shannies (and Montagu's Blennies) can survive by hiding beneath rocks and seaweeds. During this time they absorb oxygen from the air through their scaleless skin.

# MONTAGU'S BLENNY  Llyfrothen Montagu  *Coryphoblennius galerita*

Named after the English naturalist Col. George Montagu (1751–1815)  **8cm**

**KEY IDENTIFICATION FEATURES**  This fish can be identified in the field with a high degree of certainty. If you can get a close look at this blenny's head then identification is easy. Instead of the usual pair of tentacles found in most blennies, Montagu's Blenny has a single triangular flap of skin with ragged edges often referred to as a crest and behind that a line of additional, tiny skin filaments. The head and body are peppered with small pale blue spots, but these may be indistinct in older fish.

**SIMILAR SPECIES**  If you only glimpse a Montagu's Blenny then you could mistake it for a small Shanny, which has a similar overall coloration, a similar dip in the dorsal fin and is also found in rock pools. Young fish might be mistaken for shannies, so small fish need careful examination.

**BEHAVIOUR**  These little fish have been observed to nip off the cirri (feeding limbs) of barnacles.

**HABITAT**  Mostly found in rock pools and in the Britain Isles at least, seems to prefer middle shore pools lined with coral weed *Corallina* and encrusting pink algae. Further south it has been seen in shallow sublittoral water near rock faces, especially those covered in barnacles.

**DISTRIBUTION**  Confined to the south-west of Britain and Ireland from southern Wales to Dorset and Donegal to Co Cork. Very rarely it has been reported in Scotland as far north as Argyllshire. In also occurs south possibly as far as Guinea, and around the Canary Islands and in the Mediterranean.

**NATURAL HISTORY**  Look out for males guarding their eggs, laid in the summer months by females in crevices, barnacle shells and piddock holes. Males have been observed to have an orange or yellow crest and corners to the mouth. These may be breeding colours but this blenny is not often seen in winter.

**SIGHTINGS**  Almost always seen in rock pools. As this is predominantly a southern species, ocean warming may allow it to move further north. Look carefully at any blennies in rock pools in North Wales.

## MORE BLENNIES?

Other blennies usually found well to the south of the UK are also sometimes being observed. These are often difficult to identify with certainty as only photographic records are generally available which do not always show the relevant features. Some of these fish may well appear in Welsh waters sometime and any unusual blenny should be well photographed if at all possible. Recently there have been reports of both the Variable Blenny *Parablennius pilicornis* and the Striped Blenny *Parablennius rouxi* from the south English coast, but both still have to be confirmed.

# BUTTERFLY BLENNY          Llyfrothen adeiniog          *Blennius ocellaris*

**20cm**

**KEY IDENTIFICATION FEATURES** This fish can be identified in the field with a high degree of certainty The view you will usually get of this blenny is just its head sticking out of a shell or discarded tin can. This can make identification difficult but the habitat is very different from similar species such as the Tompot Blenny. Out in the open with its dorsal fin raised, the Butterfly Blenny is unmistakable. The dorsal fin is very high and clearly divided into two sections by a sharp dip. The first section is decorated by a large black eye spot, with a pale blue or white halo.

**SIMILAR SPECIES** This is the only European blenny to be found at any depth and the only Welsh one found on softer seabeds.

**BEHAVIOUR** A few observations suggest that in winter butterfly blennies may spend much of their time curled up inside or under shells – see below.

**HABITAT** The Butterfly Blenny is generally found below about 10m depth down to at least 100m and possibly 400m, on gravel, maerl, shelly sediment and sometimes sand. It shelters inside empty mollusc shells, old tyres, tin cans, bottles (especially liking old style Bovril bottles) or hides behind stones and debris, especially when guarding eggs, when empty whelk shells are much favoured.

**DISTRIBUTION** The British Isles are at the northern limit of the distribution of this species, which is found as far south as Morocco and throughout the Mediterranean. It has been recorded around most of the Welsh coast but only at scattered sites in small numbers where there is suitable habitat. It also extends up the west coast of Ireland at least as far north as the Arran Islands and Kilkieran Bay, and through the Irish Sea to the Isle of Man. It is also known from southern Scotland.

**NATURAL HISTORY** This blenny has been observed guarding eggs inside empty whelk shells (Paul Kay pers. comm.) during the summer months in both Welsh and Irish waters. As in other blennies it is the male that does all the work. Butterfly Blennies are so determined to guard their eggs that they can be trawled up still inside shells and bottles to which their eggs are attached.

**SIGHTINGS** Most sightings are by diving photographers and biologists who are looking out for interesting small animals in gravel and maerl beds – not the usual haunt of recreational divers. They are also caught in benthic trawls.

Any sightings of this species north of the English Channel are of interest, especially of males guarding eggs, as there is little information on this in Welsh waters. Winter records would also be useful as it is possible from what few observations have been made that they shelter inside or under shells, curled up and possibly remaining fairly dormant to conserve energy.

# TOMPOT BLENNY                Tompot          *Parablennius gattorugine*

**Other names: Gattorugine (Italian gatto: cat, and ruggine: rust coloured)**        **30cm**

**KEY IDENTIFICATION FEATURES**  This fish can be identified in the field with a high degree of certainty. Shape, colour and behaviour all help to identify this blenny. It is large and stout commonly up to 20cm and sometimes as much as 30cm long. It has very thick lips and large, much branched head tentacles. Most tompots are a mottled brownish-red colour with a series of vertical darker bars. The dorsal fin has no dip in the middle.

**SIMILAR SPECIES**  It would be possible to confuse a Tompot Blenny with a Butterfly Blenny, if only the head can be seen. Tompots do sometimes live in stony areas where Butterfly Blennies might be found, but in general their depth and habitat preferences are different.

**BEHAVIOUR**  In general, Tompot Blennies are inquisitive and can easily be approached. They emerge from their hidey holes to search for food and to see off intruders and will often come out and inspect visiting divers, especially at dawn and dusk when they appear to be more active. They are territorial, and divers re-visiting sites report the same individuals in the same crevices. Whether homes are retained between breeding seasons is an interesting question.

**HABITAT**  Tompot Blennies prefer shallow rocky areas with plenty of crevices and hidey holes and also frequent wrecks and other man-made structures. They are bottom-living fish and swim clumsily from cover to cover in short bursts. Most fish are spotted between about 1m to 12m depth but there are records down to at least 30m. Juveniles are sometimes found in rock pools low down on the shore.

**DISTRIBUTION**  This blenny has been recorded all round the Welsh coast. It is also found all round Ireland, along the entire Atlantic and Channel coasts of Great Britain, south to Morocco and throughout the Mediterranean. A recent record from Norfolk (Seasearch annual report 2007) suggests it may be moving up along the North Sea coast. It has also been recorded from Southend (Naylor 2005).

**NATURAL HISTORY**  Females (sometimes several) lay their sticky eggs in hidden crevices between March and May and the male guards them until they hatch a few weeks later. How far the larvae drift and swim is not well documented but juveniles are thought to settle on the seabed in summer.

**SIGHTINGS**  This blenny is usually only seen by divers or occasionally by sharp-eyed snorkelers. It is well known by underwater photographers who appreciate its habit of posing, propped up on its pelvic fins. The most usual view is of a cheeky head peering out from the fish's chosen crevice home. It is also occasionally hauled up in crab pots. Around Wales, sightings from unusual habitats or depths would be useful plus observations on feeding habits. Any records from the North Sea would be useful.

# RED BLENNY      Llyfrothen goch      *Parablennius ruber*

**Other names: Portuguese Blenny**      14cm

**KEY IDENTIFICATION FEATURES** This fish can be identified in the field with a high degree of certainty but must be carefully observed and preferably photographed as it is quite similar to the Tompot Blenny. A typical, slim blenny with a pair of branched head tentacles. As its name suggests, it is basically red in colour with a pattern of red markings overlying a paler red background. Breeding males have a large yellow-rimmed blue spot at the front of the dorsal fin. A pattern of red lines radiating from the eyes may prove to be a universal feature.

**SIMILAR SPECIES** The Red Blenny looks very similar to the Tompot Blenny *P. gattorugine*, and the two species have been extensively confused in the past. The Red Blenny has usually been dismissed as just a Tompot colour variant. After a photograph, taken in 2002 by Paul Kay, of a male red blenny off the Arran Islands, Ireland was published, more photographic records came to light, showing that these blennies are, and have been for at least the last 20 years, found all along the western coasts of Ireland and Scotland. Both habitat and behaviour should help distinguish these two species.

**BEHAVIOUR** Small groups of Red Blennies have been seen living together in the same crevice (in groups of up to 5~15). This is in contrast to the usually solitary Tompot Blenny. The Red Blenny does not appear to have the brave and inquisitive nature of the Tompot Blenny.

**HABITAT** Red Blennies seem to like very exposed rocky habitats with plenty of crevices in which to hide, typically below 10m depth, though there are some old shore records that may be erroneous. Red Blennies and Tompot Blennies are rarely seen together in the same habitat as Tompots seem to prefer more sheltered conditions.

**DISTRIBUTION** West coasts of Ireland and Scotland as least as far north as St Kilda and the Isle of Lewis. It may also occur on other exposed coasts in the UK but as yet (2008) none have been reported from England (apart from the Scilly Islands) or Wales. Further south it is known from Portugal, the Azores and Maderia.

**NATURAL HISTORY** Few *in situ* observations have been made of this species. The eggs are attached to rocks and the male probably guards them.

**SIGHTINGS** Rarely seen, even by divers as it lives in very exposed areas and disappears into crevices at the first sight of danger. Records of this species are needed to establish its current distribution, status and natural history. Look out for it at exposed sites in Wales and elsewhere.

# BLENNY-LIKE FISH

As well as the large family of true blennies (Blennidae), there are four common families of fish that are often called blennies and have some blenny-like characteristics. They are described together to help identification but the families are not all closely related.

PRICKLEBACKS (STICHAEIDAE) are represented in Welsh waters by only one species, Yarrell's Blenny. The Snake Blenny *Lumpenus lampretaeformis* is a northern species extending south as far as Scotland and North Sea coasts, whilst the Spotted Snake Blenny *Leptoclinus maculatus* does not even extend as far south as Great Britain.

GUNNELS (PHOLIDIDAE) are mainly found in the Arctic and only one species, the Butterfish or Rock Gunnel, extends as far south as Wales where it can be quite common and is described here.

EELPOUTS (ZOARCIDAE) are mainly northern and deepwater fish. The Viviparous Blenny *Zoarces viviparous* is the commonest species, but it has not yet been recorded from Welsh waters. However, it is found in nearby waters and is described here.

THREE-FIN BLENNIES (TRIPTERIGIIDAE) belong to a large family of fish that live mostly in warm and tropical waters. The Black-face Blenny *Tripterygion delaisi* is included here as it has been recorded from Dorset, Devon and Cornwall and could extend its range further north with ocean warming.

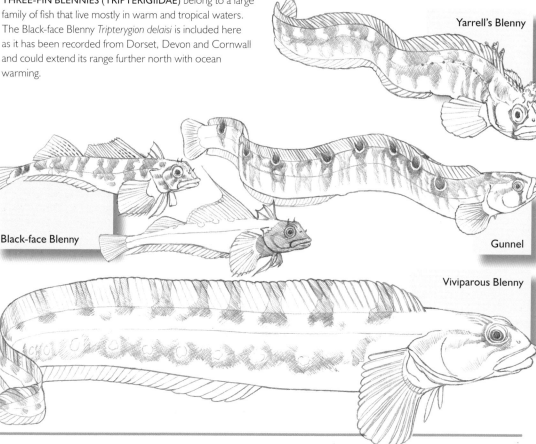

Yarrell's Blenny

Black-face Blenny

Gunnel

Viviparous Blenny

# ROCK GUNNEL       Llyfrothen       *Pholis gunnellus*

**Other names: Butterfish, Gunnel, Irish – Sleamhnóg**       **25cm**

**KEY IDENTIFICATION FEATURES** This species can be identified with a high degree of certainty in the field. Shaped like a sideways flattened eel, it grows to around 25cm long and like true blennies it has thick down turned lips and rather bulbous eyes which give it a rather sad looking expression. A striking row of 9–15 (often 12) black spots outlined in white runs along the base of the single, continuous dorsal fin, a vertical dark stripe runs through each eye and there are often dark vertical patterns along the sides.

**SIMILAR SPECIES** The markings make this fish unmistakable.

**BEHAVIOUR** A Rock Gunnel disturbed by someone turning a rock on the shore, will wriggle rapidly away out of sight. Underwater they are more easily approached especially when guarding their eggs.

**HABITAT** Search for the Rock Gunnel on the shore under rocks, amongst seaweeds and in rock pools. With the tide out, this fish can still wriggle from pool to pool and, as its alternative name of Butterfish suggests, is very difficult to pick up. In deeper water it lurks in the undergrowth amongst seaweeds or animal turfs, usually above about 20m depth. To avoid harsh winter conditions, Rock Gunnels sometimes move into deeper water and have been found down to around 100m.

**DISTRIBUTION** Common all round the coast of Wales and also all round Britain and Ireland. Essentially this is a northern species extending round the coast of Scandinavia and Russia as far as the Kanin Peninsula and White Sea. Its southern limit is in northern France. Its range also extends across the Atlantic to Iceland and east coast North America.

**NATURAL HISTORY** Females or occasionally males or both can be seen guarding their eggs in January and February around the Welsh coast. Rounded clumps of pale, sticky eggs a few centimetres in diameter are attached to rocks or other hard objects both on the shore and below. These attentive fish do not feed until the eggs hatch one to two months later. Large Rock Gunnels are a favourite food of otters and many seabirds.

**SIGHTINGS** Usually spotted on the shore, this pretty fish is a favourite find in a rock pool, but is also seen in shallow water during shore dives and snorkels. Occasionally it is caught in deeper water trawls on sediment. Around south Wales, records of shores where a thorough search has been made but no Rock Gunnels found, would be useful because as ocean warming bites, this species could possibly retract its range northwards.

## WHAT'S IN A NAME?

*Pholis* derives from Greek – a marine creature which secretes a slime which envelopes it. 'Gunnel' is said to derive from either gunwale (a comparative description of its shape given to the naturalist Ray by a fisherman!), or possibly from the Cornish word 'gun' meaning scabbard and again referring to its shape. Its 'greasy skin' has earned it the name butterfish!

# YARELL'S BLENNY    Llyfrothen Yarrel    *Chirolophis ascanii*

**25cm**

**KEY IDENTIFICATION FEATURES**  Yarrell's Blenny can be identified in the field with a high degree of certainty. It has a long, eel-like shape with a long spiny dorsal fin running all the way from head to tail. It has thick lips and bulbous eyes and its head is adorned with tentacles, a large pompom-like, fringed pair behind the eyes and, especially in males, other smaller ones between and behind these. The first few dorsal fin spines are separate and also decorated with fringed tips. It is often a greenish or yellowish brown but can be reddish and has numerous vertical brown bars and patches. The eyes are ringed with brown from which a stripe runs down across the cheeks.

**SIMILAR SPECIES**  At first glance the shape, eye stripe and colour are reminiscent of a Butterfish but this has no head tentacles. Most true blennies also have head tentacles but of different shapes and they are shorter with different coloration.

**BEHAVIOUR**  Divers report that this fish is often seen in pairs hiding in crevices. Although they can be seen out in the open in deeper, darker water they spend much of the daytime hidden.

**HABITAT**  Inshore rocky reefs and similar areas are the places to look for this fish, especially below 10m depth. It also seems to be quite partial to shipwrecks perhaps because these provide plenty of hidey holes. It extends down to several hundred metres.

**DISTRIBUTION**  Yarrell's Blenny is uncommon in Welsh waters but can be found all round the British Isles. It is a northern species that extends to Iceland, northern Norway and the Murmansk coast, but not south of the British Isles.

**NATURAL HISTORY**  The fish spawn in autumn to early winter depending on their latitude. The female lays small clusters of eggs hidden amongst rocks and it is thought that the male guards them until they hatch a few weeks later. Observations of this behaviour are needed to confirm just what happens. They feed on small invertebrates and also eat some algal material.

**SIGHTINGS**  Divers may see this fish perched on rocks, often those with rather sparse undergrowth, but near to cracks and crevices where it can hide. Usually searching rocky crevices with a torch is more productive. Most diver records are from Scotland and further north. It is very rarely found on the shore but has been found recently (2008) in rock pools in Scotland.

# SNAKE BLENNIES AND VIVIPAROUS BLENNY

Two fish belonging to different families have the name Snake Blenny. The first *Lumpenus lampraetiformis* is in the same family as Yarrel's blenny (Stichaeidae). The second *Ophidion barbatum* belongs to the Cusk-eel family Ophidiidae, and is also in a separate Order Ophidiiformes. It is included here amongst the Perciform fish simply for ease of comparison.

*Lumpenus lampraetiformis*

**SNAKE BLENNY**                          Llyfrothen fain
*Lumpenus lampretaeformis*

50cm

**KEY IDENTIFICATION FEATURES**  As its name suggests this is a long, thin snake-like fish. It has a single long, spiny dorsal fin that runs from just behind the head to the tail. Although difficult to see, this fin starts off with very short spines. The tail fin is well defined and large with a pointed tip. The colour is greyish, pale greenish or pale brown with scattered large brown blotches.

**DISTRIBUTION AND HABITAT**  This is essentially a northern fish and has not been recorded from Welsh waters although this is only just outside its known range. Around the British Isles it is rarely seen but has been recorded round Scotland, and down North Sea coasts as far south as the English Channel. It ranges north right up to Spitzbergen inside the Arctic Circle. This is a burrowing fish that lives in muddy sediments mostly below about 30m depth down to around 400m.

**SIGHTINGS**  If this species is ever recorded from Welsh waters and the Irish Sea it is likely it would be from trawls fishing for Norway Lobster *Nephrops norvegicus* in deep muddy areas offshore.

**SNAKE BLENNY**                          Cysglysywen
*Ophidion barbatum*

Other names: Cusk-eel                          25cm

**KEY IDENTIFICATION FEATURES**  This is another long thin snake-like fish, though flattened sideways and so perhaps more eel-like than snake-like. It can be recognised from its long pelvic fins which are so far forward they are under the chin. Each consists of two rays only and at first sight they look like barbels. Like eels, the dorsal, anal and tail fins are joined together as a single continuous fin which has a dark edge. It is a pale fish, mostly a bluish grey to brown colour.

**DISTRIBUTION AND HABITAT**  This is an uncommon southern species that is found in the Mediterranean and south to Senegal but only as far north as southern England. It has not yet been recorded from Welsh waters. It lives on sandy and muddy seabeds within diving depths and also down to about 150m.

**SIGHTINGS**  This is another species that, if it moves north might be trawled or dredged up off the Welsh coastline or spotted by divers, as it has been in the Mediterranean.

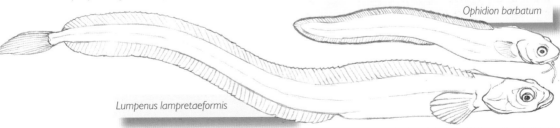

*Ophidion barbatum*

*Lumpenus lampretaeformis*

# VIVIPAROUS BLENNY

## Gweflogyn

## *Zoarces viviparous*

**Other names: Eelpout**

**30cm**

**KEY IDENTIFICATION FEATURES** Like the Snake Blenny *Ophidion barbatum* the Viviparous Blenny is a long, thin fish with a fin that runs continuously from the back, round the tail and onto the belly. A really close look will show a dip in this fin near the tail. Unlike the Snake Blenny it has short stumpy pelvic fins but large fan-like pectoral fins. It has a large head and obvious thick lips. Colour is not a good guide as it is variable depending on habitat.

**SIMILAR SPECIES** In general shape and size the Viviparous Blenny looks a bit like a Rock Gunnel but the two usually live in different habitats. It does not have the distinct tail fin and pattern of spots seen in Rock Gunnel.

**BEHAVIOUR** The fish mate in autumn and females with swollen bellies may be spotted in late autumn or winter.

**HABITAT** Although shown here amongst rocks and weed it lives mainly on and in muddy and sandy bottoms from the shore to at least 40m depth. However, it can be found in rocky areas on the shore and in shallow water.

**DISTRIBUTION** This species has only occasionally been recorded from Welsh waters. It is basically a northern fish that extends south from northern Norway and Scotland south to Cornwall and the English Channel. It is however, much less common on the west coast south of Scotland.

**NATURAL HISTORY** As its name suggests this little fish has live young, which is unusual amongst bony fish. The eggs develop and then hatch inside the female. The young larvae absorb food from the ovary and grow until they are born at about 4cm long.

**SIGHTINGS** Viviparous Blennies are sometimes found by rock poolers. It is seldom seen by divers but possibly because it lives mostly in sediment areas. It is sometimes caught in fish traps and seine nets and is fished commercially in the Baltic.

Right. Very soft (muddy) seabeds generally occur in deeper water around Wales. Smaller fish which are only found on them are seldom seen simply because deep mud is seldom visited by divers, such fish are rarely caught by anglers and they are of no commercial importance.

# BLACK-FACED BLENNY

## Llyfrothen benddu'r Gogledd
### *Tripterygion delaisi*

**Other names: *T. atlanticus* (synonym)**                                    **9cm**

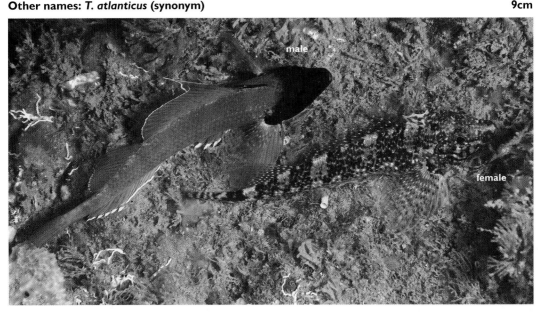

male

female

**KEY IDENTIFICATION FEATURES** This fish, especially the male, can be identified in the field with a high degree of certainty. As their other name of 'triplefins' suggests, Black-faced Blenny have three dorsal fins, the first very short and the other two long. It has a single long anal fin, peg-like pelvic fins similar to those of true blennies and a neat, triangular head. Mature breeding males are unmistakable with a bright yellow or orange body, a black head and blue edges to most fins. Females, immature fish and non breeding males are pale brown to reddish with a mottled pattern and five wide dark bars down the sides. Unlike true blennies, these fish have scales.

**SIMILAR SPECIES** Whilst there are no similar species in British waters, there are at least two others in the Mediterranean *T. melanurus*, *T. tripteronotus* and it is always possible that one of these will extend its range northwards. Photographs of Black-faced Blenny in British waters, especially from sites where they have not yet been recorded or if they look a bit different from the description, would be of great value.

**BEHAVIOUR** These fish spend much time hidden in crevices or holes or in dense undergrowth and often rest upsidedown under overhangs.

**HABITAT** The best place to look for Black-faced Blennies is under small ledges and overhangs and on steep rocks with a dense cover of fine seaweeds. This is because they prefer low light intensities. They can be found down to 40m depth.

**DISTRIBUTION** As yet, there are no records of this pretty little fish in Welsh waters. It has been regularly recorded from a number of places along the south coast of England, notably Portland and also from Wembury and Plymouth Sound (Devon), the Fleet lagoon and Swanage pier (Dorset) amongst others. It was first reported from British waters in 1972 and its spread along the coast has been slow. It is relatively common in the Channel Islands and extends south to Spain and Portugal and into the Mediterranean.

**NATURAL HISTORY** The spawning ritual of these charming fish has been filmed in Jersey by Sue Daly. The male is highly territorial and performs an elaborate, possibly figure-of-eight dance around the female to persuade her to spawn in the undergrowth in his few metres wide patch. Both male and female fish are resident all year round along the English south coast and are almost certainly breeding there. Very little appears to be known about the life history of this family in general.

**SIGHTINGS** Divers are only likely to see these fish if they search carefully in suitable areas of cliffs and bedrock reefs. Local divers in southern England often know exactly where these fish can be seen in the summer. New sightings are reported in most years and the species is slowly spreading along the south coast. Searching for them in similar habitats in Wales may eventually turn up this species, if it moves further north as the sea temperature increases. In Jersey they are sometimes found in rock pools.

male

# WOLF-FISH

FAMILY  Anarhichadidae

| **WOLF-FISH** | **Morflaidd** | *Anarhichas lupus* |
|---|---|---|

**Other names: Cat-fish**    150cm

**KEY IDENTIFICATION FEATURES**   Adult Wolf-fish are very unlikely to be mistaken for anything else, but more care is needed with juveniles. This fish has a massive head with strong, peg-like teeth and this is often all that is visible of the fish (opposite top). This photo clearly shows its tough, wrinkled grey skin. Once out in the open its long, tapered body, single long dorsal and anal fins and large pectoral fins can be seen (above). Adults are predominantly grey but have darker vertical bands. Younger fish are often brownish with very obvious banding (opposite bottom).

**SIMILAR SPECIES**  Small Juveniles (opposite bottom) could be mistaken for Butterfish or a small blenny, not surprising as they are related to the true blennies. In blennies the pelvic fins are usually obvious whereas Wolf-fish have no pelvic fins. The tiny pelvic fins in Butterfish are difficult to see but most Butterfish have a distinctive pattern of spots along the dorsal fin base.

**BEHAVIOUR**  Divers who regularly visit the same sites report that these fish are often resident and can be found in the same hidey holes from year to year. Left well alone they are not aggressive though males guarding eggs should be treated with caution.

**HABITAT**  In British waters Wolf-fish mostly live in deep water below diving depths down to about 600m, but at St. Abbs they are found in rocky areas as shallow as 12m. Divers regularly see them in Norwegian fjords on sediment or mixed sediment and rock.

**DISTRIBUTION**  This is a northern species. There are Victorian records from Barmouth in Cardigan Bay and off Anglesey, and an unconfirmed record from a survey in the 1970s. There are records from Cornwall and possibly the Bay of Biscay. Most British records are from Orkney, Shetland and St. Abbs in eastern Scotland, and just a few from western Scotland too. In the north it reaches Spitzbergen, Iceland, Greenland and Canada.

**NATURAL HISTORY**  Females lay ball-shaped clumps of eggs on the seabed in winter hiding them amongst rocks or other shelter. Males guard the eggs until they hatch two to three months later. The larvae stay near the seabed until they have used up their egg yolk, then spend a short time in mid-water before settling back onto the seabed. Wolf-fish grow slowly and can live for many years. They first reproduce around six or seven years old.

**SIGHTINGS**  There are only a few places in the British Isles where this fish has been seen in diving depths. Nevertheless keep a careful look out especially for young fish. It is caught by anglers in rocky areas and fished commercially in Norway.

# DRAGONETS

## FAMILY Callionymidae

Three species of dragonets are found in Welsh waters. These are bottom-living fish that are rather flattened from top to bottom as an adaptation to this way of life. Dragonets have a wide, pointed head that is almost triangular in shape and a tapering body, ending in a large convex tail fin. As they spend much of their time partly buried, the gill openings are small and near the top of the head. Perhaps their most spectacular features are their fins: tall, triangular first dorsal fins which may have the first ray elongated, especially in the males, and large sail-like second dorsal and anal fins. Even the pelvic fins are expanded.

**Identification problems:** Mature, male dragonets may sometimes be relatively easy to tell apart in the field. This is because they can be brightly coloured and they often 'display' with their fins erect, enabling useful identification features to be observed. These features include differences in their first dorsal fin, the coloration of the second dorsal fin and their relative head lengths, as well as head profiles – these characteristics may be visible in the field or in photographs

However both females and immature males are often not so easy to differentiate and it is all too easy to wrongly identify them. As a result, Reticulated and possibly Spotted Dragonets may be under-recorded in Wales; we believe they have often been mistaken for the much commoner Dragonet and that some illustrations and descriptions in many books are probably incorrect – many existing book's descriptions are at variance.

Dead fish can be identified by examination of the front gill cover where spines on the pre-operculum (which may need to be felt for) are distinctive (but require expert knowledge and experience) and the size, number of rays and patterning of the second dorsal fin may well help too.

The photographs shown here have been chosen because they show the classic colours of the different species but colour variations between fish in different habitats means many specimens may not fully match any of those shown! In the authors' opinion, colour and intensity of patterning are extremely variable, as shown on this page, meaning that neither can be used as a complete guide to identification.

Although not uncommon fishes, there appears to be a lack of information about dragonets that is based on direct observation and photographs of live fish. More information and images are needed to differentiate the three species, especially the females and immature males and to understand more about them and where they live.

VARIATIONS IN RETICULATED DRAGONET

Reticulated (1st dorsal fin black)

Juvenile, probably Reticulated

Possibly Reticulated (partly black 1st dorsal)

Probably Reticulated (partly black 1st dorsal)

## IDENTIFYING FEMALE AND IMMATURE DRAGONETS

| | DRAGONET *C. lyra* | RETICULATED DRAGONET *C. reticulatus* | SPOTTED DRAGONET *C. maculatus* |
|---|---|---|---|
| Head (male and female) | Large, gently sloping with long snout, 2–3 times diameter of eye – but this may be an adult male characteristic | Short, very steep profile, 45°, snout slightly longer than eye diameter | Short snout slightly shorter than eye diameter |
| First dorsal fin | Short but just taller than the 2nd dorsal fin; uniform | Short; entirely black or rear section black | Short; spotty but spots not always distinct |
| Second dorsal fin | Uniform colour or sometimes dark stripe? | Male – dark blotches in vertical or oblique rows 10 rays | Colourless. Usually 9 or rarely 8 or 10 rays |
| Front gill cover spines (male & female) | 4 | 3 | 4 |

Above. Short, steep snout of Reticulated Dragonet.
Below. Long, sloping snout of Dragonet.

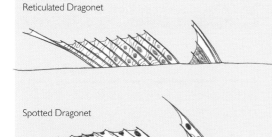

Reticulated Dragonet

Spotted Dragonet

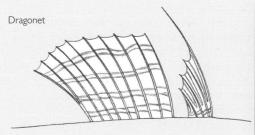

Dragonet

The characteristics in these tables and the dragonets descriptions are based on our current observations and knowledge and are a guide only. Dragonet identification in the field remains problematical with contradictory and incomplete information given in different texts.

## IDENTIFYING MATURE MALE DRAGONETS

| | DRAGONET *C. lyra* | RETICULATED DRAGONET *C. reticulatus* | SPOTTED DRAGONET *C. maculatus* |
|---|---|---|---|
| First dorsal fin | Very tall; yellow with green to blue blotches at least in breeding season | Short; often partly black | Tall; lots of spots |
| Second dorsal fin | Yellow with longitudinal green to blue stripes | Last ray branched and taller than rest. Large dark spots and bluish white wavy lines often almost vertical | Vertical rows of small alternating dark and pearly white spots. Dark spots make 4 horizontal rows |

# DRAGONET

## Bwgan dŵr

## *Callionymus lyra*

**Other names: Common or Gemmeous Dragonet**                                        **30cm**

Male

**KEY IDENTIFICATION FEATURES** See also table on page 229.

**Males** The first dorsal fin ray of the mature male is very tall and can be more than twice the height of the second dorsal fin. The face is much longer than that of the other two dragonets although it is unclear as to whether this is a characteristic of mature males only. Males may be decorated with numerous distinct blue markings (lines and blotches) on the head, body and fins which are on a variably coloured background (from pale brown to yellow) as shown in the photographs.

**Females** Even in the female the first dorsal fin is just taller than the second. Their colour appears to very variable too as it seems to vary widely depending on (and possibly to suit) the background. Many are typically a pale brown, with darker brown saddles across their backs and a number of brown blotches along their sides – all of which vary in their clarity. This is the largest species and any dragonet over about 15cm is likely to be this species; males can reach up to 30cm long and females up to 20cm.

**SIMILAR SPECIES** The females and immature males of the three dragonet species, can, as commented on in the introduction to these fishes, be very similar.

**BEHAVIOUR** Males court females by lifting and spreading out their colourful fins, especially the tall first dorsal fin, making a spectacular display. If a female approves the male, the two swim belly to belly up into the water column. Eggs and sperm are shed between the pair ensuring fertilisation. Males are territorial, will often spawn with several females and will chase out rival males.

**HABITAT** Whilst Dragonet can be found on a variety of sediments including stony areas, they are especially common on sand and muddy sand. They can be found as shallow as 5m but are usually encountered below 20m. They commonly extend down to 100m and have been recorded from 430m.

**DISTRIBUTION** The Dragonet is common all round the Welsh coastline and the British Isles. It extends north to Norway and Iceland and south to Mauritania and the Mediterranean.

**NATURAL HISTORY** Most Dragonets spawn in late winter to early spring and the eggs and larvae float in the plankton. They can live for seven years.

**SIGHTINGS** Most of the dragonets seen by divers are this species and they are a fish to look out for on any dive over sediment. Their bottom-living way of life means they are often trawled up in shrimp nets.

# RETICULATED DRAGONET  Bwgan rhwyllog  *Callionymus reticulatus*

**11cm (male); 8cm (female)**

## KEY IDENTIFICATION FEATURES

**Males and females** The first dorsal fin in both males and females is relatively short and often entirely black (probably most females) or partly black. Males and 'classic' females can have very distinct and well defined dark reddish saddles across their backs and pale blue spots along their sides. When they show this typical colour, identification is fairly certain – but they can vary.

**SIMILAR SPECIES** The females and immature males of the three dragonet species are very similar.

**BEHAVIOUR** There is little specific information on the behaviour of this species but males display their fins in a similar way to Dragonet.

**HABITAT** There is not a lot of information available on the habitat preferences of this dragonet but it seems to prefer clean sand from just below the shore down to 40m. It has also been found on stony and pebbly areas and down to 110m.

**DISTRIBUTION** This is a relatively uncommon dragonet and is recorded in Welsh waters much less often than the Dragonet (but see introduction above). Around the British Isles it has not been recorded much north of the Irish Sea and the southern North Sea but may occur as far north as Norway.

**NATURAL HISTORY** Few details of the life history are known but it is probably similar to the dragonet. Young fish ready to settle down on the seabed, are found in the plankton from May to September in the English Channel.

**SIGHTINGS** Reticulated Dragonets are not seen that often by divers, or at least not reported. As this species occurs right up to the shore, it could in theory be found in shore pools.

# SPOTTED DRAGONET     Bwgan brith     *Callionymus maculatus*

16cm (male); 13cm (female)

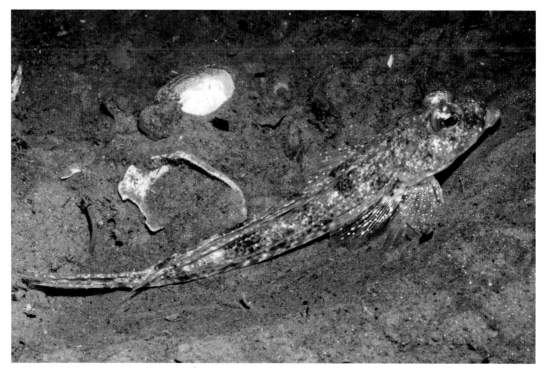

## KEY IDENTIFICATION FEATURES

**Males and females**  The first dorsal fin ray of the male tall but not as dramatically so as in the Dragonet *C. lyra*. Males and 'classic' females have a background brownish yellow colour with many dark and pearly white to bluish spots that show up especially well on the pectoral and pelvic fins (again see the photograph). There are darker brown saddles across the back as in reticulated dragonet but these may be much less well defined and not clearly delineated. Females often have two rows of conspicuous larger brown spots along the sides and fewer and duller blue spots. The face of the Spotted Dragonet may show a 'roman nose' but again how characteristic this is and whether this is just an adult male characteristic is unclear.

**SIMILAR SPECIES**  The females and immature males of the three dragonet species are very similar.

**BEHAVIOUR**  No specific details are known.

**HABITAT**  This dragonet is rarely found close inshore and mostly occurs from 70–300m, on sandy and muddy bottoms. It has however, been seen and photographed fairly often within diving depths.

**DISTRIBUTION**  Spotted Dragonets are recorded relatively infrequently around Wales but this might be because they live in deeper water, mostly below diving depths. They are found round most of the British Isles, north to southern Iceland, Norway and Denmark and south to Senegal and the Mediterranean.

**NATURAL HISTORY**  As with the Reticulated Dragonet there is not a lot of detail known about this fish's life history but it is likely to be similar to the Dragonet.

**SIGHTINGS**  Divers do see and photograph this species but much less often than the other two. It is sometimes trawled up in shrimp nets.

# MACKEREL AND TUNA

## FAMILY Scombridae

The mackerel and tuna family includes some of the most important and valuable commercial fish in the world. Most species are found in tropical and warm temperate seas and only Atlantic Mackerel is abundant and breeds in British and Welsh waters. Eleven other species are listed as occurring in British waters, most of them as rare visitors.

These fish are designed for fast swimming and are streamlined, spindle-shaped fish with the narrow tail stalk and tall, deeply forked tail fin characteristic of many strong, predatory fish. They have two dorsal fins which vary in shape and distance apart in the different species. The second dorsal fin and anal fin both end in a series of small, individual finlets. The design is so efficient that scientists are using tuna as a model to develop robot fish that 'swim' through the oceans using minimum power to collect long-term physical data from the oceans.

Mackerel and tuna are 'oily' fish that are conducive to good health in humans and they are excellent food fishes. This has led to widespread over-exploitation of stocks both in the past and the present. The larger species are near the top of the ocean food chain and as nearly top predators are vital to the health of the oceans.

Gannets have been photographed feeding on mackerel in Cardigan Bay

# ATLANTIC MACKEREL          Macrell               *Scomber scombrus*

**Other names: Joey**                                                    **60cm**

**KEY IDENTIFICATION FEATURES**  The distinctive pattern of dark, zebra-like lines worn on the back by Atlantic Mackerel makes them easy to identify and this familiar fish can be identified in the field with a very high degree of certainty. This is a slim, silvery blue green fish in which the pattern mostly ends at the lateral line. It has a pointed snout and the two dorsal fins are widely separated.

**SIMILAR SPECIES**  See 'Other mackerel' below

**BEHAVIOUR**  Mackerel are constantly in motion swimming along feeding as they go. They have voracious appetites especially after spawning and will take any small fish such as sprat, sand eels and juveniles of other species. They can also be seen with mouths wide open filtering plankton through their gill rakers. They are highly migratory moving both inshore and north in summer, and moving south, returning to deep water in winter. These movements are mostly up the west coast of Ireland and Scotland and through the English Channel rather than through the Irish Sea past Wales.

**HABITAT**  Huge schools of mackerel live and feed in the surface waters from close inshore to far out over offshore banks. In winter they can be found in water of about 250m deep but also down to 1000m.

**DISTRIBUTION**  Atlantic Mackerel is a common fish throughout Welsh waters and all round the British Isles. It is widely distributed over the continental shelf in the North Atlantic at least as far north as northern Norway and Iceland and at least as far south as the Canary Islands and throughout the Mediterranean.

**NATURAL HISTORY**  Atlantic Mackerel spawn mostly from March through July and the females shed their eggs in batches during this period. They spawn over a wide area. The eggs hatch after only a few days and the young soon start to feed on plankton. Young fish grow quickly and most are mature by three years old.

**SIGHTINGS**  Because of its open water habitat, divers seldom see Mackerel underwater. It is widely fished commercially and caught using purse seine nets, pelagic trawls and handlines. The main fishing areas in Wales are off the south coast. It is also caught by anglers, boaters and small children. There is a minimum landing size for Atlantic Mackerel in EU waters and a more stringent one in the North Sea. Both major stocks (North Sea and western) are heavily exploited.

## OTHER MACKEREL

Whilst almost all mackerel seen in Wales will be Atlantic Mackerel, there are two rare visitors that could turn up. Chub or Spanish Mackerel *Scomber japonicus* is very similar to Atlantic Mackerel and is common off Portugal and the Mediterranean. It has a larger head and eye and although the pattern on the back is similar to Atlantic Mackerel, the lines are fainter and often extend further down the sides as broken lines and patches. In dead fish the first dorsal fin spines can be counted. Atlantic Mackerel has 11–13 spines whilst Chub Mackerel has 9–11. There is at least one record of this fish from south Wales and it turns up more frequently in Cornwall.

Bullet Tuna or Frigate Mackerel *Auxis rochei rochei* looks like a large Atlantic Mackerel but has a taller, concave first dorsal fin with 10–11 fin spines. It has a dark bluish back with a pattern of nearly vertical dark bars above the lateral line. It has a worldwide distribution that just extends to the British Isles and has been recorded from Cornwall and Ireland but not specifically from Welsh waters. Frigate Tuna *Auxis thazard thazard* is a very similar species which apparently reaches the British Isles.

# TUNAS IN WELSH WATERS

Tunas are rare fish in British and Welsh waters and in northern European waters in general. A number of large, migratory tunas with worldwide distributions in tropical and warm temperate waters south of the British Isles, very occasionally stray this far north. These fish are all exceedingly rare in Welsh waters. The only tuna that is ever common in Northern European waters is Northern Bluefin Tuna *Thunnus thynnus*. Even this is uncommon now and mainly a summertime visitor from further south. Four large tunas have been recorded from Welsh waters. Excepting the Northern Bluefin Tuna which is occasionally taken by fishermen, all records are from stranded fish.

A number of small tunas have ranges that are mostly south of the British Isles, sometimes worldwide, but are regular or occasional visitors to the British Isles and sometimes beyond. Of these only Atlantic Bonito *Sarda sarda* has been recorded from Wales. A further three species have been recorded from the British Isles. These are **Plain Bonito** *Orcynopsis unicolor*, **Little Tunny** *Euthynnus alletteratus* and **Skipjack Tuna** *Katsuwonas pelamis* which extend up the west coast of Ireland and across to southern Norway. Only the latter has been recorded from southern England (Cornwall).

Tunas are not easy to identify in the field and as these fish are so rare in Welsh waters, stranded fish should always be kept if possible and sent to a specialist. If not then good close photographs showing the fins and the head will help identification.

## ALBACORE or LONGFIN TUNA
Tiwna asgell-hir
*Thunnus alalunga*    130cm

Two confirmed records from north and south Wales. This tuna is common in Biscay and the Mediterranean but a rare vagrant further north, with occasional straying as far as the British Isles in summer. The pectoral fins are longer than in any other tuna and reach back beyond the second dorsal fin lobe. The two dorsal fins are very close and almost touch.

## ATLANTIC BONITO
Bonito byrasgell
*Sarda sarda*    90cm

Recorded from south Wales. This is a regular but uncommon summer visitor to the British Isles and as far north as Oslo in southern Norway. It has a wide distribution throughout the Atlantic and Mediterranean. This small tuna is marked with a distinctive pattern of oblique black lines running across its steel blue to greenish back. It has short pectoral fins and the first dorsal fin has a straight outline sloping evenly down to very near the start of the second dorsal fin. It has a large mouth extending to the rear of the eye.

## NORTHERN BLUFIN TUNA
Tiwna mawr
*Thunnus thynnus*                    400cm

This tuna has been recorded from southern
Wales. It is a regular but uncommon summer
visitor from the Mediterranean to the British
Isles and as far north as Norway. The pectoral
fins in this tuna are very short and about the
same length as the snout. The two dorsal fins
are set close together but with a small space
between. The overall colour is bluish, dark on
the back, greenish on the sides and the belly
is white. The fins are dark blue but the finlets
and anal fin are dull yellow.

## BIG-EYE TUNA
*Thunnus obesus*                    250cm

Burry Port, Carmarthenshire, South Wales, stranded 2008. This is
only the third UK record. This is a very rare vagrant that does not
normally stray this far north and is not found in the Mediterranean.
Like the Yellowfin tuna this one also has yellow finlets but both
dorsal fins are yellow as well as the anal fin.

## YELLOWFIN TUNA
Tiwna melyn
*Thunnus albacares*        240cm

North Wales coast 1972, first UK record.
Normally found south of Biscay and does
not occur in the Mediterranean. The
front lobes of the second dorsal and anal
fins are very long and curved backwards,
especially in large fish. The pectoral fins
reach back to the beginning of the first
dorsal fin. In life it has a beautiful yellow
sheen on the sides and the finlets, edges
of the second dorsal, and anal fin are all
yellow.

# BLACKFISHES

FAMILY  Centrolphidae

## BLACKFISH                    Pysgodyn du            *Centrolophus niger*

150cm

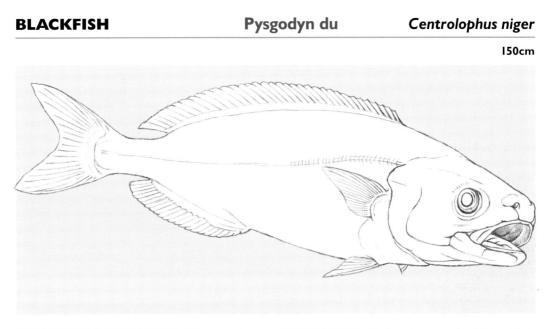

**KEY IDENTIFICATION FEATURES**  Although rarely seen, this fish should be relatively easy to identify. As its name suggests it is almost black, including the fins, shading to grey on the belly. It has a blunt face with a gently curving snout. A long-based, single dorsal fin starts well down the back, more or less at the point to which the pectoral fins stretch and it has a large forked tail. Young fish are often brownish with darker vertical bars.

**SIMILAR SPECIES**  Cornish Blackfish *Schedophilus medusophagus* are similar but are very rarely recorded in inshore waters. Adults and young remain out at sea and are relatively common in the Atlantic to the west of the British Isles. Its dorsal fin begins much further forward.

**BEHAVIOUR**  Young fish are often found with jellyfish or floating salps. It sometimes occurs in small shoals and it is its oceanic lifestyle that may bring it inshore with water currents. However, it may also actively move inshore, perhaps following jellyfish, other large plankton or small fish and squid, all of which it eats.

**HABITAT**  Blackfish are oceanic fish that are found from the surface to mid-water but not on the bottom. This species lives mostly between about 100–600m depth but young fish are found near the surface and it extends to at least 1000m.

**DISTRIBUTION**  This is a deepwater fish that is relatively common off west coasts of the British Isles and has occasionally been recorded in Welsh coastal waters. It has a wide distribution in temperate oceans in both hemispheres. In the North Atlantic it extends from Canada to Iceland, Norway and the British Isles and south to West Africa and the Mediterranean.

**NATURAL HISTORY**  Little known.

**SIGHTINGS**  Divers are unlikely to see this fish. Young fish might be caught in surface nets, and adults in deep mid-water trawls. It might also be washed ashore.

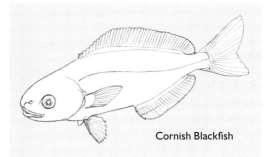

Cornish Blackfish

# FISH AND JELLYFISH

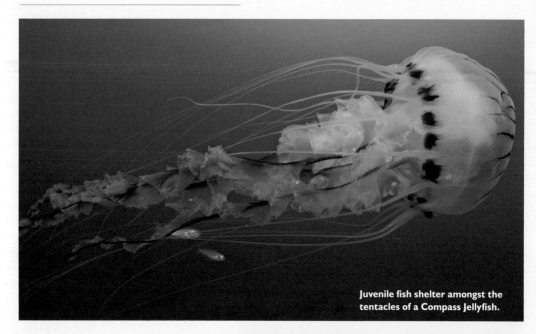

**Juvenile fish shelter amongst the tentacles of a Compass Jellyfish.**

Juveniles of some fishes are known to associate with jellyfish and it is always worth looking (carefully!) at large jellyfish such as **Lion's Mane** *Cyanea capillata* and *C. lamarckii*, **Compass** *Chrysaora hysoscella* and **Barrel** *Rhizostoma octopus*.

Fish from nine families have been recorded in association with jellyfish worldwide. Most of these are in tropical waters. In temperate waters it is mostly codfish (Gadidae) and jacks and pompanos (Carangidae). When diving in Welsh waters look out for jellyfish with juveniles of Whiting, Haddock and Cod (all gadoids) plus Horse Mackerel (a carangid). Juvenile Blackfish also associate with jellyfish but this fish is not common in Welsh waters. Records of any fish associated with jellyfish are of interest but taking photographs and identifying them is not easy.

This is thought to be a commensal relationship where the juvenile fish gain protection whilst the jellyfish is not harmed but neither does it benefit. There is some evidence for a correlation between improved survival rates of juvenile Whiting and abundance of Lion's Mane Jellyfish in the North Sea. So the relationship may be an important one for this species at least.

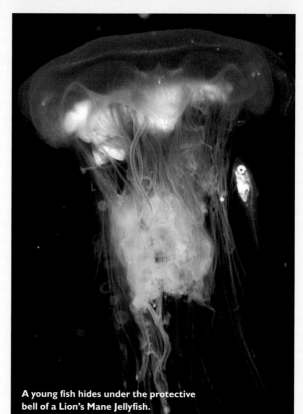

**A young fish hides under the protective bell of a Lion's Mane Jellyfish.**

# BILLFISHES

FAMILY  Xiphiidae

## SWORDFISH       Pysgodyn cleddyf cleddbysgodyn       *Xiphias gladius*

**Other names: Broadbill**                                                          **455cm**

**KEY IDENTIFICATION FEATURES**  Anyone finding one of these fish could not fail to recognise it. Its long, pointed upper snout is drawn out into a sword-shaped blade. It has a streamlined torpedo-shaped body that thins down to a powerful forked tail, with a keel on either side of the base. It has a high first dorsal fin that curves steeply down with the last few rays low. There is a second very small dorsal fin. Two anal fins follow a similar pattern. Young swordfish have both dorsal fins and both anal fins joined together. It has the typical colour of an ocean predator with a dark grey-blue back and white belly.

**SIMILAR SPECIES**  Sailfish *Istiophorus platypterus* is another similar billfish with a huge dorsal fin. It has not been recorded from Wales and records are extremely rare anywhere in northern Europe.

**BEHAVIOUR**  Highly migratory, breeding in warm areas but moving into temperate and cold waters in summer to feed. It is usually solitary but gathers in large schools when breeding. It attacks and feeds on schooling fish and there is some amazing film footage of these fish and Sailfish splitting and herding schools towards the surface.

**HABITAT**  This is an open ocean, migratory fish that ranges right across the oceans but sometimes comes into coastal waters. It ranges from the surface down to at least 800m.

**DISTRIBUTION**  Swordfish are very rare vagrants in Welsh waters and in fact anywhere north of Biscay. This beautiful fish is widespread in the Atlantic, Pacific and Indian oceans and in the Mediterranean and has been recorded as far north as Norway. The fish shown here was washed up on Barry Island Beach, Glamorgan in July 2008. There are only two other properly documented Welsh records although Travis Jenkins (1936) says that this fish was "not infrequently" taken in the Bristol Channel and the estuary of the Severn. Live fish are very occasionally seen in the south west of the British Isles.

**NATURAL HISTORY**  This is a 'warm blooded' species meaning that, like Great White Sharks it can remain an active predator even in cold water. Females mature when five or six years old and 150–170cm long, males slightly earlier. In the North Atlantic they spawn in the southern Sargasso Sea.

**SIGHTINGS**  Swordfish is one of the most highly prized by sport fishermen. Most of those caught are tagged and returned to the sea. Swordfish have been and are very heavily exploited commercially though not around the British Isles as they are too rare. The North Atlantic stock is listed as 'Endangered' in the IUCN Red List but conservation methods are having a positive effect on stocks. There is a minimum landing size and weight in EU waters.

# APPENDIX I: Annotated List of UK and Irish Marine Fishes

Appendix I lists all marine fish species that have been recorded from around the UK and Ireland, whether common, rare, or vagrant. The list was compiled from many references including www.fishbase.org and other sources, many of which are detailed in the bibliography in Appendix 2. This totals nearly 500 species. This list is as accurate as it has been possible to make it, but we have not been able to check each record back to the original sighting. There may well be errors and the list should accepted for what it is - a compilation of the marine fish for which there is some form of existent record, rather than being considered to be definitive.

Within this list, those fish that are described or mentioned in this book are coloured to show which Order they belong to. Listed fish without colours are not covered in the book. Within the whole list there are many different Orders of fish of which 28 are represented in this book.

The list is arranged in alphabetical order of the scientific names. The list will be available via www.marinewildlife. co.uk where it will be possible to arrange it as preferred, for example by Families or Orders.

Records of *Parablennius rouxi* and *Parablennius pilicornis*, (denoted by an asterisk*) are from photographs taken in UK but not yet confirmed as these species.

| Orders | Groupings in book | Colour |
|---|---|---|
| Myxiniformes<br>Petromyzontiformes | Jawless fishes | ● |
| Hexanchiformes<br>Squaliformes<br>Lamniformes<br>Squatiniformes<br>Carcharhiniformes | Sharks | ● |
| Rajiformes<br>Torpediniformes | Rays | ● |
| Chimaeriformes | Chimaeras | ● |
| Anguilliformes | Eels | ● |
| Clupeiformes | Herrings | ● |
| Salmoniformes<br>Osmeriformes | Salmon & Smelts | ● |
| Gadiformes | Codfishes | ● |
| Lophiiformes | Anglerfishes | ● |
| Zeiformes | Dories & Boarfishes | ● |
| Lampriformes | Opahs | ● |
| Ophidiiformes | Ophidiiformes | ● |
| Gobiesociformes | Clingfishes | ● |
| Atheriniformes | Sandsmelts | ● |
| Mugiliformes | Grey Mullets | ● |
| Beloniformes | Beloniformes | ● |
| Syngnathiformes | Pipefishes & Seahorses | ● |
| Gasterosteiformes | Sticklebacks | ● |
| Scorpaeniformes | Scorpaeniformes | ● |
| Pleuronectiformes | Flatfishes | ● |
| Tetradontiformes | Tetradontiformes | ● |
| Perciformes | Perciformes | ● |

| SCIENTIFIC NAME | FISHBASE NAME | Alternative Name | Family | Order |
|---|---|---|---|---|
| Acantholabrus palloni | Scale-Rayed Wrasse | | Labridae | Perciformes |
| Acipenser sturio | Sturgeon | Atlantic Sturgeon | Acipenseridae | Acipenseriformes |
| Agonus cataphractus | Hooknose | Armed Bullhead | Agonidae | Scorpaeniformes |
| Alepisaurus ferox | Longnose Lancetfish | Lancetfish | Alepisauridae | Aulopiformes |
| Alepocephalus agassizii | Agassiz' Slickhead | Agassiz' Slickhead | Alepocephalidae | Osmeriformes |
| Alepocephalus australis | Small Scaled Brown Slickhead | | Alepocephalidae | Osmeriformes |
| Alepocephalus bairdii | Baird's Smooth-Head | | Alepocephalidae | Osmeriformes |
| Alepocephalus productus | Smalleye Smooth Head | | Alepocephalidae | Osmeriformes |
| Alepocephalus rostratus | Risso's Smooth-Head | | Alepocephalidae | Osmeriformes |
| Alopias vulpinus | Thintail Thresher | Fox Shark | Alopiidae | Lamniformes |
| Alopias superciliosus | Big-Eye Thresher | | Alopiidae | Lamniformes |
| Alosa alosa | Allis Shad | Mayfish | Clupeidae | Clupeiformes |
| Alosa fallax fallax | Twaite Shad | Twait Shad | Clupeidae | Clupeiformes |
| Amblyraja hyperborea | Arctic Skate | Northern Skate | Rajidae | Rajiformes |
| Amblyraja radiata<br>Alt: Raja radiata | Thorny Skate | Starry Ray | Rajidae | Rajiformes |

| SCIENTIFIC NAME | FISHBASE NAME | Alternative Name | Family | Order |
|---|---|---|---|---|
| Ammodytes marinus | Lesser Sand-Eel | Launce | Ammodytidae | Perciformes |
| Ammodytes tobianus | Small Sandeel | Lesser Sandeel | Ammodytidae | Perciformes |
| Anarhichas denticulatus | Northern Wolfish | Blue Sea Cat | Anarhichadidae | Perciformes |
| Anarhichas lupus | Wolf-Fish | Cat-Fish | Anarhichadidae | Perciformes |
| Anarhichas minor | Spotted Wolf-Fish | | Anarhichadidae | Perciformes |
| Anguilla anguilla | European Eel | Common Eel | Anguillidae | Anguilliformes |
| Anoplagaster cornuta | Horned Fang-Toothed Fish | Common Fangtooth | Beryciformes | Beryciformes |
| Antimora rostrata | Blue Antimora | | Moridae | Gadiformes |
| Antonogadus macrophthalmus | Big-Eyed Rockling | | Lotidae | Gadiformes |
| Aphanopus carbo | Black Scabbardfish | | Trichiuridae | Perciformes |
| Aphia minuta | Transparent Goby | Transparent Goby | Gobiidae | Perciformes |
| Apletodon dentatus dentatus | Small-Headed Clingfish | | Gobiesocidae | Gobiesociformes |
| Apletodon microcephalus | None | | Gobiesocidae | Gobiesociformes |
| Apristurus aphyodes | Deep-Water Catshark | | Scyliorhinidae | Carcharhiniformes |
| Apristurus laurussonii | Iceland Catshark | | Scyliorhinidae | Carcharhiniformes |
| Apristurus manis | Ghost Catshark | | Scyliorhinidae | Carcharhiniformes |
| Apristurus melanoasper | Black Roughscale Catshark | | Scyliorhinidae | Carcharhiniformes |
| Apristurus microps | Smalleye Catshark | | Scyliorhinidae | Carcharhiniformes |
| Arctozenus risso | Ribbon Barracudina | | Paralepididae | Aulopiformes |
| Argentina silus | Greater Argentine | Atlantic Argentine | Argentinidae | Osmeriformes |
| Argentina sphyraena | Argentine | Lesser Argentine | Argentinidae | Osmeriformes |
| Argyropelecus hemigymnus | Half-Naked Hatchetfish | Axefish | Sternoptychidae | Stomiiformes |
| Argyropelecus olfersii | Silver Hatchetfish | | Sternoptychidae | Stomiiformes |
| Argyrosomus regius | Meagre | Croaker | Sciaenidae | Perciformes |
| Arnoglossus imperialis | Imperial Scaldfish | | Bothidae | Pleuronectiformes |
| Arnoglossus laterna | Scaldfish | | Bothidae | Pleuronectiformes |
| Arnoglossus thori | Thor's Scaldfish | Grohmann's Scaldfish | Bothidae | Pleuronectiformes |
| Artediellus atlanticus | Atlantic Hookear Sculpin | | Cottidae | Scorpaeniformes |
| Aspitrigla cuculus Alt: Trigla cuculus | East Atlantic Red Gurnard | Red Gurnard | Triglidae | Scorpaeniformes |
| Atherina boyeri | Big-Scale Sand Smelt | Boyer's Sand Smelt | Atherinidae | Atheriniformes |
| Atherina presbyter | Sand Smelt | Atherine | Atherinidae | Atheriniformes |
| Auxis rochei rochei | Bullet Tuna | Frigate Mackerel | Scombridae | Perciformes |
| Auxis thazard thazard | Frigate Tuna | | Scombridae | Perciformes |
| Avocettina infans | Avocet Snipe-Eel | | Nemichthyidae | Anguilliformes |
| Balistes capriscus Alt: Balistes carolinensis | Grey Triggerfish | Triggerfish | Balistidae | Tetraodontiformes |
| Bassozetus taenia | | | Ophidiidae | Ophidiiformes |
| Bathygadus melanobranchus | | | Macrouridae | Gadiformes |
| Bathylaco nigricans | Black Warrior | | Alepocephalidae | Osmeriformes |
| Bathylagus euryops | Goiter Blacksmelt | Goitre Black Smelt | Bathylagidae | Osmeriformes |
| Bathypterois dubius | Spiderfish | | Ipnopidae | Aulopiformes |
| Bathypterois longipes | Abyssal Spiderfish | | Ipnopidae | Aulopiformes |
| Bathyraja spinicauda | Spinetail Ray | Spiny-Tailed Skate | Rajidae | Rajiformes |
| Bathysaurus ferox | Deepsea Lizardfish | | Bathysauridae | Aulopiformes |
| Bathysaurus mollis | Highfin Lizardfish | | Bathysauridae | Aulopiformes |
| Bathysolea profundicola | Deepwater Sole | | Soleidae | Pleuronectiformes |
| Bathytroctes macrolepis | Koefoed's Smooth-Head | | Alepocephalidae | Osmeriformes |
| Bathytroctes michaelsarsi | Michael Sars Smooth-Head | | Alepocephalidae | Osmeriformes |
| Bathytroctes microlepis | Smallscale Smooth-Head | | Alepocephalidae | Osmeriformes |
| Belone belone | Garpike | Garfish | Belonidae | Beloniformes |
| Belone svetovidovi | | | Belonidae | Beloniformes |
| Benthosema glaciale | Glacier Lanternfish | | Myctophidae | Myctophiformes |
| Beryx decadactylus | Alfonsino | Cuvier's Berycid Fish | Berycidae | Beryciformes |
| Beryx splendens | Beryx | | Berycidae | Beryciformes |
| Blennius ocellaris | Butterfly Blenny | | Blenniidae | Perciformes |
| Bonapartia pedaliota | | | Gonostomatidae | Stomiiformes |
| Boops boops | Bogue | | Sparidae | Perciformes |
| Borostomias antarcticus | Large-Eyed Snaggletooth | | Stomidae | Stomiiformes |
| Brama brama | Atlantic Pomfret | Angel Fish | Bramidae | Perciformes |
| Brosme brosme | Tusk | Brismak | Lotidae | Gadiformes |

| SCIENTIFIC NAME | FISHBASE NAME | Alternative Name | Family | Order |
|---|---|---|---|---|
| Buenia jeffreysii<br>Alt: Gobius jeffreysii | Jeffreys's Goby | | Gobiidae | Perciformes |
| Buglossidium luteum | Solenette | Yellow Sole | Soleidae | Pleuronectiformes |
| Callanthias ruber | Parrot Seaperch | | Callanthiidae | Perciformes |
| Callionymus lyra | Dragonet | Gemmeous Dragonet | Callionymidae | Perciformes |
| Callionymus maculatus | Spotted Dragonet | | Callionymidae | Perciformes |
| Callionymus reticulatus | Reticulated Dragonet | | Callionymidae | Perciformes |
| Campogramma glaycos | Vadigo | | Carangidae | Perciformes |
| Canthidermis maculata | Spotted Oceanic Triggerfish | Spotted Triggerfish | Balistidae | Tetraodontiformes |
| Capros aper | Boarfish | | Caproidae | Zeiformes |
| Caranx chrysos | Blue Runner | | Carangidae | Perciformes |
| Careproctus aciculipunctatus | | | Liparidae | Scorpaeniformes |
| Careproctus merretti | | | Liparidae | Scorpaeniformes |
| Cataetyx alleni | | | Bythitidae | Ophidiiformes |
| Cataetyx laticeps | | | Bythitidae | Ophidiiformes |
| Centrolabrus exoletus | Rock Cook | Small-Mouthed Wrasse | Labridae | Perciformes |
| Centrolophus niger | Blackfish | | Centrolophidae | Perciformes |
| Centrophorus granulosus | Gulper Shark | | Centrophoridae | Squaliformes |
| Centrophorus squamosus | Leafscale Gulper Shark | | Centrophoridae | Squaliformes |
| Centroscyllium fabricii | Black Dogfish | | Dalatiidae | Squaliformes |
| Centroscymnus coelolepis | Portuguese Dogfish | | Dalatiidae | Squaliformes |
| Centroscymnus crepidater | Longnose Velvet Dogfish | | Dalatiidae | Squaliformes |
| Cepola macrophthalma<br>Alt: Cepola rubescens | Red Bandfish | | Cepolidae | Perciformes |
| Ceratias holboelli | Krøyer's Deep Sea Angler Fish | | Ceratiidae | Lophiiformes |
| Cetorhinus maximus | Basking Shark | | Cetorhinidae | Lamniformes |
| Chaenophryne longiceps | Can-Opener Smoothdream | | Oneirodidae | Lophiiformes |
| Cheilopogon heterurus | Mediterranean Flyingfish | Atlantic Flying-Fish | Exocoetidae | Beloniformes |
| Chelidonichthys lucerna<br>Alt: Trigla lucerna | Tub Gurnard | Sapphirine Gurnard | Triglidae | Scorpaeniformes |
| Chelidonichthys obscurus | Longfin Gurnard | Shining Gurnard | Triglidae | Scorpaeniformes |
| Chelon labrosus | Thicklip Grey Mullet | Lesser Grey Mullet | Mugilidae | Mugiliformes |
| Chimaera monstrosa | Rabbit Fish | Chimaera | Chimaeridae | Chimaeriformes |
| Chirolophis ascanii | Yarrell's Blenny | | Stichaeidae | Perciformes |
| Chlamydoselachus anguineus | Frilled Shark | | Chlamydoselachidae | Hexanchiformes |
| Ciliata mustela | Fivebeard Rockling | Five-Bearded Rockling | Lotidae | Gadiformes |
| Ciliata septentrionalis | Northern Rockling | Northern Rockling | Lotidae | Gadiformes |
| Clupea harengus harengus | Atlantic Herring | Herring | Clupeidae | Clupeiformes |
| Coelorinchus caelorhincus | Hollowsnout Grenadier | Blackspot Grenadier | Macrouridae | Gadiformes |
| Coelorinchus labiatus | Spearsnouted Grenadier | | Macrouridae | Gadiformes |
| Conger conger | European Conger | Conger | Congridae | Anguilliformes |
| Conocara macropterum | Longfin Smooth-Head | | Alepocephalidae | Osmeriformes |
| Conocara microlepis | Elongate Smooth-Head | | Alepocephalidae | Osmeriformes |
| Conocara murrayi | Murray's Smooth-Head | | Alepocephalidae | Osmeriformes |
| Conocara salmoneum | Salmon Smooth-Head | | Alepocephalidae | Osmeriformes |
| Coregonus autumnalis | Arctic Cisco | Pollan | Salmonidae | Salmoniformes |
| Coregonus lavaretus | Common Whitefish | | Salmonidae | Salmoniformes |
| Coregonus oxyrinchus | Houting | | Salmonidae | Salmoniformes |
| Coris julis | Mediterranean Rainbow Wrasse | African Rainbow Wrasse | Labridae | Perciformes |
| Coryphaena hippurus | Common Dolphin Fish | | Coryphaenidae | Perciformes |
| Coryphaenoides armatus | Abyssal Grenadier | | Macrouridae | Gadiformes |
| Coryphaenoides brevibarbis | | | Macrouridae | Gadiformes |
| Coryphaenoides carapinus | Carapine Grenadier | | Macrouridae | Gadiformes |
| Coryphaenoides guentheri | Günther's Grenadier | | Macrouridae | Gadiformes |
| Coryphaenoides leptolepsis | Ghostly Grenadier | | Macrouridae | Gadiformes |
| Coryphaenoides mediterraneus | Meditteranean Grenadier | | Macrouridae | Gadiformes |
| Coryphaenoides profundicolis | Deepwater Grenadier | | Macrouridae | Gadiformes |
| Coryphaenoides rupestris | Roundnose Grenadier | Blunt-Nose Rattail | Macrouridae | Gadiformes |
| Coryphoblennius galerita | Montagu's Blenny | | Blenniida | Perciformes |

| SCIENTIFIC NAME | FISHBASE NAME | Alternative Name | Family | Order |
|---|---|---|---|---|
| Cottunculus microps | Polar Sculpin | | Psychrolutidae | Scorpaeniformes |
| Cottunculus thomsonii | Pallid Sculpin | | Psychrolutidae | Scorpaeniformes |
| Crystallogobius linearis | Crystal Goby | | Gobiidae | Perciformes |
| Ctenolabrus rupestris | Goldsinny-Wrasse | Goldsinny | Labridae | Perciformes |
| Cubiceps gracilis | Driftfish | | Nomeidae | Perciformes |
| Cyclopterus lumpus | Lumpsucker | | Cyclopteridae | Scorpaeniformes |
| Cyclothone alba | Bristlemouth | | Gonostomatidae | Stomiiformes |
| Cynoglossus browni | Nigerian Tonguesole | | Cynoglossidae | Pleuronectiformes |
| Cyttopsis rosea | Red Dory | | Parazenidae | Zeiformes |
| Dactylopterus volitans | Flying Gurnard | | Dactylopteridae | Scorpaeniformes |
| Dalatias licha Alt: Scymnorhinus licha | Kitefin Shark | Darkie Charlie | Dalatiidae | Squaliformes |
| Dasyatis pastinaca | Common Stingray | | Dasyatidae | Rajiformes |
| Deania calcea | Birdbeak Dogfish | Shovelnosed Shark | Centrophoridae | Squaliformes |
| Dentex dentex | Common Dentex | Dentex | Sparidae | Perciformes |
| Dentex maroccanus | Morocco Dentex | | Sparidae | Perciformes |
| Diaphus metopoclampus | Spothead Lantern Fish | | Myctophidae | Myctophiformes |
| Diaphus rafinesquii | White-Spotted Lantern Fish | | Myctophidae | Myctophiformes |
| Dicentrarchus labrax Alt: Morone labrax | European Seabass | Bass | Moronidae | Perciformes |
| Diplecogaster b. bimaculata Alt: Lepadogaster bimaculatus | Two-Spotted Clingfish | | Gobiesocidae | Gobiesociformes |
| Diplodus cervinus | Zebra Seabream | | Sparidae | Perciformes |
| Diplodus sargus | White Seabream | | Sparidae | Perciformes |
| Diplodus vulgaris | Two-banded Bream | | Sparidae | Perciformes |
| Dipturus batis Alt: Raja batis | Blue Skate | Blue Grey Skate | Rajidae | Rajiformes |
| Dipturus nidarosiensis | Norwegian Skate | Black Skate | Rajidae | Rajiformes |
| Dipturus oxyrinchus Alt: Raja oxyrhinchus | Longnosed Skate | Long-Nosed Burton Skate | Rajidae | Rajiformes |
| Diretmus argenteus | Silver Spinyfin | Spiny-Fin | Diretmidae | Beryciformes |
| Dolichopterix rostrata | | | Opisthoproctidae | Osmeriformes |
| Echiichthys vipera Alt: Trachinus vipera | Lesser Weever | Weever | Trachinidae | Perciformes |
| Echinorhinus brucus | Bramble Shark | Spinous Shark | Echinorhinidae | Squaliformes |
| Echiodon drummondii | Pearlfish | | Carapidae | Ophidiiformes |
| Electrona risso | Chubby Flashlightfish | | Myctophidae | Myctophiformes |
| Enchelyopus cimbrius | Fourbeard Rockling | | Lotidae | Gadiformes |
| Engraulis encrasicolus | European Anchovy | Southern Anchovy | Engraulidae | Clupeiformes |
| Entelurus aequoreus | Snake Pipefish | | Syngnathidae | Syngnathiformes |
| Epigonus telescopus | Bulls-Eye | Bigeye | Epigonidae | Perciformes |
| Epinephelus marginatus | Dusky Grouper | Dusky Sea Perch | Serranidae | Perciformes |
| Etmopterus princeps | Great Lanternshark | | Dalatiidae | Squaliformes |
| Etmopterus spinax | Velvet Belly Lantern Shark | Velvet Belly | Dalatiidae | Squaliformes |
| Europharynx pelecanoides | Pelican Eel | | Europharyngidae | Saccopharyngiformes |
| Euthynnus alletteratus | Little Tunny | Atlantic Little Tunny | Scombridae | Perciformes |
| Eutrigla gurnardus Alt: Trigla gurnardus | Grey Gurnard | | Triglidae | Scorpaeniformes |
| Exocoetus volitans | Tropical Two-Winged Flying Fish | | Exocoetidae | Beloniformes |
| Gadiculus argenteus argenteus | Silvery Cod | | Gadidae | Gadiformes |
| Gadiculus argenteus thori | Silvery Pout | Silvery Cod | Gadidae | Gadiformes |
| Gadus morhua | Atlantic Cod | Codling | Gadidae | Gadiformes |
| Gaidropsarus argentatus | Arctic Rockling | | Lotidae | Gadiformes |
| Gaidropsarus macrophthalmus | Bigeye Rockling | | Lotidae | Gadiformes |
| Gaidropsarus mediterraneus | Shore Rockling | Mediterranean Rockling | Lotidae | Gadiformes |
| Gaidropsarus vulgaris | Three-Bearded Rockling | Threebeard Rockling | Lotidae | Gadiformes |
| Galeorhinus galeus | Tope Shark | Hundshai | Triakidae | Carcharhiniformes |
| Galeus melastomus | Blackmouth Catshark | Black-Mouthed Dogfish | Scyliorhinidae | Carcharhiniformes |
| Galeus murinus | Mouse Catshark | | Scyliorhinidae | Carcharhiniformes |
| Gasterosteus aculeatus aculeatus | Three-Spined Stickleback | Burnstickle | Gasterosteidae | Gasterosteiformes |

| SCIENTIFIC NAME | FISHBASE NAME | Alternative Name | Family | Order |
|---|---|---|---|---|
| Glyptocephalus cynoglossus | Witch | | Pleuronectidae | Pleuronectiformes |
| Gobius cobitis | Giant Goby | | Gobiidae | Perciformes |
| Gobius couchi | Couch's Goby | | Gobiidae | Perciformes |
| Gobius cruentatus | Red-Mouthed Goby | | Gobiidae | Perciformes |
| Gobius gasteveni | Steven's Goby | | Gobiidae | Perciformes |
| Gobius niger | Black Goby | | Gobiidae | Perciformes |
| Gobius paganellus | Rock Goby | | Gobiidae | Perciformes |
| Gobiusculus flavescens Alt: Gobius flavescens | Two-Spotted Goby | | Gobiidae | Perciformes |
| Gonostoma bathyphilum | Spark Angelmouth | | Gonostomatidae | Stomiiformes |
| Gonostoma elongatum | Elongated Bristlemouth Fish | | Gonostomatidae | Stomiiformes |
| Grammatostomias flagellibarba | | | Stomiidae | Stomiiformes |
| Guttigadus latifrons | | | Moridae | Gadiformes |
| Gymnammodytes semisquamatus | Smooth Sandeel | Smooth Sandeel | Ammodytidae | Perciformes |
| Halargyreus johnsonii | Slender Codling | Morid Cod | Moridae | Gadiformes |
| Halosauropsis macrochir | Abyssal Halosaur | | Halosauridae | Notacanthiformes |
| Harriotta raleighana | Narrownose Chimaera | Bentnose Rabbitfish | Rhinochimaeridae | Chimaeriformes |
| Helicolenus dactylopterus dactylopterus | Blackbelly Rosefish | Bluemouth Rockfish | Sebastidae | Scorpaeniformes |
| Heptranchias perlo | Sharpnose Sevengill Shark | | Hexanchidae | Hexanchiformes |
| Hexanchus griseus | Bluntnose Sixgill Shark | Atlantic Mud Shark | Hexanchidae | Hexanchiformes |
| Himantolophus groenlandicus | Atlantic Footballfish | | Himantolophidae | Lophiiformes |
| Hippocampus guttulatus Alt: Hippocampus ramulosus | Long-Snouted Seahorse | Spiny Seahorse | Syngnathidae | Syngnathiformes |
| Hippocampus hippocampus | Short-Snouted Seahorse | | Syngnathidae | Syngnathiformes |
| Hippoglossoides platessoides | American Plaice | Long Rough Dab | Pleuronectidae | Pleuronectiformes |
| Hippoglossus hippoglossus | Atlantic Halibut | Halibut | Pleuronectidae | Pleuronectiformes |
| Hirundichthys rondeletii | Black Wing Flyingfish | Blackwing Flyingfish | Exocoetidae | Beloniformes |
| Histiobranchus bathybius | Deepwater Arrowtooth Eel | | Synaphobranchidae | Anguilliformes |
| Holocentrus adscensionsis | Squirrel Fish | | Holocentridae | Beryciformes |
| Holosaurus johnsonianus | Halosaur | | Halosauridae | Notacanthiformes |
| Holtbyrnia anomala | Bighead Searsid | | Platytroctidae | Osmeriformes |
| Hoplostethus atlanticus | Orange Roughy | | Trachichthyidae | Beryciformes |
| Hoplostethus mediterraneus mediterraneus | Mediterranean Slimehead | Black-Mouthed Alfonsin | Trachichthyidae | Beryciformes |
| Hydrolagus affinis | Smalleyed Rabbitfish | | Chimaeridae | Chimaeriformes |
| Hydrolagus mirabilis | Large-Eyed Rabbitfish | | Chimaeridae | Chimaeriformes |
| Hydrolagus pallidus | Ghost Rabbitfish | | Chimaeridae | Chimaeriformes |
| Hymenocephalus italicus | Glasshead Grenadier | | Macrouridae | Gadiformes |
| Hyperoglyphe perciformis | Barrelfish | | Centrolophidae | Perciformes |
| Hyperoplus immaculatus | Greater Sand-Eel | Corbin's Sandeel | Ammodytidae | Perciformes |
| Hyperoplus lanceolatus | Great Sandeel | | Ammodytidae | Perciformes |
| Icelus bicornis | Twohorn Sculpin | | Cottidae | Scorpaeniformes |
| Ilyophis arx | | | Synaphobranchidae | Anguilliformes |
| Ilyophis blachei | | | Synaphobranchidae | Anguilliformes |
| Ilyophis brunneus | Muddy Arrowtooth Eel | | Synaphobranchidae | Anguilliformes |
| Istiophorus albicans | Atlantic Sailfish | | Istiophoridae | Perciformes |
| Isurus oxyrinchus | Shortfin Mako | Atlantic Mako | Lamnidae | Lamniformes |
| Katsuwonus pelamis | Skipjack Tuna | Atlantic Bonito | Scombridae | Perciformes |
| Labrus bergylta | Ballan Wrasse | | Labridae | Perciformes |
| Labrus mixtus Alt: Labrus bimaculatus | Cuckoo Wrasse | Red Wrasse (Female) | Labridae | Perciformes |
| Lagocephalus lagocephalus lagocephalus | Oceanic Puffer | | Tetraodontidae | Tetraodontiformes |
| Lamna nasus | Porbeagle | Beaumaris Shark | Lamnidae | Lamniformes |
| Lampanyctus crocodilus | Jewel Lanternfish | | Myctophidae | Myctophiformes |
| Lampanyctus intricarius | | | Myctophidae | Myctophiformes |
| Lampanyctus macdonaldi | Rakery Beaconlamp | | Myctophidae | Myctophiformes |
| Lampanyctus pusillus | None | | Myctophidae | Myctophiformes |
| Lampetra fluviatilis | European River Lamprey | Lampern | Petromyzontidae | Petromyzontiformes |
| Lampetra planeri | European Brook Lamprey | | Petromyzontidae | Petromyzontiformes |

| SCIENTIFIC NAME | FISHBASE NAME | Alternative Name | Family | Order |
|---|---|---|---|---|
| Lampris guttatus | Opah | Jerusalem Haddock | Lampridae | Lampriformes |
| Lebetus guilleti | Guillet's Goby | | Gobiidae | Perciformes |
| Lebetus scorpioides | Diminutive Goby | | Gobiidae | Perciformes |
| Lepadogaster candolii | Connemarra Clingfish | Connemara Sucker | Gobiesocidae | Gobiesociformes |
| Lepadogaster purpurea Alt: Lepadogaster l. purpurea | Cornish Sucker | | Gobiesocidae | Gobiesociformes |
| Lepidion eques | North Atlantic Codling | | Moridae | Gadiformes |
| Lepidocybium flavobrunneum | Escolar | | Gempylidae | Perciformes |
| Lepidopus caudatus | Silver Scabbardfish | Scabbard Fish | Trichiuridae | Perciformes |
| Lepidorhombus boscii | Fourspotted Megrim | | Scophthalmidae | Pleuronectiformes |
| Lepidorhombus whiffiagonis | Megrim | | Scophthalmidae | Pleuronectiformes |
| Leptochilichthys agassizii | Agassiz' Smooth-Head | | Leptochilichthyidae | Osmeriformes |
| Leptoclinus maculatus | Daubed Shanny | Spotted Snake Blenny | Stichaeidae | Perciformes |
| Leptostomias gladiator | | | Stomiidae | Stomiiformes |
| Lesueurigobius friesii Alt: Gobius freisii | Fries's Goby | | Gobiidae | Perciformes |
| Leucoraja circularis Alt: Raja circularis | Sandy Ray | | Rajidae | Rajiformes |
| Leucoraja fullonica Alt: Raja fullonica | Shagreen Ray | Dun Cow | Rajidae | Rajiformes |
| Leucoraja naevus Alt: Raja naevus | Cuckoo Ray | Butterfly Skate | Rajidae | Rajiformes |
| Limanda limanda | Dab | Common Dab | Pleuronectidae | Pleuronectiformes |
| Liparis liparis liparis | Striped Sea Snail | Sea Snail | Liparidae | Scorpaeniformes |
| Liparis montagui | Montagu's Sea Snail | | Liparidae | Scorpaeniformes |
| Lipophrys pholis Alt: Blennius pholis | Shanny | | Blenniidae | Perciformes |
| Liza aurata | Golden Grey Mullet | Golden Mullet | Mugilidae | Mugiliformes |
| Liza ramado | Thinlip Mullet | Grey Mullet | Mugilidae | Mugiliformes |
| Lobianchia gemellarii | Coco's Lantern Fish | | Myctophidae | Myctophiformes |
| Lophius budegassa | Black-Bellied Angler | European Anglerfish | Lophiidae | Lophiiformes |
| Lophius piscatorius | Angler | Monk | Lophiidae | Lophiiformes |
| Lumpenus lampretaeformis | Snakeblenny | Snake Blenny | Stichaeidae | Perciformes |
| Lutjanus ehrenbergii | Blackspot Snapper | | Lutjanidae | Perciformes |
| Luvarus imperialis | Luvar | Louvar | Luvaridae | Perciformes |
| Lycenchelys alba | | | Zoarcidae | Perciformes |
| Lycenchelys sarsii | Sar's Wolf Eel | | Zoarcidae | Perciformes |
| Lycodes esmarkii | Greater Eelpout | | Zoarcidae | Perciformes |
| Lycodes terraenovae | | | Zoarcidae | Perciformes |
| Lycodes vahlii | Vahl's Eelpout | | Zoarcidae | Perciformes |
| Lyconus brachycolus | | | Merlucciidae | Gadiformes |
| Macroramphosus scolopax | Longspine Snipefish | Snipe-Fish | Centriscidae | Syngnathiformes |
| Macrourus berglax | Onion-Eye Grenadier | | Macrouridae | Gadiformes |
| Magnisudis atlantica | Duckbill Barracudina | | Paralepididae | Aulopiformes |
| Malacocephalus laevis | Softhead Grenadier | | Istiophoridae | Perciformes |
| Makaira nigricans | Blue Marlin | | Macrouridae | Gadiformes |
| Maulisia mauli | Maul's Searsid | | Platytroctidae | Osmeriformes |
| Maurolicus muelleri | Pearlsides | Muller's Bristlemouth Fish | Sternoptychidae | Stomiiformes |
| Megalops atlanticus | Tarpon | Atlantic Tarpon | Megalopidae | Elopiformes |
| Melanogrammus aeglefinus | Haddock | | Gadidae | Gadiformes |
| Merlangius merlangus | Whiting | | Gadidae | Gadiformes |
| Merluccius merluccius | European Hake | Cornish Salmon | Merlucciidae | Gadiformes |
| Micrenophrys lilljeborgii Alt: Cottus lilljeborgi | Norway Bullhead | | Cottidae | Scorpaeniformes |
| Microchirus azevia | | | Soleidae | Pleuronectiformes |
| Microchirus boscanii | Lusitanian Sole | | Soleidae | Pleuronectiformes |
| Microchirus theophila | Bastard Sole | | Soleidae | Pleuronectiformes |
| Microchirus variegatus | Thickback Sole | Bastard Sole | Soleidae | Pleuronectiformes |
| Micromesistius poutassou | Blue Whiting | Couch's Whiting | Gadidae | Gadiformes |
| Microstoma microstoma | Slender Argentine | | Microstomatidae | Osmeriformes |
| Microstomus kitt | Lemon Sole | Lemon Dab | Pleuronectidae | Pleuronectiformes |

| SCIENTIFIC NAME | FISHBASE NAME | Alternative Name | Family | Order |
|---|---|---|---|---|
| Mobula mobular | Devil Fish | | Myliobatidae | Rajiformes |
| Mola mola | Ocean Sunfish | Sunfish | Molidae | Tetraodontiformes |
| Molva dypterygia | Blue Ling | | Lotidae | Gadiformes |
| Molva macrophthalma | Spanish Ling | Blue Ling | Lotidae | Gadiformes |
| Molva molva | Ling | European Ling | Lotidae | Gadiformes |
| Mora moro | Common Mora | Morid Cod | Moridae | Gadiformes |
| Mugil cephalus | Flathead Mullet | Black True Mullet | Mugilidae | Mugiliformes |
| Mullus barbatus barbatus | Red Mullet | Striped Mullet | Mullidae | Perciformes |
| Mullus surmuletus | Red Mullet | Striped Red Mullet | Mullidae | Perciformes |
| Muraena helena | Mediterranean Moray | Marbled Moray | Muraenidae | Anguilliformes |
| Mustelus asterias | Starry Smooth-Hound | Smooth-Hound | Triakidae | Carcharhiniformes |
| Mustelus mustelus | Smooth-Hound | Grey Mouth Dog | Triakidae | Carcharhiniformes |
| Myctophum punctatum | Spotted Lanternfish | | Myctophidae | Myctophiformes |
| Myliobatis aquila | Common Eagle Ray | Eagle Ray | Myliobatidae | Rajiformes |
| Myoxocephalus scorpius Alt: Acanthocottus scorpius | Shorthorn Sculpin | Bullhead | Cottidae | Scorpaeniformes |
| Myxine glutinosa | Hagfish | Common Hag | Myxinidae | Myxiniformes |
| Myxine ios | White-Headed Hagfish | | Myxinidae | Myxiniformes |
| Nansenia groenlandica | Greenland Argentine | | Microstomatidae | Osmeriformes |
| Nansenia oblita | | | Microstomatidae | Osmeriformes |
| Narcetes stomias | Blackhead Salmon | | Alepocephalidae | Osmeriformes |
| Naucrates ductor | Pilotfish | | Carangidae | Perciformes |
| Nemichthys scolopaceus | Slender Snipe Eel | Atlantic Snipe Eel | Nemichthyidae | Anguilliformes |
| Neocyttus helgae | False Boarfish | | Oreosomatidae | Zeiformes |
| Neoraja caerulea | Blue Ray | | Rajidae | Rajiformes |
| Nerophis lumbriciformis | Worm Pipefish | | Syngnathidae | Syngnathiformes |
| Nerophis ophidion | Straightnose Pipefish | | Syngnathidae | Syngnathiformes |
| Nesiarchus nasutus | Black Gemfish | | Gempylidae | Perciformes |
| Nezumia aequalis | Common Atlantic Grenadier | Smooth Grenadier | Macrouridae | Gadiformes |
| Normichthys operosus | Multipore Searsid | | Platytroctidae | Osmeriformes |
| Notacanthus bonaparte | Shortfin Spiny Eel | | Notacanthidae | Notacanthiformes |
| Notacanthus chemnitzii | Spiny Eel | Spiny-Eel | Notacanthidae | Notacanthiformes |
| Notolychnus valdiviae | Topside Lampfish | | Myctophidae | Myctophiformes |
| Oblada melanura | Saddled Bream | | Sparidae | Perciformes |
| Oncorhynchus gorbuscha | Pink Salmon | Humpback Salmon | Salmonidae | Salmoniformes |
| Oncorhynchus kisutch | Coho Salmon | Hoopid Salmon | Salmonidae | Salmoniformes |
| Oncorhynchus mykiss | Rainbow Trout | Coast Angel Trout | Salmonidae | Salmoniformes |
| Oneirodes carlsbergi | | | Oneirodidae | Lophiiformes |
| Oneiroides eschrichtii | Bulbous Dreamer | | Oneirodidae | Lophiiformes |
| Ophidion barbatum | Snake Blenny | Cusk Eel | Ophidiidae | Ophidiiformes |
| Opisthoproctus soleatus | Barrel-Eye | | Opisthoproctidae | Osmeriformes |
| Orcynopsis unicolor | Plain Bonito | | Scombridae | Perciformes |
| Osmerus eperlanus | European Smelt | Sparling | Osmeridae | Osmeriformes |
| Oxynotus centrina | Angular Roughshark | | Dalatiidae | Squaliformes |
| Oxynotus paradoxus | Sailfin Roughshark | Kite-Fin Shark | Dalatiidae | Squaliformes |
| Pachycara bulbiceps | Snupnose Eelpout | | Zoarcidae | Perciformes |
| Pachycara crassiceps | | | Zoarcidae | Perciformes |
| Pagellus acarne | Axillary Seabream | | Sparidae | Perciformes |
| Pagellus bogaraveo | Blackspot Seabream | Common Sea Bream | Sparidae | Perciformes |
| Pagellus erythrinus | Common Pandora | Becker | Sparidae | Perciformes |
| Pagrus pagrus | Common Seabream | Couch's Sea-Bream | Sparidae | Perciformes |
| Pampus argenteus | Silver Pomfret | White Pomfret | Stromateidae | Perciformes |
| Parablennius gattorugine Alt: Blennius gattorugine | Tompot Blenny | | Blenniidae | Perciformes |
| Parablennius pilicornis* | Variable Blenny | | Blenniidae | Perciformes |
| Parablennius rouxi* | Striped Blenny | | Blenniidae | Perciformes |
| Parablennius ruber | Red Blenny | Portuguese Blenny | Blenniidae | Perciformes |
| Paralepis coregonoides Alt: Paralepis coregonoides borealis | Sharpchin Barracudina | Lancet Fish | Paralepididae | Aulopiformes |
| Paraliparis abyssorum | | | Liparidae | Scorpaeniformes |

| SCIENTIFIC NAME | FISHBASE NAME | Alternative Name | Family | Order |
|---|---|---|---|---|
| Paraliparis bathybius | Black Seasnail | | Liparidae | Scorpaeniformes |
| Paraliparis bipolris | | | Liparidae | Scorpaeniformes |
| Paraliparis hystrix | | | Liparidae | Scorpaeniformes |
| Pegusa lascaris Alt: Solea lascaris | Sand Sole | French Sole | Soleidae | Pleuronectiformes |
| Peristedion cataphractum | African Armoured Searobin | Armed Gurnard | Peristediidae | Scorpaeniformes |
| Petromyzon marinus | Sea Lamprey | Great Sea Lamprey | Petromyzontidae | Petromyzontiformes |
| Pholis gunnellus | Rock Gunnel | Butterfish | Pholidae | Perciformes |
| Phrynorhombus norvegicus | Norwegian Topknot | Norwegian Topknot | Scophthalmidae | Pleuronectiformes |
| Phycis blennoides | Greater Forkbeard | Forked Hake | Phycidae | Gadiformes |
| Platichthys flesus | Flounder | Butt | Pleuronectidae | Pleuronectiformes |
| Pleuronectes platessa | Plaice | European Plaice | Pleuronectidae | Pleuronectiformes |
| Pollachius pollachius | Pollack | Callagh | Gadidae | Gadiformes |
| Pollachius virens | Saithe | Coalfish | Gadidae | Gadiformes |
| Polycanthonotus challengeri | Longnose Tapirfish | | Notacanthidae | Notacanthiformes |
| Polycanthonotus rissoanus | Smallmouth Spiny Eel | | Notacanthidae | Notacanthiformes |
| Polymetme corythaeola | | | Phosichthyidae | Stomiiformes |
| Polymetme thaeocoryla | | | Phosichthydae | Stomiiformes |
| Polyprion americanus | Wreckfish | Atlantic Wreckfish | Polyprionidae | Perciformes |
| Pomatoschistus lozanoi | Lozano's Goby | | Gobiidae | Perciformes |
| Pomatoschistus microps Alt: Gobius microps | Common Goby | | Gobiidae | Perciformes |
| Pomatoschistus minutus Alt: Gobius minutus | Sand Goby | One Spotted Goby | Gobiidae | Perciformes |
| Pomatoschistus norvegicus | Norway Goby | | Gobiidae | Perciformes |
| Pomatoschistus pictus Alt: Gobius pictus | Painted Goby | | Gobiidae | Perciformes |
| Poromitra crassiceps | Crested Bigscale | | Melamphaidae | Stephanoberyciformes |
| Prionace glauca | Blue Shark | Blue Dog | Carcharhinidae | Carcharhiniformes |
| Protomyctophum arcicum | Arctic Telescope | | Myctophidae | Myctophiformes |
| Psetta maxima Alt: Scophthalmus maximus | Turbot | Breet | Scophthalmidae | Pleuronectiformes |
| Pseudonezumis flagellicauda | | | Macrouridae | Gadiformes |
| Pseudotriakis microdon | False Catshark | | Pseudotriakidae | Carcharhiniformes |
| Pteroplatytrygon violacea | Pelagic Stingray | | Dasyatidae | Rajiformes |
| Pterycombus brama | Atlantic Fanfish | Rough Pomfret | Bramidae | Perciformes |
| Pungitius pungitius | Nine-Spined Stickleback | Ten-Spined Stickleback | Gasterosteidae | Gasterosteiformes |
| Raja brachyura | Blonde Ray | | Rajidae | Rajiformes |
| Raja clavata | Thornback Ray | Maiden Ray | Rajidae | Rajiformes |
| Raja microcellata | Small-Eyed Ray | Owl Ray | Rajidae | Rajiformes |
| Raja montagui | Spotted Ray | Homelyn Ray | Rajidae | Rajiformes |
| Raja undulata | Undulate Ray | Undulate Painted Ray | Rajidae | Rajiformes |
| Rajella bathyphila | Deepwater Ray | | Rajidae | Rajiformes |
| Rajella bigelowi | Bigelow's Ray | | Rajidae | Rajiformes |
| Rajella fyllae | Round Ray | Round Skate | Rajidae | Rajiformes |
| Rajella kukujevi | Mid-Atlantic Skate | | Rajidae | Rajiformes |
| Raniceps raninus | Tadpole Fish | Lesser Forkbeard | Gadidae | Gadiformes |
| Ranzania laevis | Slender Sunfish | Slender Sunfish | Molidae | Tetraodontiformes |
| Regalecus glesne | King Of Herrings | Giant Oarfish | Regalecidae | Lampriformes |
| Reinhardtius hippoglossoides | Greenland Halibut | Black Halibut | Pleuronectidae | Pleuronectiformes |
| Remora remora | Common Remora | Shark-Sucker | Echeneidae | Perciformes |
| Rhinochimaera atlantica | Spearnose Chimaera | Atlantic Knife-Nose Chimaera | Rhinochimaeridae | Chimaeriformes |
| Rinoctes nasutus | Abyssal Smooth-Head | | Alepocephalidae | Osmeriformes |
| Rostroraja alba Alt: Raja alba | Bottlenosed Skate | Bordered Skate | Rajidae | Rajiformes |
| Rouleina attrita | Softskin Smooth-Head | | Alepocephalida | Osmeriformes |
| Rouleina maderensis | Madeiran Smooth-Head | | Alepocephalida | Osmeriformes |
| Ruvettus pretiosus | Oilfish | | Gempylidae | Perciformes |
| Saccopharynx ampullaceus | Gulper Eel | | Saccopharyngidae | Saccopharingiformes |
| Sagamichthys schnakenbecki | Schnakenbeck's Searsid | | Platytroctidae | Osmeriformes |

| SCIENTIFIC NAME | FISHBASE NAME | Alternative Name | Family | Order |
|---|---|---|---|---|
| Salmo salar | Atlantic Salmon | Black Salmon | Salmonidae | Salmoniformes |
| Salmo trutta trutta | Sea Trout | Blacktail | Salmonidae | Salmoniformes |
| Salvelinus alpinus alpinus | Charr | Alpine Char | Salmonidae | Salmoniformes |
| Sarda sarda | Atlantic Bonito | Belted Bonito | Scombridae | Perciformes |
| Sardina pilchardus | European Pilchard | Sardine | Clupeidae | Clupeiformes |
| Sarpa salpa | Salema | Goldline | Sparidae | Perciformes |
| Schedophilus medusophagus | Cornish Blackfish | | Centrolophidae | Perciformes |
| Schedophilus ovalis | Imperial Blackfish | | Centrolophidae | Perciformes |
| Sciadonus galatheae | | | Aphyonidae | Ophidiiformes |
| Scomber japonicus Alt: Scomber colias | Chub Mackerel | Big-Eyed Mackerel | Scombridae | Perciformes |
| Scomber scombrus | Atlantic Mackerel | Joey | Scombridae | Perciformes |
| Scomberesox saurus saurus | Atlantic Saury | Garfish | Scomberesocidae | Beloniformes |
| Scopeloogadus beanii | | | Melamphaidae | Stephanoberyciformes |
| Scopelosaurus lepidus | Blackfin Waryfish | | Notosudidae | Aulopiformes |
| Scophthalmus rhombus | Brill | | Scophthalmidae | Pleuronectiformes |
| Scorpaena porcus | Black Scorpionfish | Small-Scaled Scorpionfish | Scorpaenidae | Scorpaeniformes |
| Scorpaena scrofa | Largescaled Scorpionfish | Large-Scaled Scorpion Fish | Scorpaenidae | Scorpaeniformes |
| Scyliorhinus canicula | Small-Spotted Catshark | Lesser-Spotted Dogfish | Scyliorhinidae | Carcharhiniformes |
| Scyliorhinus stellaris | Nursehound | Bull Huss | Scyliorhinidae | Carcharhiniformes |
| Scymnodon obscurus | Smallmouth Velvet Dogfish | | Dalatiidae | Squaliformes |
| Scymnodon ringens | Knifetooth Dogfish | | Dalatiidae | Squaliformes |
| Zameus squamulosus Alt: Scymnodon squamulosus | Velvet Dogfish | | Dalatiidae | Squaliformes |
| Searsia koefoedi | Koefoed's Searsid | | Platytroctidae | Osmeriformes |
| Sebastes marinus | Ocean Perch | Red-Fish | Sebastidae | Scorpaeniformes |
| Sebastes viviparus | Norway Redfish | Norway Haddock | Sebastidae | Scorpaeniformes |
| Seriola carpenteri | Guinean Amberjack | | Carangidae | Perciformes |
| Seriola dumerili | Greater Amberjack | | Carangidae | Perciformes |
| Seriola rivoliana | Almaco Jack | | Carangidae | Perciformes |
| Serranus cabrilla | Comber | Gaper | Serranidae | Perciformes |
| Solea solea Alt: Solea vulgaris | Common Sole | Sole | Soleidae | Pleuronectiformes |
| Somniosus microcephalus | Greenland Shark | Ground Shark | Dalatiidae | Squaliformes |
| Sparus aurata | Gilthead Seabream | Gilthead | Sparidae | Perciformes |
| Spectrunculus grandis | Pudgy Cuskeel | | Ophidiidae | Ophidiiformes |
| Sphoeroides pachygaster | Blunthead Puffer | Puffer | Tetraodontidae | Tetraodontiformes |
| Sphyraena viridensis | Yellowmouth Barracuda | | Sphyraenidae | Perciformes |
| Sphyrna zygaena | Smooth Hammerhead | Common Hammerhead Shark | Sphyrnidae | Carcharhiniformes |
| Spinachia spinachia | Sea Stickleback | Fifteen-Spined Stickleback | Gasterosteidae | Gasterosteiformes |
| Spondyliosoma cantharus | Black Seabream | | Sparidae | Perciformes |
| Sprattus sprattus sprattus | European Sprat | Brisling | Clupeidae | Clupeiformes |
| Squalus acanthias | Piked Dogfish | Blue Dog | Squalidae | Squaliformes |
| Squatina squatina | Angelshark | Angel Fiddle Fish | Squatinidae | Squatiniformes |
| Sternoptyx diaphana | Diaphanous Hatchet Fish | Diaphanous Hatchetfish | Sternoptychidae | Stomiiformes |
| Stomias boa ferox | Boa Dragonfish | | Stomiidae | Stomiiformes |
| Sudis hyalina | | | Paralepididae | Aulopiformes |
| Symbolophorus veranyi | Large Scale Lantern Fish | | Myctophidae | Myctophiformes |
| Symphodus bailloni Alt: Crenilabrus bailloni | Baillon's Wrasse | Vielle | Labridae | Perciformes |
| Symphodus melops Alt: Crenilabrus melops | Corkwing Wrasse | | Labridae | Perciformes |
| Synaphobranchus kaupii | Kaup's Arrowtooth Eel | | Synaphobranchidae | Anguilliformes |
| Syngnathus acus | Greater Pipefish | Common Pipefish | Syngnathidae | Syngnathiformes |
| Syngnathus rostellatus | Nilsson's Pipefish | Lesser Pipefish | Syngnathidae | Syngnathiformes |
| Syngnathus typhle | Broad-Nosed Pipefish | | Syngnathidae | Syngnathiformes |
| Taractes asper | Rough Pomfret | | Bramidae | Perciformes |
| Taractichthys longipinnis | Bigscale Pomfret | Long-Finned Bream | Bramidae | Perciformes |
| Taurulus bubalis Alt: Acanthocottus bubalis | Longspined Bullhead | Sea Scorpion | Cottidae | Scorpaeniformes |

| SCIENTIFIC NAME | FISHBASE NAME | Alternative Name | Family | Order |
|---|---|---|---|---|
| *Tetrapturus albidus* | Atlantic White Marlin | White Marlin | Istiophoridae | Perciformes |
| *Thallassobathia pelagica* | | | Bythitidae | Ophidiiformes |
| *Thorogobius ephippiatus* | Leopard-Spotted Goby | | Gobiidae | Perciformes |
| *Thunnus alalunga* | Albacore | Albacore Tuna | Scombridae | Perciformes |
| *Thunnus albacares* | Yellowfin Tuna | Allison's Tuna | Scombridae | Perciformes |
| *Thunnus obesus* | Big-Eye Tuna | | Scombridae | Perciformes |
| *Thunnus thynnus* | Northern Bluefin Tuna | Bluefin Tunny | Scombridae | Perciformes |
| *Torpedo marmorata* | Spotted Torpedo | Common Crampfish | Torpedinidae | Torpediniformes |
| *Torpedo nobiliana* | Atlantic Torpedo | Electric Ray | Torpedinidae | Torpediniformes |
| *Trachinotus ovatus* | Derbio | Pompano | Carangidae | Perciformes |
| *Trachinus draco* | Greater Weever | Greater Weever | Trachinidae | Perciformes |
| *Trachipterus arcticus* | Deal Fish | | Trachipteridae | Lampriformes |
| *Trachurus trachurus* Alt: *Caranx trachurus* | Atlantic Horse Mackerel | Horse Mackerel | Carangidae | Perciformes |
| *Trachyrincus murrayi* | Roughnose Grenadier | | Macrouridae | Gadiformes |
| *Trachyrincus scabrus* | Roughsnout Grenadier | | Macrouridae | Gadiformes |
| *Trachyscorpia cristulata echinata* | Spiny Scorpionfish | | Sebastidae | Scorpaeniformes |
| *Trichiurus lepturus* | Largehead Hairtail | Atlantic Cutlassfish | Trichiuridae | Perciformes |
| *Trigla lyra* | Piper Gurnard | | Triglidae | Scorpaeniformes |
| *Trigloporus lastoviza* Alt: *Chelidonichthys lastoviza* | Streaked Gurnard | | Triglidae | Scorpaeniformes |
| *Triglops murrayi* | Moustache Sculpin | | Cottidae | Scorpaeniformes |
| *Trigonolampa miriceps* | Threelight Dragonfish | | Stomiidae | Stomiiformes |
| *Tripterygion delaisi* | Black-Faced Blenny | | Tripterygiidae | Perciformes |
| *Trisopterus esmarkii* | Norway Pout | | Gadidae | Gadiformes |
| *Trisopterus luscus* | Pouting | Bib | Gadidae | Gadiformes |
| *Trisopterus minutus* | Poor Cod | | Gadidae | Gadiformes |
| *Umbrina cirrosa* | Shi Drum | Corb | Sciaenidae | Perciformes |
| *Uranoscopus scaber* | Atlantic Stargazer | | Uranoscopidae | Perciformes |
| *Urophycis chuss* | Red Hake | Ling | Phycidae | Gadiformes |
| *Valenciennellus tripunctulatus* | Constellationfish | | Sternoptychidae | Stomiiformes |
| *Venefica proboscidea* | Bluntnose Smooth-Head | | Nettastomatidae | Anguilliformes |
| *Xenodermichthys copei* | Bluntsnout Smooth-Head | Altantic Gymnast | Alepocephalidae | Osmeriformes |
| *Xiphias gladius* | Swordfish | Broadbill | Xiphiidae | Perciformes |
| *Zenopsis conchifer* | Sailfin Dory | | Zeidae | Zeiformes |
| *Zeugopterus punctatus* | Topknot | Bastard Brill | Scophthalmidae | Pleuronectiformes |
| *Zeugopterus regius* Alt: *Phrynorhombus regius* | Eckström's Topknot | | Scophthalmidae | Pleuronectiformes |
| *Zeus faber* | John Dory | Atlantic John Dory | Zeidae | Zeiformes |
| *Zoarces viviparus* | Viviparous Blenny | Eelpout | Zoarcidae | Perciformes |

# APPENDIX II: Where to find out more

This book is as comprehensive as we have been able to make it and should allow you to identify most of the fish you see. However, it is often useful to consult more than one book and to use websites. The following lists those sources of information that we have found particularly useful. Many of the out of print books can be found by searching on the internet. Numerous scientific publications are also available, many as PDF downloadable files, and we would recommend careful use of search engines to try to locate information about any particular species of interest.

## Books and references

Dipper, F.A. (2001) (2nd ed.). *British Sea Fishes*. Underwater World Publications. ISBN 0 946020 31 0.

Forrest, H.E. (1907). *The Vertebrate Fauna of North Wales*. Witherby & Co. (out of print).

Goodwin, C.E. and Picton, B.E. (2007). The red blenny *Parablennius ruber* in the British Isles, with notes on field identification characteristics and ecology. *J. Mar. Biol. Ass. U.K.* 87, 1309-1313.

Henderson, P.A. (1994). Wildlife reports. *British Wildlife* 6, 124-125.

Herdman, W.A. and Dawson, R.A. (1902). *Fish and Fisheries of the Irish Sea*. Philip & Son (out of print).

Jenkins, J. Travis (1936) (2nd ed). *The Fishes of the British Isles both fresh water and salt*. Frederick Warne, London.

Lythgoe, J. & Lythgoe, G. (1991). *Fishes of the Sea: the North Atlantic and Mediterranean*. Blandford Press ISBN 0-7137-2225-8 (out of print).

Miller, P. & Loates, M. (1997). *Collins Pocket Guide: Fish of Britain and Europe* ISBN 0 00 219945 9 (out of print).

Moen, F.E. & Svensen, E. (2004). *Marine fish and invertebrates of Northern Europe*. Aquapress. ISBN 0-9544060-2-8

Naylor, P. (2005). *Great British Marine Animals* 2nd Edition. Sound Diving Publications. ISBN 0 9522831 5 8

Stebbings, A.R.D et al. (2002). Immigration of southern fish species to SW England linked to warming of the North Atlantic (1960-2001). *JMBA* 82, 177-180.

Vas, P. (1991). *A Field Guide to the Sharks of British Coastal Waters*. Field Studies Council Publication 205, reprinted from Field Studies Vol.7 No.4 (1991).

Wheeler, A. (1969). *The Fishes of the British Isles and North West Europe*. Macmillan and Co. (out of print).

Wheeler, A. (1978). *Key to the Fishes of Northern Europe*. Frederick Warne. ISBN 0 7232 2064 6 (out of print).

Wheeler, A. (1995). *Field Key to the Shore Fishes of the British Isles*. Field Studies Council Publication 225, reprinted from Field Studies, Vol.8, No.3 (1994) ISBN 1 85153 225 0 .

Whitehead, P.J.P. et al. (1986). *Fishes of the North-eastern Atlantic and Mediterranean* (3 volumes) UNESCO ISBN 92-3-002215-2 (out of print but available in digital format).

## Websites

Searches on scientific names are usually very productive, but the following are especially useful:

www.fishbase.org - a vast amount of data on fish worldwide (both marine and freshwater).

www.fishonline.org – information from the Marine Conservation Society on the status and management of commercial fish in British waters allowing readers to choose which fish to eat.

www.marlin.ac.uk - the Marine Life Information Network (also see below); UK information including marine fish.

www.nbn.org.uk - information, records and distribution maps of UK animals and plants including many Welsh fish.

# APPENDIX III: Where and how to record your finds

## Recording schemes

A variety of schemes are in operation that will allow you to contribute towards our knowledge of Welsh fish by recording details of fishes seen or caught. These schemes are likely to vary over the coming years with some finishing and other new schemes appearing. As with all web links, these may change over time so it may well be worth searching using terms such as Welsh Marine Fish Identification Records, in case new or additional schemes and/or information become available. At the time of writing the following schemes are in operation:

*British Marine Life Study Society*
www.glaucus.org.uk
Members post their records and sightings on the website.

*The Countryside Council for Wales*
http://www.ccw.gov.uk
The Countryside Council for Wales is the Government's statutory advisor on sustaining natural beauty, wildlife and the opportunity for outdoor enjoyment in Wales and its inshore waters.

*Marine Conservation Society*
www.mcsuk.org
The Marine Conservation Society is the UK charity dedicated to caring for our seas, shores and wildlife. It runs conservation campaigns and projects and the website has links to marine recording schemes.

*MarLIN The Marine Life Information Network of Britain and Ireland*
www.marlin.ac.uk/welsh_fish
This organisation is based at the Marine Biological Association in Plymouth and this link will allow you to supply records of marine fish on-line after registering. Sightings of rare, vagrant and non-native species can be also be entered, this time at www.marlin.ac.uk/rml.

*Marine Wildlife Photo Agency*
www.marinewildlife.co.uk
More information about Welsh marine fish will be available from and through Paul Kay's Marine Wildlife website.

*National Biodiversity Network*
www.nbn.org.uk
The NBN Gateway was developed by NBN to communicate and share biodiversity data using the internet. Many of the other recording schemes described here feed their data sets into this scheme. It is not designed to input individual records.

*National Marine Aquarium*
www.national-aquarium.co.uk
Runs the United Kingdom Marine Fish Recording Scheme which collects and collates records or rare and unusual fish.

*Porcupine Marine Natural History Society*
www.pmnhs.org
This society is an informal society interested in marine natural history and recording particularly in the NE Atlantic and Mediterranean. Details of how to record your sightings are given on the website.

*Seasearch*
www.seasearch.org.uk
Seasearch is a project for recreational divers run by the Marine Conservation Society. Divers collect information about marine habitats, animals and plants including fishes. Seasearch fish identification courses are run throughout UK.

*The Shark Trust*
www.sharktrust.org
The Shark Trust, based in Plymouth, provides options on their website for recording sightings of skates and rays and their egg cases.

# INDEX

# THE AUTHORS

**Paul Kay** studied Scientific Photography before working as a volunteer at the Sherkin Island Marine Station in County Cork, Ireland where his lifelong fascination in marine life began. He gained a Fellowship of the Royal Photographic Society with the first digitally printed submission of natural history photographs – all of temperate marine life from around Britain and Ireland. His previous books include *The shallow seas of Wales*, *Ireland's Marine Life* and *Underwater Photography* and his photographs have been used throughout the world, in numerous publications. He has been diving and taking underwater photographs for over 25 years and has dived in locations as diverse as Tahiti and the Falkland Islands, The Caymans and New Zealand, but still prefers the waters surrounding Britain and Ireland. He now freelances as a photographer – specialising in underwater photography and videography. He shot the underwater footage used in Natur Cymru for S4C. He is especially interested in photographing the fish found around Britain and Ireland, and finds the gobies – some of which are extremely difficult to identify – to be both rewarding and a challenge.

www.marinewildlife.co.uk

**Frances Dipper** has always loved the sea, in spite of being brought up on a farm in deepest Warwickshire. She is now an independent marine consultant, lecturer and author and has been studying marine life for over 30 years. Her interest in fishes was fired whilst doing her PhD on British wrasses at Port Erin, Isle of Man. She has dived extensively in the UK, Middle East and Far East and is currently a volunteer with the MCS working on coral reef survey and monitoring in the Semporna Islands, Borneo. She has run numerous expeditions and courses for divers and naturalists and has written many books on marine and freshwater biology and ocean environments for both children and adults. In 2003 her Dorling Kindersley children's book, *Guide to the Oceans* won the Aventis Prize for junior Science Books. She was also an author and consultant on Dorling Kindersley's acclaimed *Ocean* and *Animal Life* and other books include *Extraordinary Fish* (BBC/Toucan Books) written to tie-in with the BBC's *Blue Planet* publishing programme and *British Sea Fishes* (Underwater World Publications) www.marinedipper.co.uk.